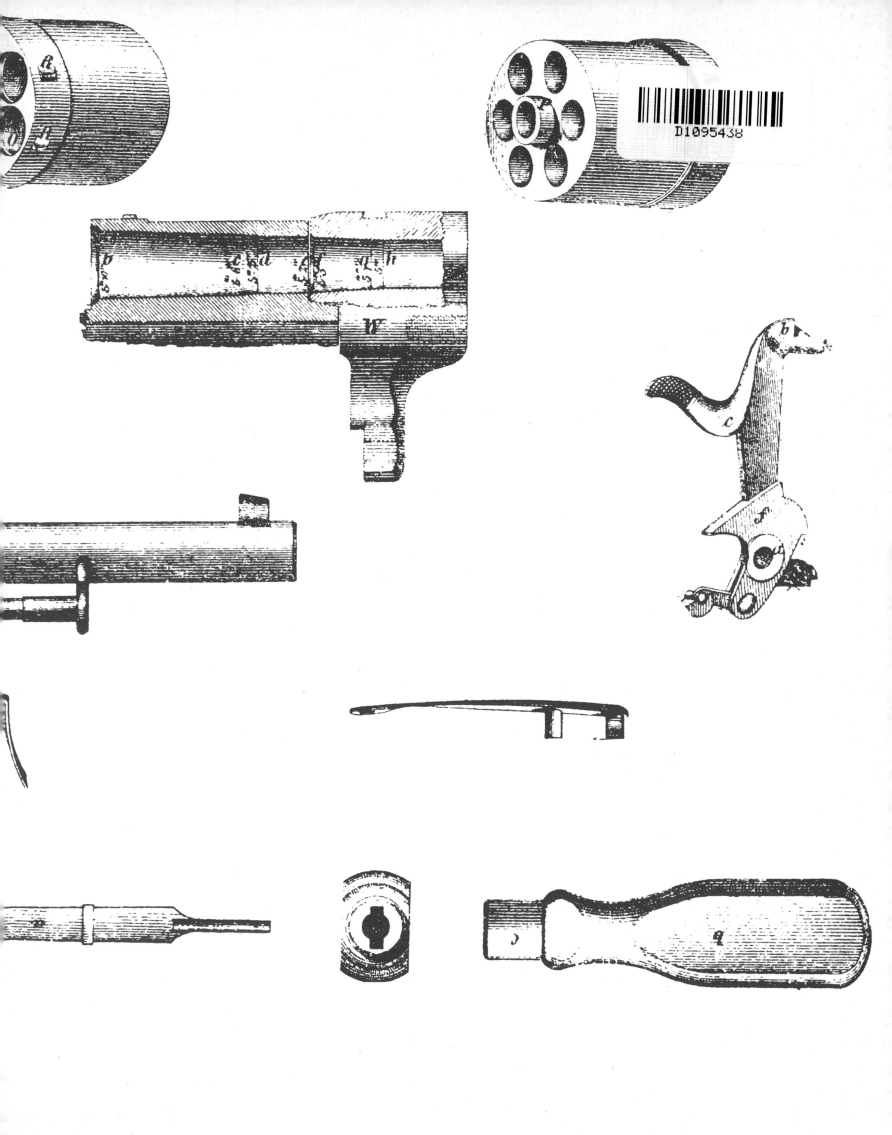

The
Great Century
of
GUNS

Branko Bogdanović   Ivan Valenčak

The Great Century of GUNS

GALLERY BOOKS

An Imprint of W. H. Smith Publishers Inc.
112 Madison Avenue
New York City 10016

Concept and general editing:
Nena Mićunović,
BESSA International Publishing,
Lucerne

Text and technical drawings
for the air-brush illustrations:
Branko Bogdanović

Translation:
Madge Phillips-Tomasević
Una Tomasević

Air-brush illustrations:
Ivan Valenčak

Design:
Gane Aleksić

Editing, picture procuration,
technical drawings, portraits,
cartography and photography:
SPECTRA, Belgrade

Consultants:
Colonel S. Corda
Prof. Dr. D. Petrović
Dipl.-Ing. S. Hartmann

Lithography: Sebi, Milan
Printing and binding:
Sagdos, Brugherio/Milan
Printed in Italy

First American edition
ISBN 0-8317-4070-1

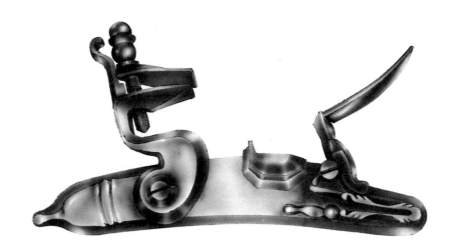

Prussian Lock M.1723.

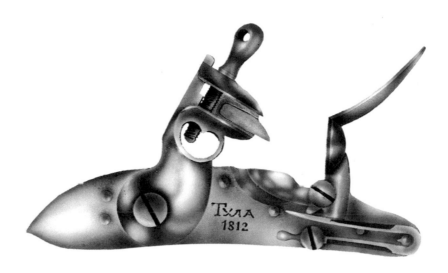

Russian Lock M.1808.

Austrian Lock M.1835.

Russian Lock M.1849.

Contents:

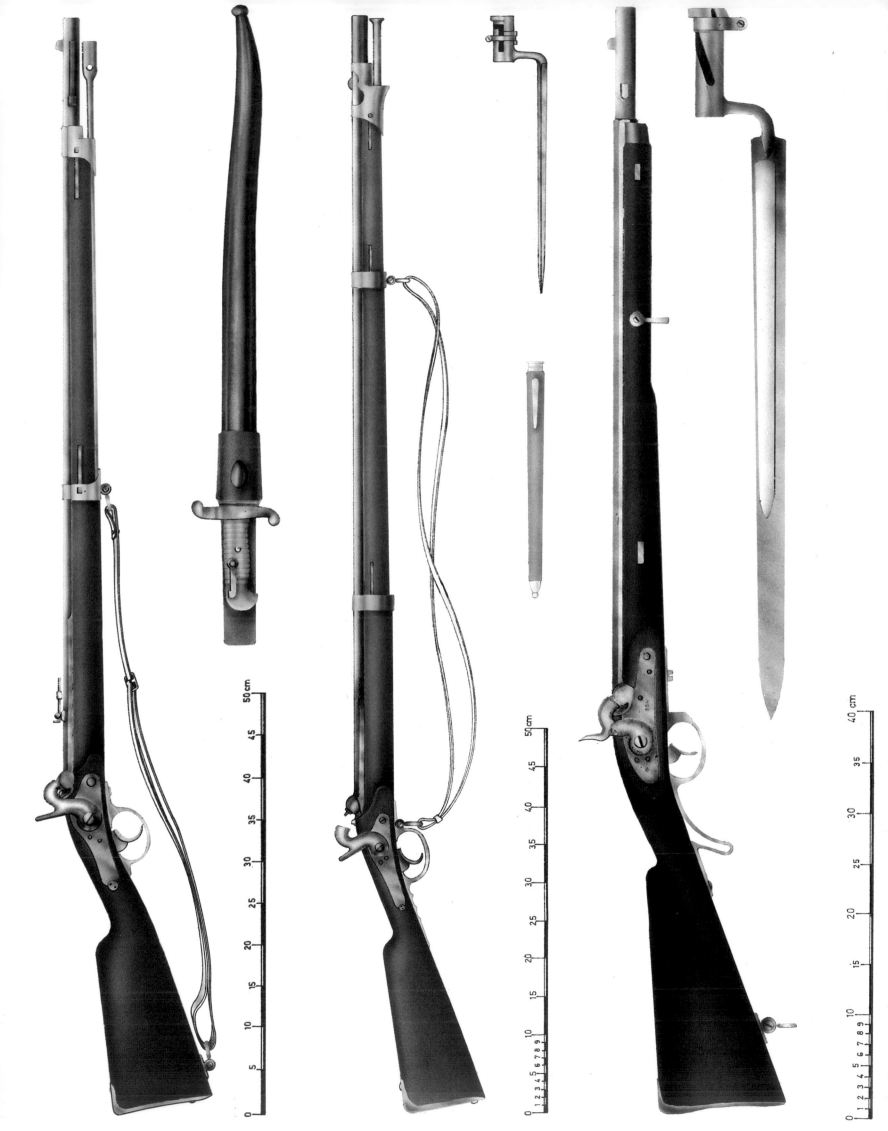

Foreword

Hand guns have a 600-year tradition behind them. When studying their development over this period, one dominant epoch immediately stands out. This roughly corresponds to the 19th century, or rather, the period from the Napoleonic Wars to the end of World War I. By all its characteristics, this period may rightly be called THE GREAT CENTURY OF GUNS.

This is not, of course, to belittle the significance of previous innovations: by the end of the 18th century muskets and pistols had become indispensable military tools, completely replacing sharp-edged waepons in importance. However, the mode of functioning and production, as well as the tactical-technical characteristics of guns at the dawn of the 19th century were based on principles almost 200 years old. European armies entered the Napoleonic Wars with muzzle-loading flintlock muskets whose basic principles had already been set in the 16th century! On the other hand, only 100 years later, World War I ended with breech-loading magazine and automatic guns, whose main characteristics have not undergone any significant change to this day. It was this progression from flintlook muskets to the automatic rifle that made this the great century of guns.

The obvious question that springs to mind is: what caused such a dynamic development of military technology in a relatively short period of time? The century or so which separated the two major wars was marked by numerous local and colonial conflicts, i.e. wars of limited scope. These provided opportunities for testing and improving arms; sometimes, indeed, bitter experiences and the awakening of expansionist territorial aspirations, directly accelerated the development of military technology. There had been large-scale wars in earlier ages, but these did not have any significant influence on the modernization of arms.

Far more important, in this respect, was the organization of regular armies that required large quantities of military supplies. However, the most significant factor was undoubtedly the industrial revolution, which made possible the mass production and improvement of arms.

The industrial revolution was born in Great Britain in the mid-18th century with the construction of James Watt's steam engine. This provided the basis for the rapid development of industry and its movement away from large rivers, until then the main source of power. Furthermore, metallurgy made great progress thanks to the use of coke and a number of technological innovations. Economic liberalism, new means of production and new materials encouraged constructors to try their hand in all fields, from the textile industry to arms. Only when viewed against the background of the progress of technology, engineering and transport does the sudden development of weapons in the 19th century become fully understandable.

From the functional aspect, hand guns passed through four phases in this time period. The first was the use of the archaic muzzle-loading flintlock weapons. The next step was the application of caps in rifles and pistols still loaded through the muzzle. A great improvement in quality was obtained by the introduction of breech-loading single-shot guns which used cartridges with paper and later metal cases. Finally, the last phase was that of repeating magazine guns, which relatively soon became automatic.

All four phases were marked by innumerable constructions, most of them economical and practical, but some on the verge of the fantastic.

It is virtually impossible to include in a single volume even all the solutions that were in fairly wide use in the period between the Napoleonic Wars and World War I. We therefore decided to make a selection of only those constructions that really left their mark on this great century of guns. The choice was not based exclusively on the guns' tactical-technical importance, but also took into account their historical, political and economic significance. As such a broad and free approach to the matter cannot be entirely objective, we must beg the indulgence of the attentive reader if a particular type or construction of gun has been neglected or even omitted.

THE AUTHOR

Opposite, from left to right:

French "à Tige" M.1846 rifle.

Russian M.1853 rifle.

Austrian M.1854 rifle.

Introduction

The first hand guns appeared in Europe in the first third of the 14th century. The earliest representations are probably the drawings made in 1327 by the chaplain of King Edward III of England, Walter de Milmete. In fact, they were no more than simple metal barrels through which metal or stone bullets or arrows were ejected. The powder was lit by a piece of red-hot metal, at first through the muzzle, later through the barrel vent or touch hole. The end of the 14th century and the early years of the 15th saw the first significant changes in guns — the transfer of the barrel vent from the top to the right side of the barrel and the introduction of the flash pan.

A few decades later simple precursors of firing mechanisms, taken from the crossbow, were added to these primitive weapons. The first mechanism, called the "serpent", was an S-shaped bar which had a fixed smouldering fuse or tinder at one end; it was connected to the butt in the middle by its axle, while the lower part served as the trigger. Pressure on the trigger caused the upper end of the bar to fall into the flash pan and ignite the gunpowder. It is difficult to say precisely when such a mechanism first appeared, but as early as 1439 smiths who made them are mentioned in the accountancy books of Presburg.

A much improved type of fire-lock, developed from the serpent mechanism, was to achieve its peak in the late 16th and the 17th century. This improved match-lock consisted of a system of levers, a return spring, a tumbler and a cock, combined on a lock plate. This mechanism allowed for the cocking of the match holder and permitted steadier firing and simpler handling.

The early 16th century saw the development of a completely new type of weapon, the harquebus, its name derived from the English transcription of the German term *Hackenbüchse (Hacken = hook, büchse = firearm)*. The harquebus had a metal hook on the lower side of the front of the barrel which, to offset the recoil, rested during use on some solid object. As part of Emperor Maximilian I's military reforms, in 1499 a section of the *Landsknecht* was equipped with light variants of the harquebus. This was the first time that firearms were used in larger quantities in an army.

During the second decade of the 16th century, a new type of gun mechanism came into use — the wheel-lock. The basic parts of the wheel-lock were the lock plate, hammer, wheel-lock legend, the mainspring an a lever system with a chain. The iron legend with indented edges passed through the flash pan and was connected to the mainspring by a system of levers and a chain. The legend was wound a certain part of the circle and locked there by a special key. A piece of pirytes was lowered onto the edge of the legend ans secured in the jaw of the hammer. The pulling of the hammer released the legend which, moved by the mainspring, turned quickly. The friction of the pirytes and the iron teeth of the legend produced sparks which ignited the powder in the flash pan.

This type of fire-lock was almost certainly German in origin. One of the first to publicise its construction was Martin Löffelholz of Nuremberg, in 1505. A similar solution of the mechanism, at about the same time, was published by Leonardo da Vinci in his *Codex Atlanticus*.

The new mechanism soon caught on in Europe but never achieved popularity beyond its borders. On the other hand, the armies of the Old World never used the wheel-lock to any great extent, since it was too expensive and complicated for a simple infantryman. Wheel-lock guns were accepted only by the cavalry because the earlier match-lock guns were almost useless for fighting on horseback. Thus the wheel-lock mechanism remained the exclusive privilege of huntung guns, luxury and cavalry weapons.

It was the participation of the soldiers of the Duke of Alba in the pacification of the Netherlands from 1567 — 1573 that introduced Europe to a new infantry gun — the musket, created in Spain in the second decade of the 16th century. In comparison with the harquebus, it had a much greater range and a butt ergonomically adapted to rest against the shoulder. The new weapon almost exclusively used the simple and cheap match-lock mechanism. These characteristics helped the musket become the main attribute of the European infantry and retain this status until the late 17th century. The famous Turkish janissaries also had muskets as early as the reign of Suleiman the Magnificent. Through the intervention of the Dutch and the Portugese, match-lock muskets even reached Japan, where they remained in use until the mid-19th century!

The difficulty of maintaining a smouldering fuse in bad weather, and the flames and smoke which constantly revealed the position of the troops and made aiming difficult prompted constructors to seek a better fire-lock solution. Naturally, it had to be safer, simpler and cheaper than the existing wheel-lock

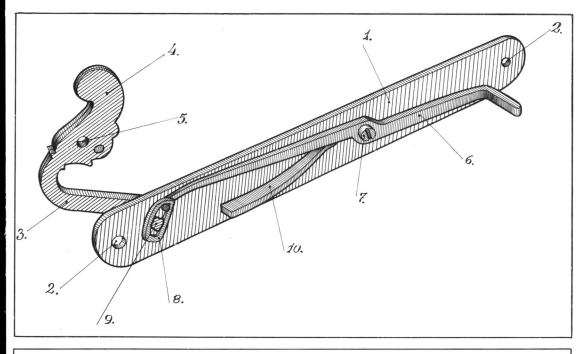

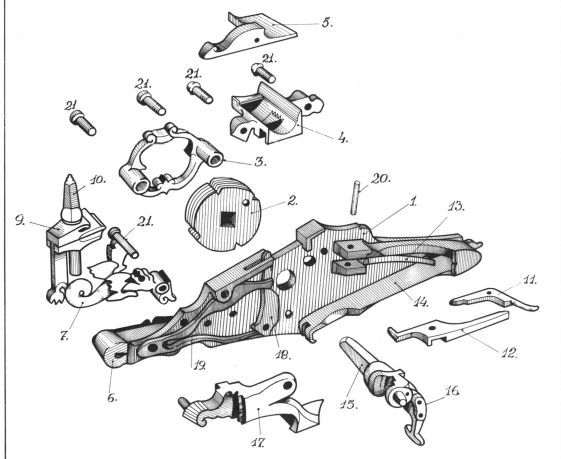

MATCH-LOCK
1. lock plate; 2. lock screw holes; 3. match-holder; 4. jaws; 5. jaw screw holes; 6. operating lever; 7. operating lever screw; 8 – 9. nuss.

WHEEL-LOCK
1. lock plate; 2. wheelock legend; 3. wheel housing ring; 4. flash pan; 5. pan cover; 6. hammer or doghead spring; 7. hammer or doghead; 8. pyrites; 9. top jaw; 10. top jaw screw; 11. primary sear; 12. secondary sear; 13. sear spring; 14. mainspring; 15. spindle; 16. chain; 17. wheel arbor brindle; 18. pan cover shaft; 19. pan cover friction spring; 20. pin; 21. screws.

system. Thus the mid-16th century saw the appearance of a new type of mechanism which, though still imperfect, combined almost all the best features of its predecessors. The Florentine decree of 1547 forbidding the bearing of arms within the city walls mentions "... *archibusi ... da acciaiuolo ...*" *Acciaiuolo* in Italian meant a kind of steel. In fact, this referred to the most advanced arms to date – snaphance muskets and pistols. From the earlier wheel-locks, snaphance guns inherited the hammer with a piece of flint fixed in its jaw. Under the action of the mainspring, the hammer with the flint struck the steel, causing sparks which ignited the powder in the flash pan. The name of this mechanism derived either from the transcription of the Dutch term *snap-hahn* (chicken thieves) or, more likely, from the German *Schnapp-hahn* (pecking fowl). It is interesting that the other name of the Spanish snaphance – Miquelet – was also connected, in legend, with thieves and robbers: it is said to come from the Spanish nickname for robbers – *miquelites*.

During the 16th and 17th centuries several local types of flint-lock mechanisms were invented. They differed mostly in the arrangement and shape of the elements, while the functioning principle remained constant. Of these early, imperfect, mechanisms, the Miquelet was used most widely and for the longest period of time, first and foremost because of its use in weapons of Turko-Balkan origin.

In the early 17th century the most perfect type of snaphance mechanism – the classic flintlock – was made in France. The gunsmith family of Le Bougeoys, of Lisieux in Normandy, certainly deserved most credit for its development. In the French flintlock all the vital parts of the mechanism were placed on the inside of the lock plate. The steel and the pan cover together formed one element, the frizzen battery, which had its own spring. The hammer could be cocked to the first or second degree. This fire-lock was first applied to military arms in its country of origin – France. During the early 18th century, the flintlock also came to be used more in other European countries, completely ousting all the other, archaic mechanisms. From this time onwards, military muskets did not change significantly until the appearance of the most advanced percussion mechanisms.

FLINT-
LOCK
MUSKETS
AND
PISTOLS

The Battle of Leipzig: Prince Karl Schwarzenberg brings news of the victory to the three monarchs.

French M. 1777 and M.AN. IX Muskets

France is regarded as the cradle of the flintlock mechanisms. Nevertheless, the vainglorious king who said of himself, *"L'Etat, c'est moi"*, strongly opposed the introduction of this innovation into the army. Le Tellier (1603 – 1685) Louis XIV's Secretary of War, included an article in the Constitution of 1665 which strictly forbade the use of flintlock by the troops. Moreover, members of military commissions were responsible for ensuring the destruction of such weapons during inspections, and their replacement with traditional ones, at the expense of the captain who had broken the law. Whatever may have induced this otherwise far-sighted man to such a conservative step, already at the time when his son, Louvois (1639 – 1691) took over from him, the flintlock musket started to replace the old match-lock. In 1717, France became the first country to adapt the flintlock musket for the arming of its entire forces.

It was also the first country to issue a royal decree on the production of cartridges. Until then, weapons were loaded either directly, or with paper cartridges. In the former case, a measure of powder was poured from a special horn into the muzzle of the gun, the bullet was then inserted and all this was finally tamped down with a paper or tow stopper by means of a ramrod. The paper cartridge, on the other hand, consisted of a precisely weighed amount of powder and a metal bullet wrapped in paper. Before use in battle, the paper cartridge was usually torn open with the teeth, the powder was poured into the barrel and the bullet was forced down with the remaining paper by a ramrod.

In 1738 Louis XV issued a regulation on the making of uniform cartridges, thereby simplifying the supply of troops with ammunition.

Far-reaching changes in its armament, supply system and organization raised the French Army to the highest level in Europe. At the same time, the M. 1717 musket became a model zealously copied by all continental armies.

During 1776 the French made a number of changes to their muskets. As a starting point for the reconstruction of the gun, the gunsmiths used the 1763 weapon, a descendant of the M. 1717 musket. It had a 17.5 mm calibre barrel, a flintlock mechanism with a flat lock plate, a reinforced flat-faced hammer, an iron pan and a cylindrical touch hole. The shape of the lock plate was also altered in this weapon, in that the rear end of the lock plate terminated in a rounded point. In

Napoleon I Bonaparte (1769 – 1821).

addition, the hammer was further strengthened and the iron pan replaced by one of brass with a forward inclination. At the same time, the touch hole was inclined downwards, simplifying the connection between the fine powder in the pan and the powder in the barrel. The new musket, called the M.1777, had a maximum range of 900 and an effective range of 250 m. These were excellent characteristics for the second half of the 18th century, so that the M.1777 was also copied by other countries of Europe and America. The M.1777 musket was retained, thanks to its good qualities, until almost the middle of the 19th century, and in some African countries is still used.

It should be said at once that the French also knew of the far more accurate rifled weapon. After its experiences of the bloody Seven Years' War, in which the Hessen sharpshooters inflicted so many losses, France started experimenting with these guns. However, the growth of the Army during the revolutionary wars demanded a steady inflow of recruits, and there was insufficient time for the instruction of these mostly unskilled and uneducated men in the complicated handling of rifled weapons. This was the main reason why Napoleon stopped further use of rifles in the Army in 1805. France thus went through all the wars of the Napoleonic era with its old M.1777 musket, albeit somewhat modified in 1800/1801. The lock plate and hammer were given a convex form on the outside, the butt became lighter and slimmer, and the overall length of the weapon was slightly increased. This improved musket was marked as the M.AN.IX. This name may con-

The battle of Caldiero, October 29th, 1805.

fuse, but one must recall that in 1793 the Gregorian calendar was replaced in France by the new Republican. According to the latter, years were counted from the date of the proclamation of the Republic, i.e. November 22, 1792.

The French marshal, Bugeaud, in his work *Aperçus sur quelques détails de guerre,* speaks of the great enthusiasm but also the poor training of French recruits. Describing a battle during the Peninsular War, he states that already one kilometre from the English lines, the French soldiers showed signs of agitation. They covered their nervousness by talking and shouting to one another. The march gradually turned into an undisciplined race. Soon they tossed their shakos on their bayonets and started shouting: *"Vive l'Empereur! En avant, à la baïonette!"*

Duke of Wellington alias Old Nosey, remained still, seemingly unconcerned. This had a demoralising effect on the French recruits: they started slowing down, their steps faltering, and soon fell silent. Only then did the Britons raise their guns and fire on command. Their united and loud "Hoorah!" turned the French ranks into a mass retreating in panic.

These objective words, written down by a marshal, merely confirmed Napoleon's belief that it would be absurd to arm such inexperienced young men with rifles that called for great patience and dexterity in handling.

The huge French army naturally required corresponding quantities of weapons. Manufacturers in Charleville, Saint Etienne, Mutzig, Tulle, Versailles, Liège, Turin, Rouen and Culenborg all produced guns for the needs of the mil-

FRENCH MUSKET M. 1777
- Calibre .... 17.5 mm
- Rifling .... —
- Capacity 1
- Length .... 1,137 mm
- Length of barrel .... 1,520 mm
- Weight ....

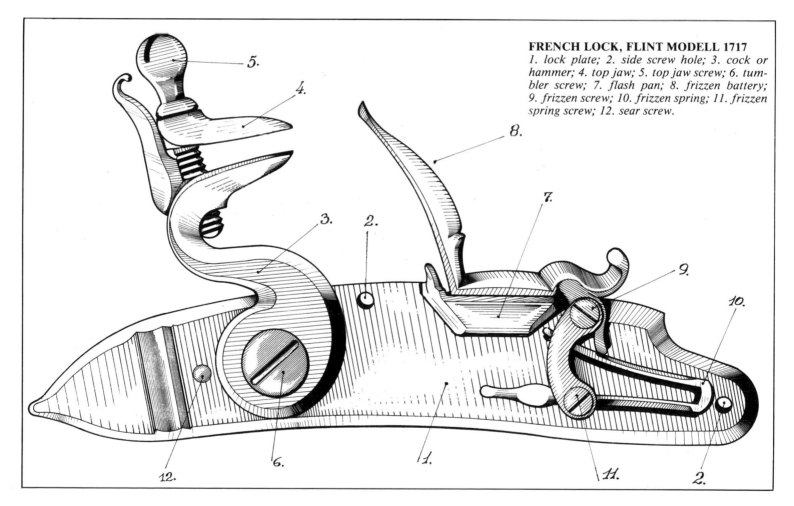

FRENCH LOCK, FLINT MODELL 1717
1. lock plate; 2. side screw hole; 3. cock or hammer; 4. top jaw; 5. top jaw screw; 6. tumbler screw; 7. flash pan; 8. frizzen battery; 9. frizzen screw; 10. frizzen spring; 11. frizzen spring screw; 12. sear screw.

All this time, the English Army stood motionless, like a thin red line, calmly holding their guns to foot. The French came closer and the first shots came from their ranks. Although the distance between the opposing forces was only 300 paces, the experienced veterans for the

itary forces. Since even this did not satisfy the demand, Napoleon did not hesitate to give his troops captured arms as well. During the occupation of Vienna in 1805 and 1809, about 100,000 Austrian guns of various types were carried away from the *Wiener Zeughaus.*

Overleaf:
French musket M. 1777/AN. IX, M. 1777 bayonet and Grenadierring.

15

M^{re} R^{ale}
de Tulle

FUSIL

Valenčak

Baïonnette Mle 1777

ODELE 1777/AN IX

Prussian M.1723/40, Nothardt and Neupreussisch Muskets

PRUSSIAN MUSKET M. 1723/40	
- Calibre	19 – 20 mm
- Rifling	—
- Capacity	1
- Length	1,450 mm
- Length of barrel	1,040 mm
- Weight	4,770 gr

Potsdam GF

Unlike Britain and France, which had their own manufacturers as early as the 17th century, Prussia was obliged to import firearms from Holland, Suhl and Liège. During the reign of Frederick I, in the period between 1713 and 1722, the main supplier of the Prussian Army was the Liège gunsmith, F. Henoul (or Henouville, as he sometimes signed himself). For exceptional services rendered in the arming of the military forces, Henoul was honoured with the title of *Grand Armurier de Sa Majesté le Roy de Prusse.* His influence was decisive as regards both the shape of the mechanism and the overall design of later Prussian flintlock muskets.

Frederick the Great, the famous *Soldatenkönig,* had great amibitions for the organization of the Army. He was well known for his enthusiasm for giant Guardsmen, or *Großen Kerle* as he fondly called them. However, the organization of a powerful army made it necessary to have an arms manufacturing industry, so that the first important Prussian weapons factory was opened in Potsdam in 1722. The organization of this workshop was aided by F. Henoul's son, Philipp, serving as technical consultant, whilst the whole project was financed by bankers from Berlin-Spandau, Splittgerber and Daum.

One of the first products of this workshop was the famous *Infanterie-Flinte* M.1723. The word *Flinte,* used throughout Europe in the 18th century for flintlock muskets, came from the English, flint. The M.1723 was characterised by the serpent shape of its sideplate and escutcheon with the ruler's initials. But this Prussian musket differed most in its butts, resembling a cow's foot in shape, and frequently called just that – *Kuhfuß.* The barrel of the musket was connected to the forestock by a nail. Were it not for this characteristic butt, these Prussian arms would be hard to distinguish from the early Brown Bess muskets. The first important change in the infantry flintlock musket was made six decades later, in 1780, when the *Kuhfuß* butt was replaced by the more modern French type. An innovation of far greater importance was the introduction of a conical touch hole which significantly simplified filling of the flash pan with powder from the barrel. This construction also had one major fault – when the gun was fired, the touch hole let out more flames and gasses than was the case with the traditional solution, and it was thus dangerous for the user. To overcome this, in 1790 the Prussians adopted a six-year-old Austrian idea, the so-called *Feuerschirm* – basically a simple metal shield mounted on the flash pan.

Another similarity between the Prussian and British muskets was the calibre – c. 19.5 mm. During the Napoleonic Wars both Prussian and British soldiers were able to use captured French ammunition of smaller calibre.

Regardless of this advantage, and ignoring the constant threat of France, in the early 19th century Prussia decided to reduce the calibre of its muskets to 15.7 mm. The sources give two different dates as the year of design of this new, "small-calibre", so-called *Nothardt* musket – 1801 and 1805. Already in 1806 war broke out with France. The fact that Prussia brought only six batallions of Guards armed with Nothardt guns to the battlefields near Jena and Auerstädt best showed what an inopportune moment had been chosen to modify infantry arms. To make matters worse, according to the Peace of Tilsit, Berlin was compelled not only to cede France the regions west of Laba, but also to hand over all the M.1801/1805 guns produced!

Only two years later the Prussians forgot their bitter experiences with the Nothardt and started the design of a new, so-called *Neupreußisch* musket. The M.1809 is the best example of how even the practical Germanic spirit succumbed to the charm and quality of the French M.1777/M.AN.IX musket. After all, they had had plenty of occasions on which to verify all the characteristics of this gun to their own detriment. The *Neupreußisch* musket adopted the typical French front bands, also known as the *Grenadierring.* The mechanism took on the form of the AN.IX model, though the *Feuerschirm* was kept on the flash pan and the barrel was connected to the forestock for the first time by bands.

In the famous Battle of Waterloo, the troops of Field-Marshal Prince Gebhard Blücher von Wahlstädt were partly armed with this musket. The *Neupreußisch* M.1809 musket stayed in use in the Prussian infantry until the end of the 1830s, when it was adapted for percussion firing.

Opposite:
Detail of M.1723/40 Prussian musket with Feuerschirm and Serpent type sideplate.

INFANTERIE-FLINTE M. 1725/40

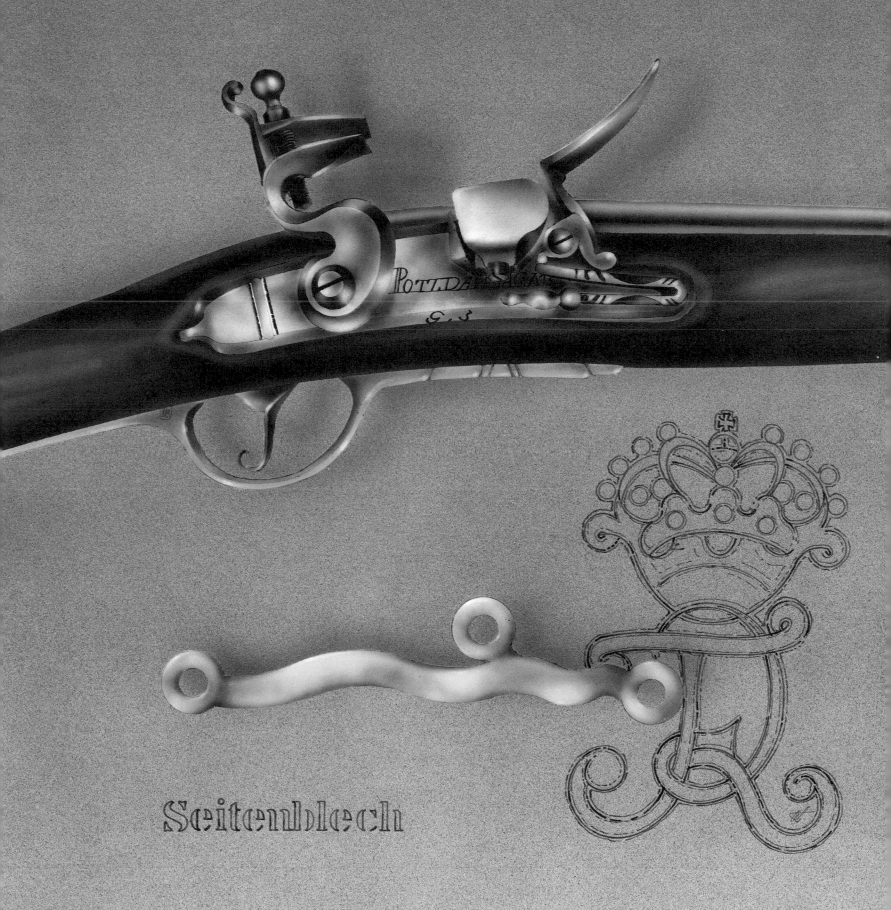

Seitenblech

British Brown Bess Muskets

TOWER

SNAPHANCE LOCK
1. lock plate; 2. cock or hammer; 3. battery or frizzen; 4. pan; 5. pan cover (sliding); 6. pan cover spring; 7. mainspring; 8. sear; 9. sear spring; 10. tumbler; 11. pan cover opening bar.

OLD BREECH PLUG SCREW
1. barrel; 2. bullet; 3. chamber; 4. breech-plug; 5. touch-hole; 6. breech-tang; 7. rear sight.

Soon after France, its opponent across the Channel also introduced flintlock muskets for its forces. Tradition has it that the man responsible for this, in the reign of Queen Anne (1702–1714), was John Churchill, first Duke of Marlborough. In fact, the first examples of British flintlock muskets date from the period between 1725 and 1735. As far as is known today, this weapon originally had brass furniture, a wooden ramrod and a 0.75-inch calibre barrel, connected to the forestock by a nail. It is precisely the lack of bands that differentiated British and continental weapons for almost a century.

By the mid-18th century the English musket had acquired a standard form. Because of its length, 1.6 m, it came to be known as the *Long Land Musket*. During 1765, the barrel of the same weapon was shortened by 100 mm for purely practical reasons. In order to distinguish it from the archaic long muskets, by a decree of 1768 the new gun was named the *Short Land Musket*. The "short" musket was given to the militia and the Army as well as the Royal Navy.

The popular nickname, *Brown Bess,* used for all British flintlock muskets, first appeared in 1785. Its origin has not been satisfactorily explained: of several versions, the most convincing is that *Bess* is an anglicised version of the German *Büchse*. And since in the 18th century the butt of military weapons was mostly painted black, the British reddish-brown colour probably explains the adjective *Brown*.

In the midst of the Napoleonic Wars, Britain decided to make its arms more economical. This led, in 1797, to the removal of the forestock reinforcement and the excessive brass furniture, producing the *New Land Pattern Musket* which, in its naval version, was also called the *Sea Service Musket*. At the same time, manufacturers in Birmingham and London produced the *India Land Pattern Musket* for the needs of the semi-private East India Company. This weapon, 1.4 m long, had a butt without an escutcheon and was made of cheap wood of poorer quality. But this well-conceived diversification of several types of guns for different arms and services was never fully carried through in practice. Due to the ever-increasing needs of the army which was suffering losses in the wars with France, the infantry was armed, of necessity, with the old *Brown Bess* types and the somewhat

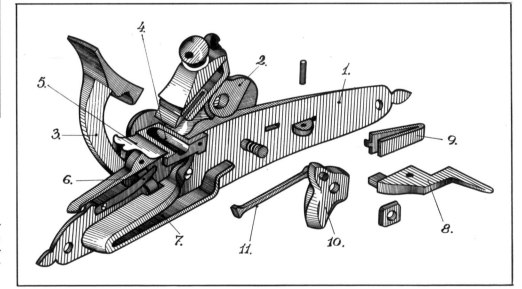

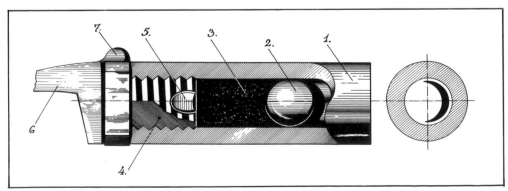

despised *India Land Pattern Muskets* as well. The privilege of bearing the modern *New Land Pattern Muskets* was retained exclusively by the Guards.

In the hands of veterans, the older arms lost nothing of their deadliness, although they required more careful maintenance and handling. Likewise, it was essential to ensure that the powder in the flash pan and barrel remained dry, so that the gun would not misfire at the crucial moment. Otherwise it was necessary to start the long process of "drawing the shots": fresh, dry powder would be poured into the flash pan and ignited by releasing the hammer, thus partly drying the charge in the barrel. The process would be repeated several times, until the powder in the chamber had dried out.

There is a well known episode which happened on the legendary damp morning of the Battle of Waterloo. The veterans of the 42nd Royal Highlanders, the *Black Watch,* found that their powder was damp. Taught by their experience in Spain, the Scots calmly released the hammers of their muskets, drying the charge in the barrel. Tense before the battle, Old Nosey, surveying the position of his troops, was astonished by their behaviour. Wellington obviously did not know *Brown Bess* muskets as well as his men. Afraid that the regiment would not be ready for the decisive battle, he irritably chided Sir Thomas Picton for allowing this. The old commander of the 5th Division to which the *Black Watch* belonged, knew very well what his Highlanders were doing. Out of respect for the Duke, however, he answered that he, too, was surprised by the behaviour of these experienced fighters.

With the arrival of peace after the Congress of Vienna, the old *Brown Bess*

The battle of Waterloo, June 18th, 1815.

muskets were retired, the East India Company received its *India Land Pattern Muskets* and only the *New Land Pattern* guns remained in the Empire's arms. These last faithfully served British soldiers until the mid-19th century.

Overleaf:
European muskets of the 18th and 19th centuries: 1. French M.1777 musket; 2. British Brown Bess New Land Pattern musket; 3. Prussian M.1723/40 (Kuhfuss) musket; 4. Austrian Kommissgewehr M.1754.

1.

2.

3.

4.

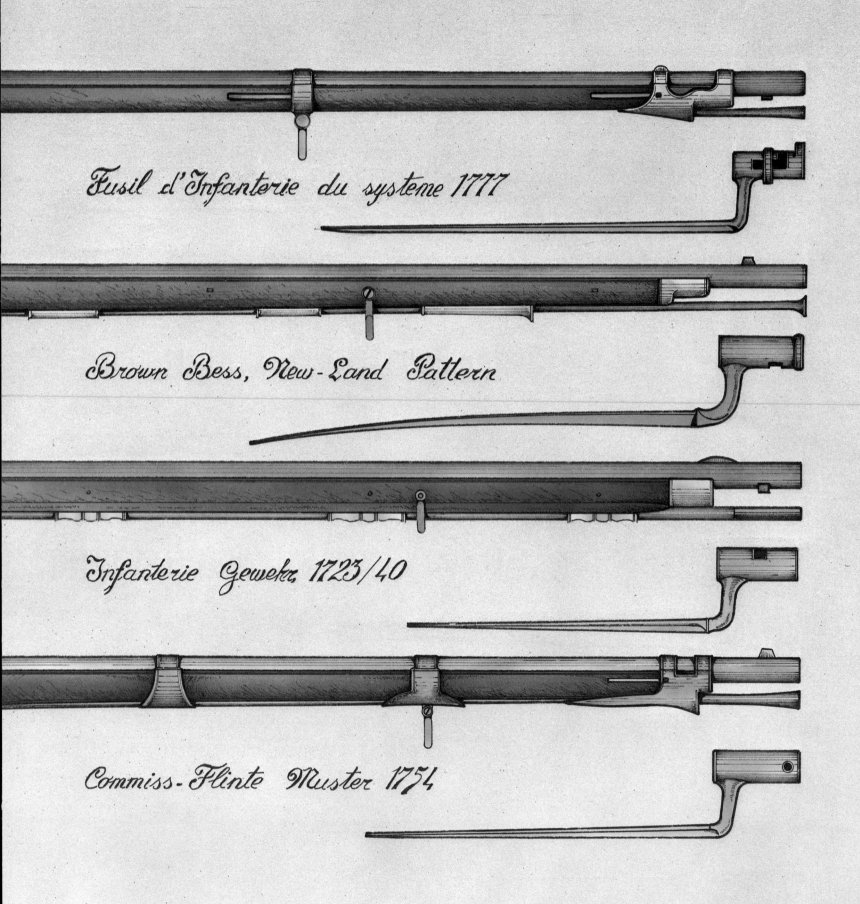

Fusil d'Infanterie du système 1777

Brown Bess, New-Land Pattern

Infanterie Gewehr 1723/40

Commiss-Flinte Muster 1754

Austrian Muskets

From the time of Emperor Maximilian I, Austria by tradition carefully followed all innovations in the field of military technology. In line with this, and in order to free the country of its dependence on imports, in 1656 his descendant, Ferdinand III, settled 17 Dutsch master-gunsmiths and 36 apprentices in Wiener Neustadt. These men were the founders and first workers of the first sizeable Austrian workshop. The imperial army became familiar with flintlocks as early as in 1666. At that time the discerning field marshal, Prince Raimondo Monteuccoli, armed part of his forces with 2000 flintlock muskets bought in Italy. The production of similar guns in the country started at the end of the 17th century, but the first Austrian-made flintlock was not introduced into the army until 1722. The so-called *Ordinäre Flinte* had iron furniture without bands, a wooden ramrod and a 3/2-löth calibre barrel. In the 18th century, the calibre was usually expressed in weights, i.e. the number of lead shot in one pound. Concretely, a 3/2-löth bullet was an 18.3 calibre.

The Austrian commissar Johan Schmied designed a new Austrian gun in 1745, for the first time adopting bands for fixing the barrel to the forestock. Schmied's gun was tested for three years and introduced into the army by the resolution of April 8, 1748. Only six years later, in 1754, a military-technical commission was set up to establish a uniform model of infantry arms. Four different solutions were submitted at the open competition, but it seems that none satisfied all the conditions. This forced the members of the commission to design their own gun, resulting in the M.1754 Kommiss Flinte, a musket which was to be used in the Austrian army over the next 100 years.

The Commission musket retained the old 18.3 mm calibre and set of iron furniture, but was also given a front *Grenadierring*. In the best Austrian tradition of thriftiness, the butt of the M.1754 was of cheap beechwood, painted black. There was an interesting detail on the gun, however: a button on the trigger guard. A cover for the mechanism was attached to

it in bad weather, and during exercises it served to tighten the belt of the gun, so that it would not catch on the equipment.

The Kommiss Flinte was given a conical touch hole in 1781, with the Prussian gun as model. For reasons already mentioned, in 1784 Austria was also the first to introduce the *Feuerschirm*. The new gun, M.1754/84, was used on almost all the battlefields of Europe, serving the imperial army in warfare against the French and the Turks.

Like other continental armies, the Austrian, too, discovered the undoubted high quality of its adversaries' guns during wars with France. In 1798 the Unterberger commission was formed, and by October of the same year had designed a whole family of infantry and cavalry guns based on the French M.1777 and M.1800/01 models. The M.1798 infantry musket had a reduced calibre of 17.68 mm (5/4 löth), a hammer with reinforce and a brass pan. Originally all the furniture was brass, but as early as 1807 the manufacturers returned to the cheaper iron. Only the workshop in Brescia continued the production of a luxurious version of the gun.

Two names are used for the Unterberger gun: M.1798 and M.1808, the latter of which is wrong as it denotes only the date of the musket's mass introduction into the army. Because of operations in the Napoleonic Wars, the rearming of the military forces stagnated for fully ten years! Moreover, a year after the expansion of production, Napoleon carried off a considerable number of these new weapons from the Viennese arsenal.

In the early 19th century the Kommiss guns were given to frontier troops in the *cordon militaria* towards Turkey and to the *Landwehr,* while some were put in the *Zeughaus* as army reserves. This gun was also the subject of legal and illegal trade with rebels on the territory of the Ottoman Empire. It is interesting to note that the M.1798 muskets, used by the infantry, were adapted in the 1840s to the percussion system. The old Kommiss guns, however, faithfully served until the mid-19th century exclusively in their original form.

The battle of Khulm, August 30th, 1813.

AUSTRIAN M. 1754/84 "KOMMISS" MUSKET	
- Calibre	18.3 mm
- Rifling	—
- Capacity	1
- Length	1,510 mm
- Length of barrel	1,120 mm
- Weight	4,860 gr

Opposite:
Detail of the Austrian Kommissgewehr M. 1754 and Grenadierring M. 1754.

COMMISS-FLINTE MUSTER 1754

Cylindergewehr

GRENADIERRING

Kaiferin Maria Therefia

Russian Muskets

As early as the first years of the 18th century Russia was acquainted with the Swedish type of Snapphahn mechanism. Under Peter the Great, these archaic models were slowly replaced by Prussian flintlock types. The same ruler also founded the first state institution for the manufacture of guns, on February 15, 1712 in Tula. Soon after this, the Russians became obsessed with changing muskets: within the first two decades of the 18th century their army changed models no less than five times. Consequently, towards the end of the 18th century, certain infantry regiments were armed with muskets of four or five different calibres and the dragoons with eighteen! During the same century, the effect of infantry fire was consistently underestimated in the Russian army. It is true that a 75% hit-rate was considered an excellent result for muskets at 100 paces. But regardless of their imprecision, exaggerated insistence on the use of bayonets was equally unfounded. From 1709, when this edged weapon was introduced into the Russian army, the emphasis in infantry training was laid on fighting at close quarters with the bayonet. This reached its peak during the reign of Catherine the Great (1762 – 1796), when General Suvorov made up the slogan: "Brave is the bayonet – and stupid the bullet." True, the well-trained and patriotic Russian soldier of the time was unsurpassed in the use of the bayonet, with which he settled almost every battle, while foreign merce-

Congress of Vienna, September 1814 – June 1815.

26

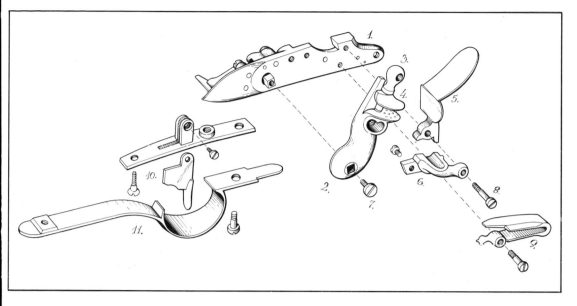

RUSSIAN M. 1839 CARBINE	
- Calibre	16.51 mm
- Rifling	8
- Capacity	1
- Length	730 mm
- Length of barrel	325.1 mm
- Weight	3,030 gr

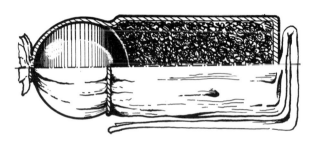

RUSSIAN M.1808 FLINT-LOCK MECHANISM

1. lock plate; 2. cock or hammer; 3. top jaw screw; 4. top jaw; 5. frizzen battery; 6. flash pan; 7. tumbler screw; 8. frizzen screw; 9. frizzen spring; 10. trigger; 11. trigger guard.

PAPER CARTRIDGE FOR SMOOTH--BORE MUZZLE-LOADERS

naries in other European armies were afraid of bayonets. Friedrich II even pledged his men that they would not have to advance on bayonets during battle. With the changes in tactics and the increase in infantry numbers, resulting in a greater density of shot, this type of fighting lost a great deal of its import.

It was not until the death of Paul II (1796 – 1801) that the tragic epoch ended for the Russian army, an epoch marked by inflexible tactics and blind copying of Prussian models. When Alexander I (1801 – 1825) came to the throne, the more advanced French spirit startet to penetrate Russia, and this was to be reflected in the modernization of military arms. Already in 1805 and 1809 two new rifles were designed in Russia, retaining all the better qualities of the M.1777/AN.IX. Although these laid the cornerstone of modern armament, the imperial army retained its love of diversity: all forms of cavalry (dragoons, uhlans, cuirassiers, hussars and cossacks) and the infantry were armed with different types of guns. Fortunately, all these carbines, muskets, rifles and pistols were produced in three Russian workshops – Tula, Sestroreck and Izhevsk.

In the early 19th century, the Tula works were capable of turning out 100,000 weapons a year. In reality, due to lack of raw materials and bad organization, not more than 46,000 had been produced by 1806! Because of a possible French invasion, in 1810 the Ministry of War made every effort to increase the production of the new M.1808 and M.1809 guns. But instead of the planned 146,000, the Army received only 99,000.

The situation changed drastically when the French troops crossed the Russian border in 1812. In production, as in the army, patriotism worked miracles. The workers of the Tula works suddenly managed to turn out 10,000 guns a month as well as repair 3,000 damaged ones. Twelve private workshops located in the same town delivered 3,000 different guns to the army in just one month, and the workshops in Izhevsk and Sestroreck managed, in the most critical period, to produce 18,614 guns and 2,400 pistols!

In the cruel year of 1812, Napoleon felt the power of Russian arms at Borodino.

In the total silence of the morning of August 26th, 110,000 Russian bayonets shimmered in the rosy rays of the dawn. The icon of the Virgin of Smolensk was carried along the long, straight line of soldiers each of whom fell to his knees before it and prayed for the glory of Russian arms. These peasants were defending their fields, led by their adored Kutuzov. This was the same Kutuzov of whom it was said that a great eagle of victory rose and flew over him and who, on hearing that Moscow was burning was to exclaim in anger that the fire would be quenched with the enemy's blood. In the fierce battle, stopped only by nightfall, these men refused to yield an inch of the Borodino fields to the 130,000 Frenchmen.

Four months later, Russian soil was free of "... Gauls or any of their 25 tongues ..."

After the Congress of Vienna, the Russian Army again allowcd itsclf to relax. Just as it was believed that thc *status quo ante bellum* could be maintained on the map of Europe, so the Russian military circles believed that the M.1808 was good enough not to undergo any change. It was not until 1826 and 1828 that Generals Staden and Bontan managed in the face of much opposition to obtain some improvements. They shortened the barrel of the M.1808 by 90 mm, added a rear sight and moved the front sight from the *Grenadier-ring* to the front of the barrel.

A significant change was the increase in the angle of the butt, reducing the recoil. The obstinacy of conservative circles is best illustrated by the absurd fact that in 1839, when almost all of Europe was thinking about or actually changing to percussion weapons, the Russian cavalry was given a new, although rifled, flintlock *stutz!*

Overleaf:
Russian cavalry carbine M.1839, ramrod and initial of Czar Alexander I Romanov.

КРЕМНЕВЫЙ КАВАЛЕРИЙСК

Cavalry Sh

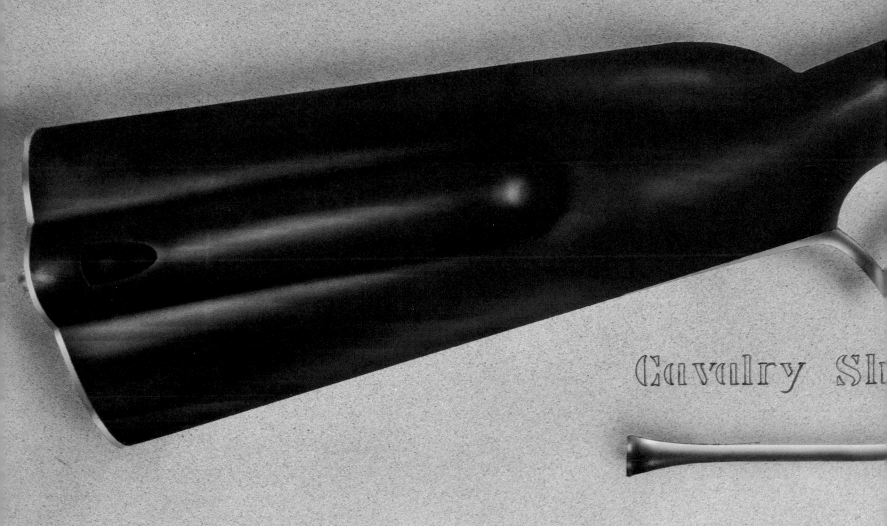

ТУЛА

Й ШТУЦЕР ОБРАЗЦА 1859

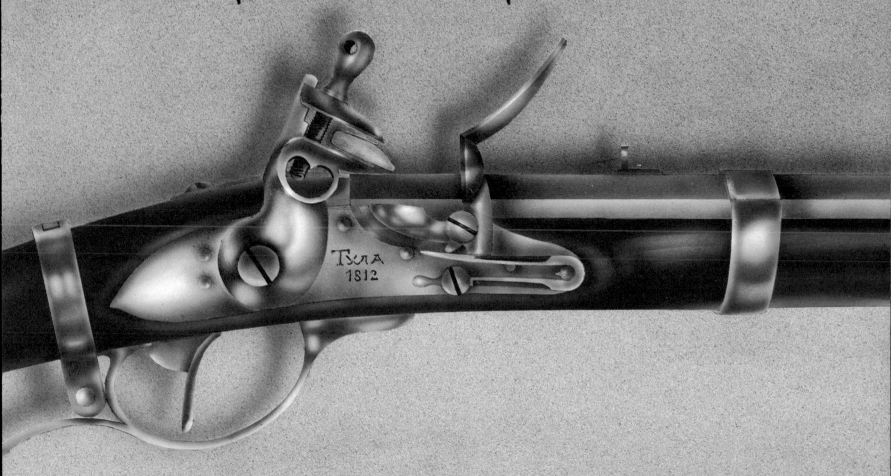

Тула
1812

rt Rifle Model 1859

ШОМПОЛ   Ramrode

American Muskets

In the mid-18th century, guns were a part of everyday life in the 13 British colonies on the North American continent. Almost every colonist had a gun which he used for hunting, personal protection or service in the local militia. This gun was popularly known as the Kentucky or Pennsylvania rifle. Because hunting was its primary function, the Kentucky differed considerably from the classic military muskets. Its tactical-technical characteristics were most similar to the German *Jäger-stutzen*.

In about 1710, a large number of German emigrants who had fled to the New World for religious reasons, settled on the territory of Pennsylvania. Among these were many gunsmiths, who continued the production of their favourite rifled flintlocks in their new homeland. In time, these weapons underwent several changes in America which only added to its quality. To start with, the barrel was considerably lengthened and the calibre reduced to 0.45 inches. The barrel was rifled with seven grooves which curved lengthways to the left for 3/4 of a circle. The relatively small butt of the Kentucky gun was usually made of maplewood and decorated with various motifs in bronze or silver. Thus modified, these rifles attained a wide, even legendary popularity in the New World. Finally, Old Betsy, Philadelphia's gift to Davy Crockett, was also a Kentucky rifle.

At the outbreak of the American Revolution, these guns were the main firing power of the rebels. Good hunters and scouts, veterans of many skirmishes with the French and the Indians, the Americans proved to be excellent marksmen in the war with Britain as well. General Gage's "Redcoats" first felt the precision of the Kentucky rifles in April 1775, during operations near Lexington and Concord. The story recounted by the British Major George Hanger in his book *To All Sportsmen,* is well known. According to Hanger, one American sharpshooter managed to kill the horse of an orderly-bugler with his Kentucky rifle from the then incredible distance of 350 m!

Nevertheless these rifles were not all-powerful. Their great faults were the length of time needed for loading, the fact that a bayonet could not be mounted onto them, and the use of wooden ramrods. Fighters equipped with Kentuckys were at a disadvantage in open combat with the closed formations of an enemy armed with muskets and bayonets. The commander of the Hessen Infantry Regiment, von Heerigen, in his commentary ridiculing the length of time necessary for loading, stated that he could easily hunt down such fighters with just a bayonet. For the same reason, the American general, "Mad Anthony" Wayne, also employed bayoneted muskets against the rifled guns. The Kentucky rifles were therefore used primarily for guerilla warfare, special units and parts of local militia. The young American army, born during the Revolution, needed to be equipped with real, reglemented muskets. The few captured British Brown Bess muskets and some old French guns were certainly not enough. Soon after the outbreak of hostilities at Lexington Green, the local authorities founded the Committees of Safety, whose main job was the organization of production of muskets (quite good copies of the Brown Bess) in local workshops. A year later, on February 23, 1776, the Continental Congress organized its own committee, with the task of dawing up a contract on the production of muskets with bayonets for the needs of the US. Soon after this, the job was given the factories of Lancaster and Trenton, for $ 10,000.

With the surrender of Lord Cornwallis at Yorktown in 1781, the thirteen states of North America were virtually free of London. This was acknowledged *de jure* two years later by the articles of the Peace of Versailles. Regardless of the then seven-year-old Declaration of Thomas Jefferson and the somewhat later Eternal Union, the Confederation still lacked unified and stable foundations. George Washington was once again obliged to enter the scene − during his presidency, the convention in Philadelphia finally accepted the Constitution of the USA in 1787.

According to the Constitution, the Continental army was maintained as the instrument of the new, federal state. It needed, however, a uniform model of musket which would finally put an end to the chaotic diversity of types of infantry arms. The first step in that plan was the act of Congress of April 2, 1794, which founded the Federal Armory in Springfield, Massachussetts. Then followed the decision regarding the best foreign model which could be produced in the country. From the economic and tactical-technical standpoint, the choice of the French M.1763 musket was a very wise decision. This excellent weapon, which had proved its qualities on several continents, was relatively easy and cheap to copy in the USA. The M.1763 musket was also called the Charleville, after one of the French state workshops.

The production of the regular US musket M.1795 started first in the north, in Springfield, and later in the south, at Harper's Ferry. This was a faithful copy of the Charleville musket, which did not detract from its importance. Moreover, the Americans based all their later flintlocks on French models. Thus the M.1808, M.1812 and M.1816 guns were based on the M.1777/M.AN.IX, while the last US flintlock the M.1835, adopted the design and conical touch hole of the French M.1822 musket.

Opposite:
Detail of the mechanism and butt of the American Kentucky rifle.

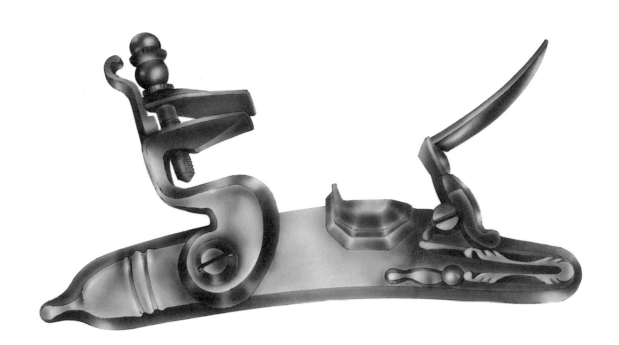

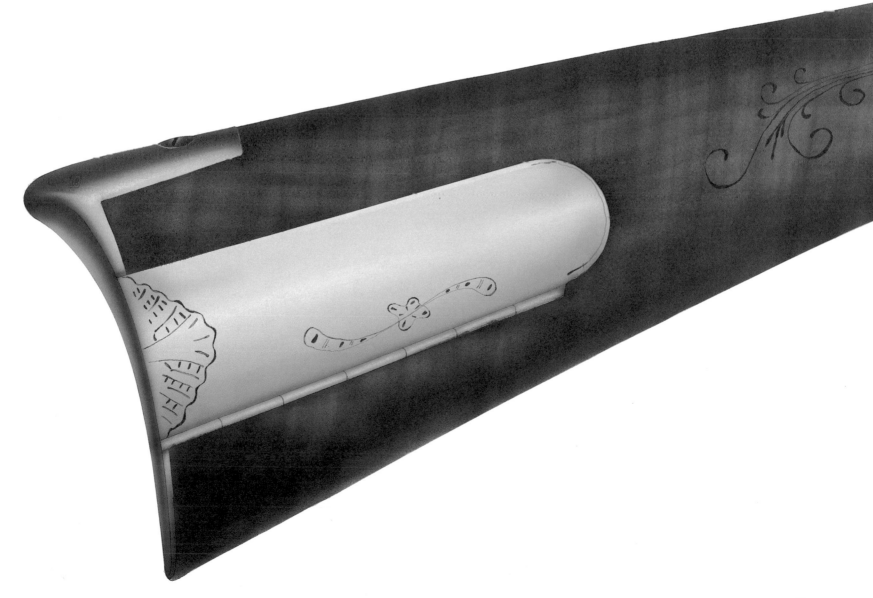

French Cavalry Pistols

French military circles treated the question of cavalry arms as a matter of secondary consideration in the overall military problem, in which the infantry came first. The easiest solution was to use a scaled-down version of musket mechanisms for cavalry pistols, which consequently bore the same model numbers as the guns. The first example of this was M.1763, based on the famous Charleville musket. This cavalry pistol of 17.1 mm calibre had iron furniture, a strong front band and a mechanism which was, in fact, a miniature version of the infantry prototype.

A far more interesting solution was the famous *Pistolet d'arcon à la Mandrin,* or simply the M.1777, in which the whole frame was cast in bronze. The wooden handle ended in a butt-cap shaped like a bronze calotte, and a belt-hook was mounted on the back of the mechanism. This belt-hook, also used on wheel-lock pistols, so-called *puffers,* was soon eliminated from the arms of the French cavalry. The M.1777 pistol is believed to have been designed and constructed by the comptroller and main organizer of arms manufacture at Saint Etienne, Honoré Blanc.

During 1800/1801, the classical M.A-N.IX pistol with a wooden forestock and brass front band in the shape of the infantry Grenadierring was produced for the cavalry. This weapon was of 17.5 mm calibre, and its total length was increased by 20 mm. All the models that followed, M.AN.XIII, M.1816 and M.1822, were practically identical to that of 1800, apart from variations in the shape of the front ring and the head of the ramrod.

The Napoleonic Wars were the period when light cavalry firearms lost their importance, serving almost solely for the personal protection of the rider. Cavalry pistols were most widely used during the 16th and 17th centuries, i.e. after the battle of Dreux in which the German cuirassiers introduced the caracoling. This manoeuvre consisted of a cavalry charge arranged in several rows. When the first row was close enough to fire, they would do so and move back by stepping to the

FRENCH CAVALRY PISTOL M.1777 MECHANISM
1. frame; 2. lock plate; 3. cock or hammer; 4. top jaw; 5. top jaw screw; 6. frizzen battery or steel; 7. bridle; 8. mainspring; 9. mainspring screw; 10. trigger; 11. trigger guard.

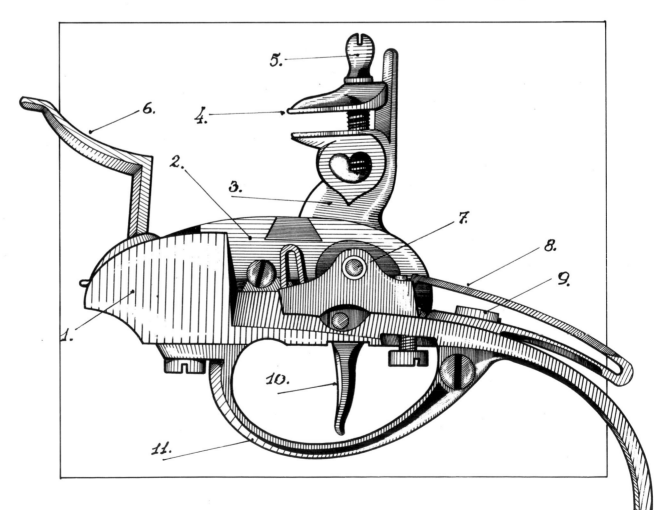

FRENCH M.1777 CAVALRY PISTOL	
- Calibre	17.1 mm
- Rifling	—
- Capacity	1.
- Length	350 mm
- Length of barrel	189 mm
- Weight	1,300 gr

left, opening their ranks for the next row to fire. During the Thirty Years' War, King Gustavus Adolphus of Sweden changed the tactics to a direct-attack method. His famous order was: "Don't fire until you see the whites of the enemy's eyes". The cavalry would gallop straight at the enemy, fire their pistols and then continue to do battle with swords.

During the 18th and 19th centuries, the tactics and purpose of the cavalry changed completely. The attitude of the soldier of the last century to cavalry pistols is perhaps best illustrated by quoting Blume: "A cavalry which uses firearms at a moment at which it can act with the sword should have its horses taken away and its spurs removed."

The battle of Wagram, July 6th, 1809.

The cavalry General Marmont completely ignoring the existence of pistols, claimed: *"La lance doit être l'arme principale et le sabre une arme auxiliaire"* (The lance should be the principal weapon, the sabre auxiliary).

Overleaf:
French cavalry pistol M.1777.

33

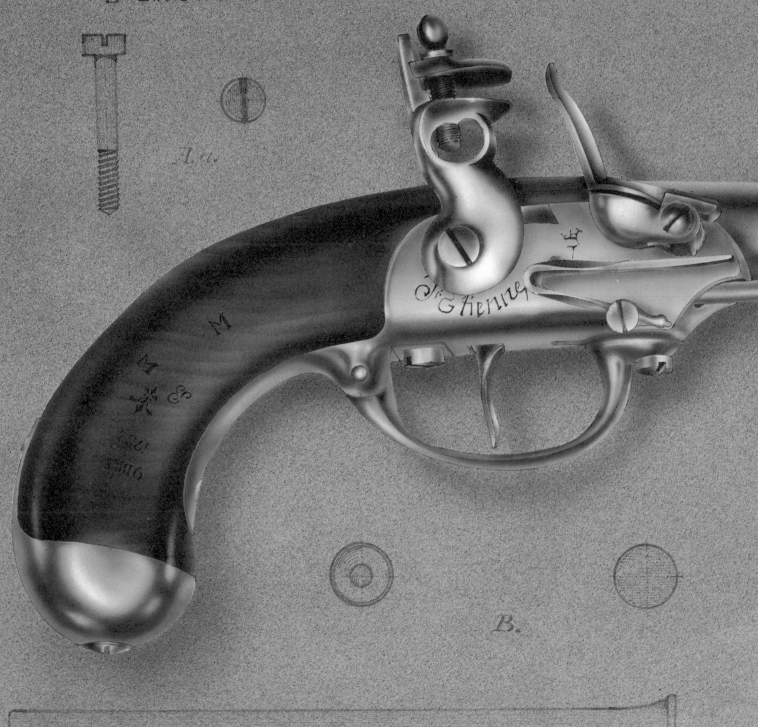

Pistolet d'arcon á la Mandrin

St. Etienne

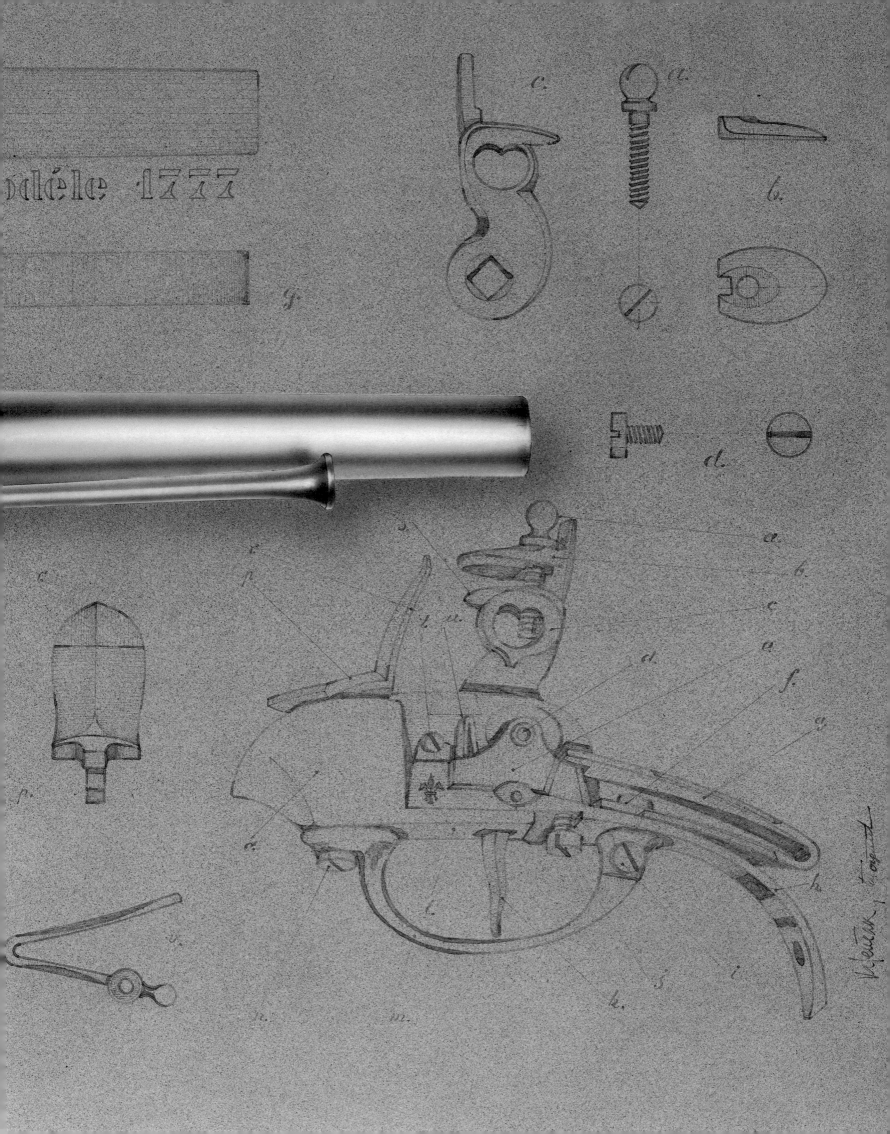

Modéle 1777

Austrian Cavalry Pistols

Regardless of the fact that the Austrian Cavalry also considered firearms inferior to edged weapons, during the 18th century Vienna experimented with the calibre and type of pistol. The regulation cavalry pistols of 1744 and 1746 were often of different forms. During 1781, 50 pairs of cavalry pistols of the Prussian type were also ordered from Potsdam, and tested in squadrons stationed in Vienna.

After the bad experiences of the 1798 campaign, the Unterberger commission prescribed several types of cavalry weapons as well as the infantry gun. Thus the long dragoon and short hussar carbine, the cavalry *Stutz* and cavalry pistol appeared. This last was, in effect, the first standardized and high-quality pistol of the Austrian cavalry. It had a smooth 17.6 mm calibre barrel, the one-piece butt was made of walnut and all the furniture of brass. The early version of the mechanism, adopted from the French model, from the M.1798 musket, had a flat type of lock-plate with a brass pan and a flat-faced hammer with reinforce. Because of its shape, in Austria this type of hammer was called *Herzformige Hahn* (heart-shaped hammer).

After Unterberger's death, a cavalry colonel, B. Bianchini, became the *generaldirector* and president of the arms committee. Though this officer, previously in the service of Italy, spoke little German, he contributed greatly to the development of Austrian arms — with the aid of his interpretor, Captain Pilsak. It is difficult to determine, however, whether it was under Bianchini's influence that the mechanism of the M.1798 cavalry pistol, produced in the first decades of the 19th century, acquired the rounded hammer. In any case, it seems that the design of this pistol satisfied Austrian military circles to such an extent it was not changed until the end of the 1850s! On the other hand, the mechanism was twice adapted to the more modern percussion system. Even so, this weapon was used in frontier and Landwehr regiments in its original flintlock form until the mid-19th century.

It is difficult to say to what extent Austrian cavalrymen used their pistols in battle. Marbot's detailed account of the battle of Austrian and French cuirassiers at Eckmühl (April 22, 1809) provides a vivid description of the fierce cavalry fighting.

"... The enemy charged towards each other like lightning. Trampling everything in front of them, the mass of iron clashed furiously, turning into a huge bloody tangle. In the dusk, touched by the pale light of the rising moon, thousands of bright sparks caused by heavy *pallaschs* striking against the steel of helmets and cuirasses created a wondrous image. The shouts of the soldiers were drowned by the clash of swords and armour. The French and the Austrians were equal in strength, valour and equipment, but the French had both breast and backplate of cuirass whilst the Austrians had only their

Austrian cavalry at the battle of Dürnstein, November 13th, 1805.

breast protected. Thus the French did not need to watch their backs, and inflicted terrible wounds on the enemy with their *pallaschs*. After a few minutes, regardless of their bravery, the Austrians had to withdraw because of their losses. At that moment the battle turned into slaughter. The French cuirassiers pursued the fugitives, striking at their unprotected backs. In the end, it was only thanks to a Hungarian grenadier regiment that a handful of Austrian troopers were saved ..."

According to the author, each French soldier killed cost the Austrians thirteen of their own men! Regardless of the great losses, it seems that neither side at any time reached for the pistols that hung from the pommel of their saddles. It is difficult to believe that Marbot, in his detailed description which goes as far as morbid trivialities, would have forgotten

to mention pistol shots. He, like Marmont, speaks exclusively of the terrible efficiency of swords and the importance of protective equipment, completely ignoring cavalry pistols.

Austrian cavalry at the battle of Dürnstein, November 13th, 1805.

AUSTRIAN M. 1798 CAVALRY PISTOL

- Calibre	17.58 mm
- Rifling	—
- Capacity	1
- Length	453 mm
- Length of barrel	261 mm
- Weight	1,387 gr

Overleaf:
Austrian cavalry pistol M. 1798.

Russian Cavalry Pistols

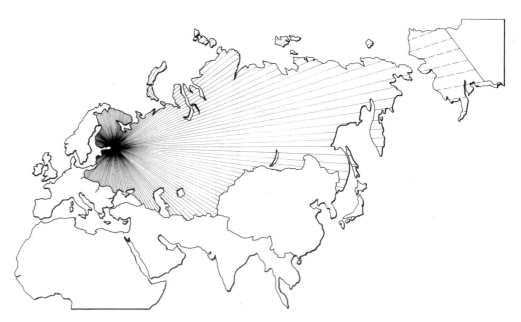

The first Russian dragoon regiment was founded in 1631, and four decades later there were already 11,500 dragoons. The arming of such a powerful cavalry certainly demanded much more attention than in other countries. In 1715, during the reign of Peter the Great, the first stereotyped 6.8 *linien* (17.3 mm) calibre cavalry pistol was issued, giving the Russians enough time to realise all the faults of this short firearm. According to some sources, towards the end of the 18th century a hit by a pistol from the distance of 30 paces was considered a real wonder. This drove St. Petersburg military circles to the other extreme: wishing to equip the cavalry with more accurate weapons, they issued a whole collection of carbines. The large variety of weapons was a consequence of the division of the Russian cavalry into dragoons, uhlans, cuirassiers, hussars and jaegers, all of which, for some curious reason, had to have different guns and pistols. Yet it soon became obvious that horsemen armed with carbines did not gain anything in precision. Because of the awkwardness of loading muzzle-loaders, the carbines had to have as short a barrel as possible. Thus the dragoon and cuirassier carbine M.1809 was 942 mm long, the hussar carbine only 637,5 mm! The percentage of hits in a target 1.2 × 1.8 m at a distance of 160 paces was 50%, from 240 paces, only 25%! To make the carbines at least somewhat more effective, the Russians also worked on constructions with rifled barrels. This led to the cavalry *Stutz* M.1788, 16 mm calibre, and the family of rifled carbines of 6.5 *linien* (16.5 mm): the M.1803 (length of barrel 322.5 mm), M.1818 (length of barrel 331 mm) and M.1839 (length of barrel 325.1 mm).

Because of the complicated and expensive production process, the workshops in Oloneck, Izhevsk, Tula and Sestroreck never managed to deliver a sufficient number of these excellent weapons. Du-ring the Napoleonic Wars, each dragoon, cuirasse, and uhlan regiment had only 16 M.1803 *Stutz* each.

For the above reasons, the pistol retained its title as the main cavalry firearm. As in France and Austria, in Russia, too, pistols, in fact, only followed the development of muskets. All the most important qualities of the gun designed in 1808 were used for the making of the M.1809 cavalry pistol. The appearance of this pistol differed little from other European types, especially as French influence in Russia was apparent in its construction. The only reminder of the previous Prussian domination was the escutcheon with the monogram of the ruler.

The M.1809 pistol was used in the Russian cavalry for almost half a century, though in 1839 it was slightly modified by the removal of part of the forestock, thus reducing its weight.

Mention must also be made here of the partisan cavalry which, in the 1812 campaign eliminated almost one third of Napoleon's army. The character of these regiments was determined by the number of Cossacks in them. Cunning and brave, unsurpassed riders and swordsmen, the Cossack soldiers had one great fault: they were undisciplined and mostly individualists who had little chance in an open battle with regular cavalry formations. Their whole method of fighting, based on sudden, fast attacks with swords, virtually excluded the use of pistols.

In his memoirs, the Russian poet Denis Davidov, a hussar officer, describes a scene which best illustrates the weakness of the Cossacks in the face of well-trained regular troops, expert at handling firearms. His partisan unit, composed mostly of irregular Cossacks, operated in the rear and the flanks of the enemy. One day, they unexpectedly came accross a French Guard division surrounding Napoleon personally. Unthinkingly, in keeping of their usual tactics ... "colonels, officers,

Evolution of the Russian Empire during the 19th century.

Ὤ Ἐρα Στατο вεликомνека Георгίа

non-commissioned officers and a large number of ordinary Cossacks charged the enemy. The (French) lines formed into ranks and repulsed the assault with fire-arms, laughing at the Cossacks' riding skill which was useless here ... The Guard, with Napoleon in its centre, rode through the Cossacks lines as a warship would cut through a fleet of fishing boats."

RUSSIAN M. 1809/39 CAVALRY PISTOL
- Calibre .... 17.78 mm
- Rifling .... —
- Capacity 1
- Length .... 400 mm
- Length of barrel .... 250 mm
- Weight .... 1,400 gr

Icon of St. George, 19th century.

Overleaf:
Russian cavalry pistol M. 1809/39.

СТРЦК
1845

ПИСТОЛЕТ КАВАЛЕРИЙ

CAVALRY PISTOL

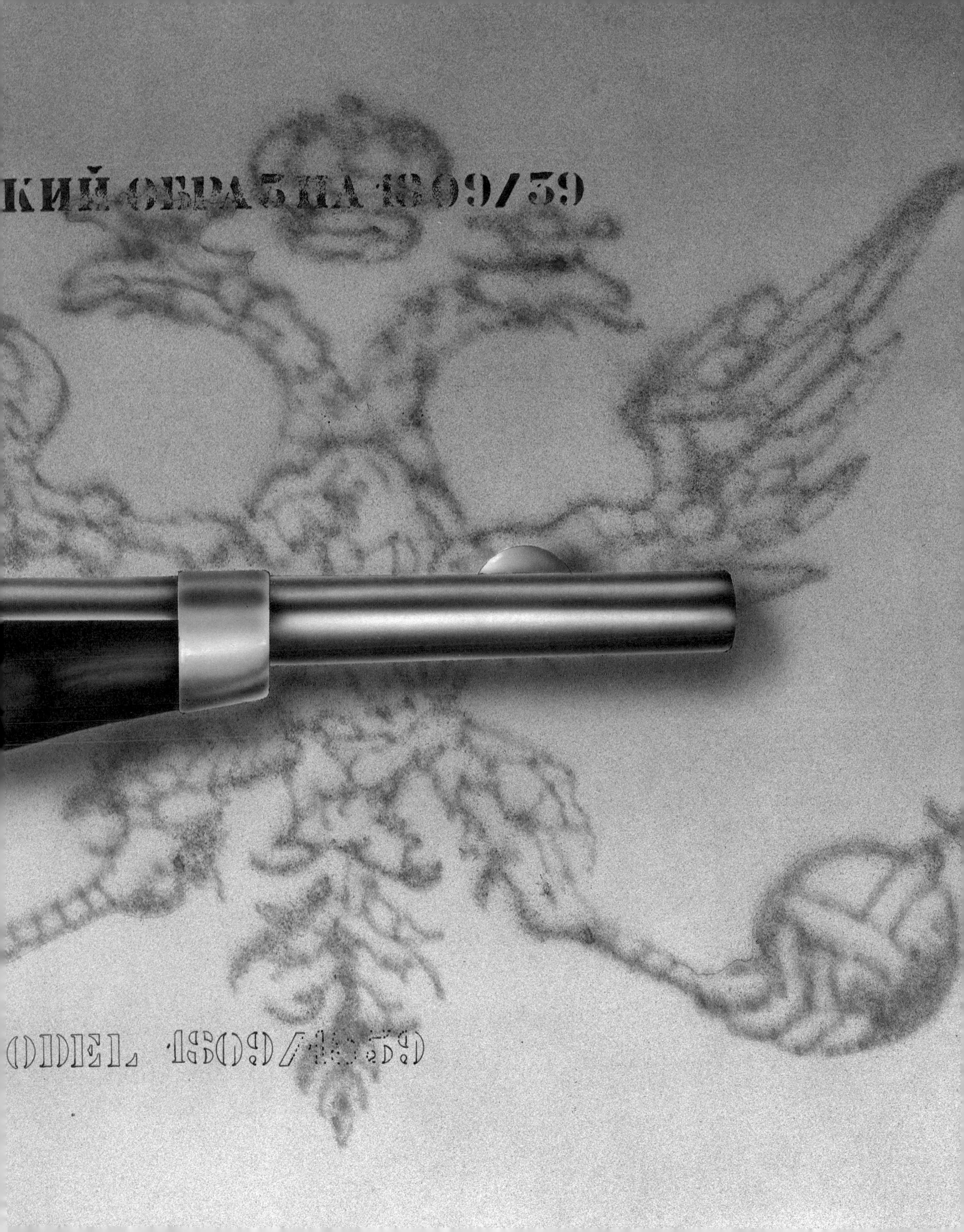

КИЙ ОБРАЗЦА 1809/59

ODEL 1809/1959

MUZZLE-LOADING PERCUSSION MUSKETS, RIFLES AND PISTOLS

Clash of Hungarian hussars and Austrian infantry, 1849.

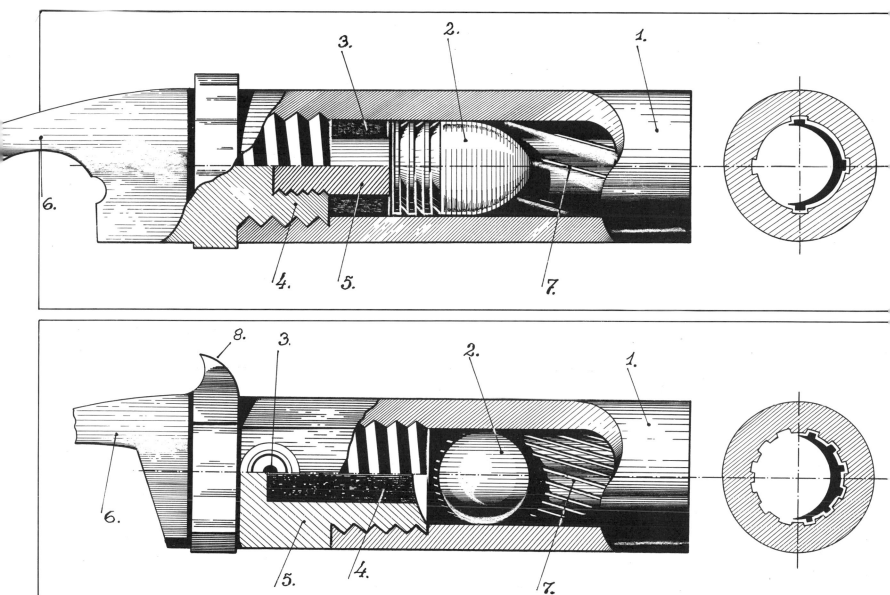

DELVIGNE SYSTEM BREECH-PLUG
1. barrel; 2. bullet; 3. touch-hole; 4. chamber; 5. breech-plug; 6. breech-tang; 7. grooves; 8. rear sight.

THOUVENIN BREECH-PLUG "A Tige"
1. barrel; 2. bullet; 3. chamber; 4. breech-plug; 5. nipple; 6. breech-tang; 7. grooves.

the attention of constructors in the early 19th c. was mostly concentrated on devising a better firing-system. One of the most significant moments in the evolution of fire-arms was the discovery of explosive mixtures activated mechanically (by percussion). Claude Louis Barthollet laid the foundations of explosives by inventing potassium-chloride (KCLO3) in 1786. The unfortunate inventor paid dearly for this invention: his factory in Esonne blew up! Thirteen years later a Briton, Charles E. Howard, whilst attempting to improve Berthollet's invention, discovered mercury fulminate. At this point a clergyman became involved in the history of arms. In 1805, a Scottish Presbyterian minister, Alexander Forsythe, constructed a gun which was the first to use mercury fulminate. In 1807 the Scotsman patented his invention, obliging numerous constructors to seek other percussion-weapons solutions.

Austrian Console System Guns

The practical application of explosive mixtures posed a number of problems for the constructors. The first that had to be solved was the packing of this sensitive preparation. To start with, the explosive powder was compressed into the shape of a tablet or a straw and covered with varnish or wax. This type of "cap" was usually used in old flintlock mechanisms. The straw or tablet was placed either inside or next to the touch-hole, covered by the pan-cover, and the hammer would strike the steel, its impact detonating the explosive mixture.

Naturally, such partial solutions did not meet military standards. On the other hand, the attitude of the military circles in denying *a priori* that percussion weapons could have any future, was inexcusable. An obvious example of this was the attitude of the Austrian commission for weapons' testing. Vienna had experimented with percussion solutions of French origin since 1825. Finally, Beronaldo's commission came to the conclusion that explosive straws and tablets were too small and delicate for rough soldiers' hands, and the mixture itself so hydroscopic as to make it useless in wet weather.

Regardless of the unfavourable attitude of the military, in 1830 a financial official from Milan, Giuseppe Console, constructed the first Austrian percussion gun. He adapted the old M.1798 mechanism by adding a double lever instead of the frizzen and tightening the metal firing pin in the jaw of the hammer. The explosive mixture, compressed into the shape of a straw attached to string (to allow easier manipulation by "rough" soldiers' hands) was inserted in the touch hole and the lever, struck by the hammer, was lowered onto it.

In the same year, Console replaced the bare straw by a tubular cap produced according to Joseph Manton's patent (No. 4285). In 1818, this well-known English gunsmith packed the mixture in a copper tube, thus producing a cap much easier and safer to handle. Similarly, Console filled his copper tube, 3 mm wide and 15 long, with a mixture of powder and potassium chloride. The new cap added to safety and ease of handling Console's mechanism. Only after this did he gather enough courage to submit his solution to the Austrian governor. During 1835, the military commission in Vienna, chaired by Schneider and Augustin, decided to use Console's solution for the adaptation of some flintlocks. The choice fell on the rifled hunting Stutz, M.1807, which with Console's mechanism was given the official designation of Jaegerstützen M.1835. Two years later the jaeger batallions stationed in the Tyrol and Moravia were equipped with this weapon.

However significant the Console mechanism may have been for the introduction of the percussion system into the Austrian Army, it nevertheless was not widely used. However, a certain number of M.1798 cavalry pistols were adapted according to the same principle and the Principality of Modena applied it to its guns. The mass of Austrian infantry still went on using the flintlock system, awaiting the appearance of some better percussion solution.

CONSOLE SYSTEM M. 1835 JÄGERSTUTZEN	
- Calibre	13.9 mm
- Rifling	7
- Capacity	1
- Length	1,050 mm
- Length of barrel	660 mm
- Weight	3,550 gr

Opposite:
Austrian Jägerstutzen (Short rifle) M.1835 Console system and detail of bayonet.

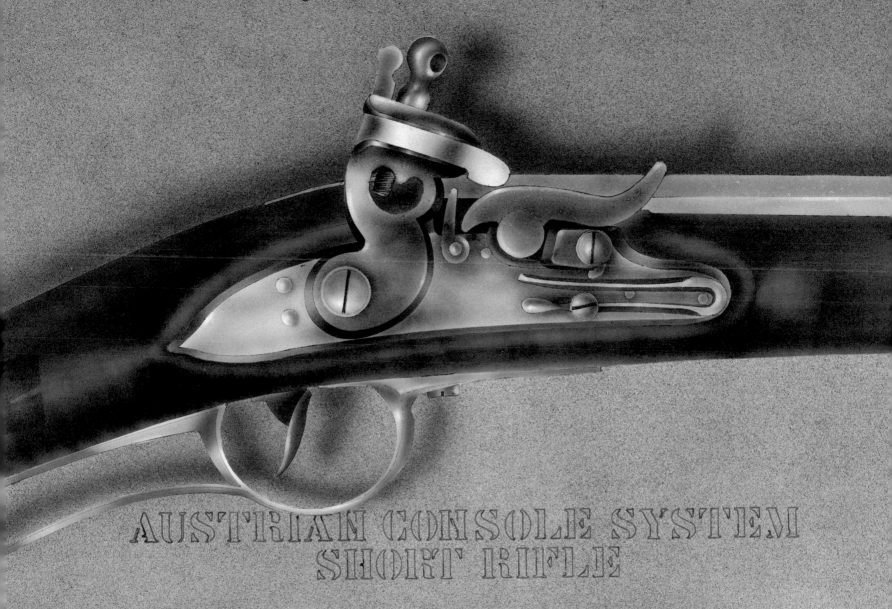

AUSTRIAN CONSOLE SYSTEM
SHORT RIFLE

Bajonett M. 1807

Austrian Augustin and Lorenz System Guns

Augustin, Vinzenz, born March 27, 1780, in Pest, died March 6, 1859, in Vienna. Austrian officer. In 1814, founded Austrian rocket battery. Raised to the rank of *Feldzeugmeister* in 1849, and later appointed general director of the Artillery. From 1848 was in charge of the building of the Vienna Arsenal.

During 1840, the president of the commission for the choice of arms, Field Marshal Baron Vinzenz Augustin, took on the modernization of Console's construction. By Order 3426 of December of the same year, his modification of the mechanism was introduced for all arms of the Austrian Army. Augustin actually added a new pan to the old mechanism into which the tubular touch-hole partially entered. A special pan cover through which a massive firing pin passed was lowered onto the pan. The hammer was given a new, monolithic form with a flattened head. The cap was pushed into the touch hole and the pan cover was lowered onto it. The flattened part of the hammer struck the firing pin which transferred the impetus to the cap. Augustin also changed the composition of the cap: a brass rolled tube was filled with a mixture of KCLO3, charcoal and sulphur. The cap was covered with mastic for protection against the damp and was attached with wire to the paper cartridge. At first the Austrians only adapted the old flintlocks to the Augustin system. By a decree of 1841, a new Augustin mechanism was introduced into the army, the M.1842, made by a special casting procedure. After this, M.1840 guns with adapted mechanisms (about 80,000 of them) were issued to garrisons in Vienna and Moravia and in 1846, to all batallions of the II Line *Landwehr*. Some frontier regiments entered the war with these weapons in 1859, and it was still to be found in arsenals in 1863.

Baron Augustin also greatly improved the ballistics of Austrian guns. For easier loading, the closer fit of the bullet and the barrel and the compressing of the bullet into the grooves, he adapted the Delvigne powder chamber to the M.1842 Stutz. Five years later, Augustin developed Theuvenin's *"à tige"* (nipple) idea, combining it with the Delvigne-Tamisier cylindrical-conical bullet.

Thus by the mid-century the Austrian Army had a whole collection of Augustin solutions. However significant they may have been for the improvement of guns, they also created a real problem regarding different calibres, ammunition and mechanisms. The first step towards unification of guns was only made by the work of K.k. Oberwerkführer Lorenz.

During 1852, Lorenz, working in the Vienna Arsenal, developed the so-called "compression bullet" on the basis of Wilkinson's ideas. Since it had a calibre 0.1 mm less than the diameter of the barrel, the compression bullet could be easily slipped down the rifles to the powder charge. Following detonation, as a result of the pressure of powder gasses and its own inertia, the bullet was compressed, thereby increasing in diameter and pressing into the grooves. Manufactured exclusively in 13.9 mm calibre, the gun with Lorenz's bullet had outstanding ballistic qualities for its time.

Lorenz also exploited the old idea of a cap in the shape of a copper tip filled with a friction mixture. Even today there are conflicting views as to whether this solution was devised by the Englishman Joseph Egg or the American Joshua Shaw. This question certainly did not bother Lorenz. He adopted the simple lug screwed into the barrel, on which the cap was

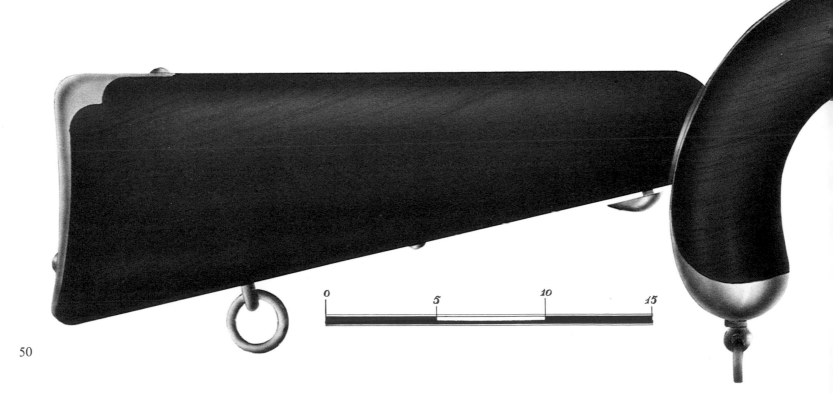

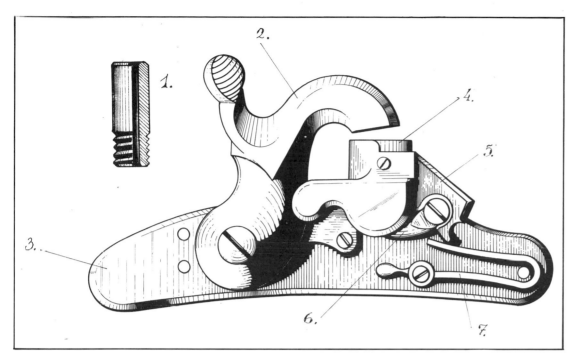

designed until 1859. The quality of Lorenz's weapons was demonstrated in the war of 1859. But in time it became outdated. Although some Austrian guns were improved during 1862 by the introduction of steel barrels, in the war of 1866 the percussion muzzle-loading systems could not compete with the Prussian breech-loading arms.

Frequent changes on the Austrian percussion weapons resulted in the accumulation in arsenals of a large number of guns that had been successively withdrawn. In fact, these were adaptations of Augustin's models from 1840 and Lorenz's rifles with iron barrels from 1854. The Austrians never had the same commercial spirit as, for example, the Belgians and the French, but they nevertheless managed to sell a considerable number of these outdated weapons, their best customers certainly being the neighbouring Balkan principalities. The Civil War in America opened up a new market which absorbed virtually everything offered it. In 1861 the New York firm, Kruse, Drexel and Schmidt, imported 12,000 old and 13,000 "new" guns of the Augustin M.1840 system. Following the defeat at Bull Run, the situation became so critical for the North that almost any weapon was welcome. Consequently, General Fremont purchased all 25,000

AUGUSTIN SYSTEM PERCUSSION MECHANISM
1. barrel-vent; 2. hammer; 3. lock-plate; 4. striker; 5. pan cover; 6. pan; 7. pan cover spring.

Austrian M.1860 Lorenz system cavalry pistol with disassembling butt.

LORENZ SYSTEM M. 1860 CAVALRY PISTOL
- Calibre .... 13.9 mm
- Rifling 4
- Capacity 1
- Length with butt ... 660 mm
- Length of barrel ... 265 mm
- Weight .... 2,300 – 2,575 gr

placed. A direct blow of the hammer on the cap caused detonation which ignited the powder charge through the channel of the lug. In this way the percussion mechanism was simplified to the maximum extent without any loss of safety. Pleased with Lorenz's construction, in 1854 the government in Vienna adopted it for the weapons of all the armed forces. The only exception was the cavalry, which since 1850 had used Augustin's M.1844 pistol adapted to the conventional cap and lug. Lorenz's new cavalry gun, calibre 13.9 mm (with four grooves), was not

Augustin guns for his troops. It must be admitted that this was not a very satisfactory purchase, for Augustin's tubular caps were hard to find, and a part of this consignment had to be adapted to the conventional cap and lug.

During 1862, Colonel Schuyler placed an order for 70,048 Lorenz M.1854 guns, opening up the American market to this Austrian weapon. By the end of the Civil War, the Americans had imported about 200,000 Lorenz guns, some of which were adapted for use with 0.58-inch ammunition.

51

Belgian Percussion Guns

In the early 19th century, Liège in Belgium was one of the world's major arms manufacturing centres, and the astute arms merchants of this city managed to sell these goods on virtually all continents. Their weapons were relatively cheap and in no way inferior to other European products. The quality of Belgian arms had been considerably raised by the rigorous law on testing all finished products which had been passed back in 1816, in the time of Dutch rule. After the establishment of the monarchy under Leopold I, this law was confirmed in 1838, and eight years later made more precise. It did, however, contain a clause which was to lead to a decline in the quality of civilian weapons manufactured for the European commercial market: such weapons intended for sale abroad did not have to bear a stamp. They were packed in sealed crates which were not to be opened on the territory of Belgium, nor could such weapons be sold in the country.

The Belgian priciple of adapting old flintlock arms was to play a very important role in a number of foreign armies. Around 1838, the Belgians closed the old touch-hole of flintlock weapons, drilled the barrel on the upper right-hand side of the powder chamber and screwed a traditional lug into the opening. All unnecessary parts were removed from the mechanism, and a new hammer of massive form with an indented head was mounted on it. This simple and cheap solution could be applied to all types of flintlock, and was safer than the solution with tubular straws and required only a minimal change in the arsenal.

By 1840 Belgium had modified all its infantry weapons in this manner, so that it could now turn to exporting. The firm, J. Lemille, alone manufactured 60 different types of guns for the needs of Austria, Bavaria, Belgium, Denmark, France, Great Britain, the Hanseatic League, Holland, Italy, Luxemburg, Mexico, Norway, Oldenburg, Piedmont, Prussia, Spain, Sweden, Switzerland and Venezuela. Realizing the advantages of the Belgian system, many countries which were reluctant to spend money on the production of new weapons in view of the huge quantities of flintlock muskets at their disposal, bought the licence and started adapting their own arsenals.

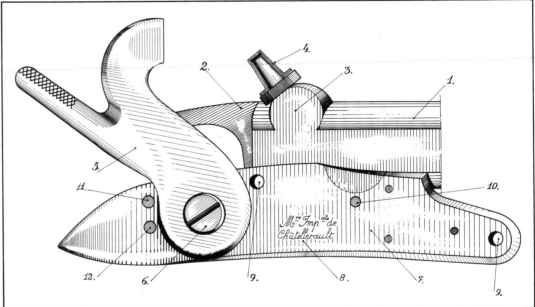

FLINTLOCK PLATE MODIFIED TO PERCUSSION M.1841
1. barrel; 2. breech-tang; 3. lug; 4. cap; 5.hammer; 6. tumbler screw; 7. sideplate; 8. maker's name; 9. side screw holes; 10. mainspring screw; 11. sear spring screw; 12. sear screw.

Opposite:
Belgian percussion rifle, mid-19th century.

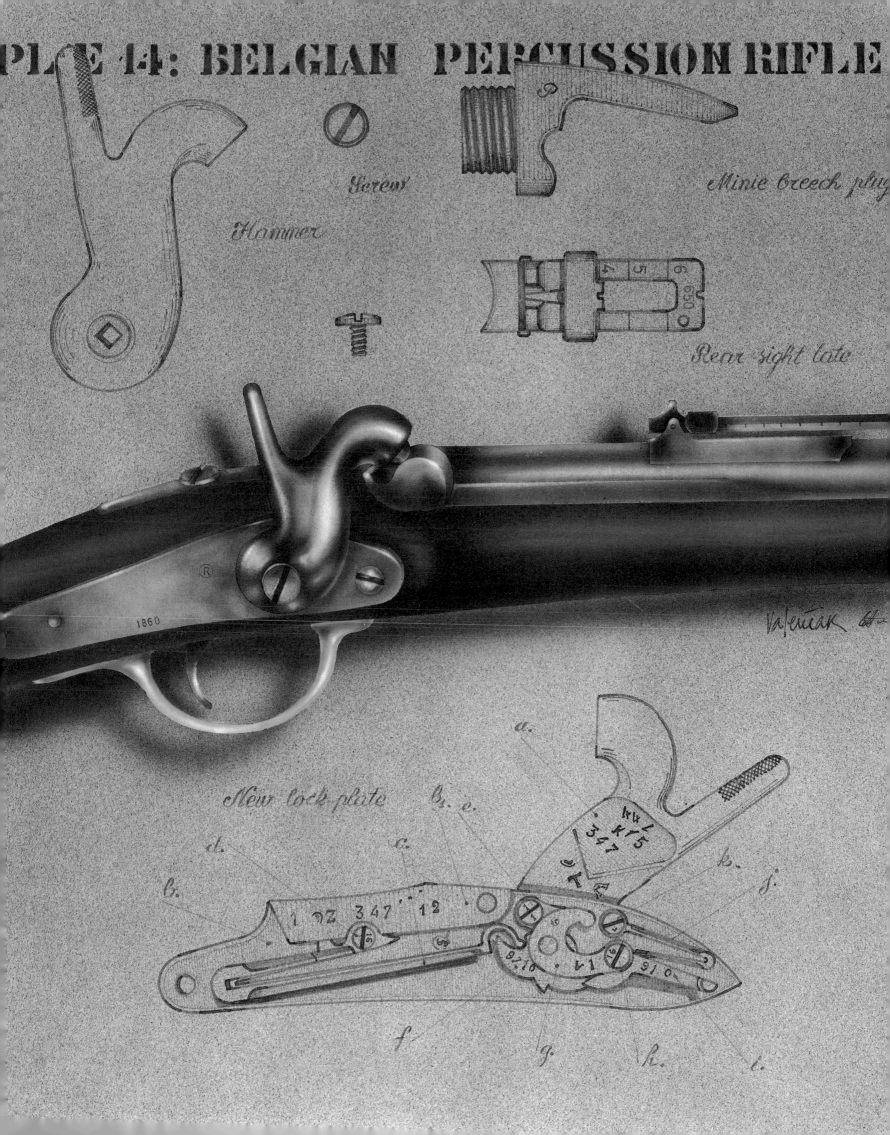

Screw

Minie breech plug

Hammer

Rear sight late

New lock plate

1860

French Percussion Guns

France was one of the first states in which experiments with percussion firing were carried out. Nevertheless, its military circles decided, on July 17, 1840, in favour of the Belgian system of adaptation, which had proved to be the cheapest and most practical. A year later the French deviated from this principle to a certain extent, moving the nipple to the right-hand side of the powder chamber. In fact, the newly designed French gun made use of an original back-action mechanism. This type was first applied by Pontcharra as early as 1835, and was adopted by the Belgians and all the nations who followed in their footsteps.

Relatively satisfied with the percussion system, the French decided to turn their attention to the ballistic qualities of their arms. In this connection they made a mistake in 1842 by increasing the calibre of smooth-bore guns from 17.5 to 18 mm, firmly convinced that a heavier bullet would show a better ballistic perfomance! Regardless of this error which was later to cause serious problems, the French sharpshooter school at Vincennes was to play

a role of crucial importance for the ballistics of these weapons. Stationed at Vincennes was the VI Battalion of the Duke of Orleans' *Chasseurs d'Afrique,* an experimental unit whose officers also engaged in the construction of weapons. In the 1830s, Captain Delvigne devised a separate powder chamber. Following his idea, the breech plug, which was screwed into the barrel, was lengthened and a powder chamber with a diameter less than the calibre of the barrel was drilled in it. During loading, the powder lay free in the chamber, and the bullet easily slid to its edge. Under the heavy blows of the ramrod, the bullet was compressed, increased in diameter, pressed into the grooves, and at the same time perfectly filled the clearance. Shortly afterwards, Delvigne designed a new, cylindrical-conical bullet. This type of gun had good ballistic qualities, and for this reason the Duke of Orleans equipped his troops with it during the Algerian campaign. One episode from this colonial adventure eloquently testifies to the quality of Delvigne's gun. While out reconnoitering, the

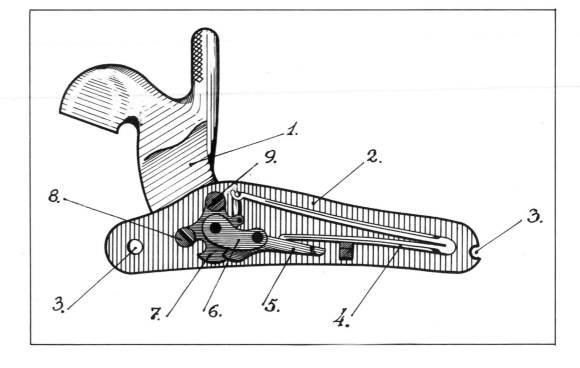

FRENCH "à Tige" M. 1846 RIFLE	
- Calibre	17.75 – 17.795 mm
- Rifling	4
- Capacity	1
- Length	1,285 mm
- Length of barrel	865 mm
- Weight	4,200 gr

BACK ACTION PERCUSSION LOCK M.1846
1. hammer; 2. lock plate; 3. side screw holes; 4. mainspring; 5. sear; 6. bridle; 7. tumbler; 8 – 9. tumbler screw.

DELVIGNE SYSTEM PAPER CARTRIDGE

Duke was irritated by the provocative behaviour of an Arab sheik who kept at a safe distance of almost 600 m. Furious, the Duke of Orleans offered five francs to any soldier who shot the Arab. A chasseur stepped forward and brought down the "impudent" sheik with a bullet through the heart!

In 1846 Captain Thouvenin patented the new *"à tige"* solution of a breech plug with a nipple. The charge lay free around the nipple, 38 mm long, which was screwed into the breech plug. The base of the cylindrical-conical bullet which as with Delvigne, was compressed by the blows of the ramrod, rested on the head of the tige.

This breech-plug solution enabled the constructors at Vincennes to pay greater attention to the rifling of the old smooth-bore barrel. But first of all it was necessary to solve the problem created by the previous increase in the calibre of muzzle-loaders. Boring had considerably thinned the walls of the barrel, particularly at the muzzle. Practical necessity therefore imposed the idea of grooves of progressive depth. This was the brain-child of officers Minié and Tamisier, who introduced grooves that were 0.5 mm deep at the powder chamber and only 0.005 mm at the muzzle!

Parallel with innovation on the breech plug and grooves, efforts were made at Vincennes to improve the actual bullet. Captain Claude Etienne Minié improved Delvigne's projectile by shaping the top. To achieve a flatter ballistic trajectory,

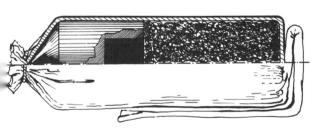

Captain Tamisier moved the centre of gravity of Minié's bullet towards the top, at the same time introducing wider rim grooves which increased air resistance behind the central point of gravity. Immediately after that, Nesler, commander of the Vincennes school, designed what is known as the expansive bullet. This had a hollow at the base which permitted the bullet under pressure of powder gasses to expand and fit into the grooves of the barrel. In this way the problem of the slow compression of the bullet by ramrod was

overcome. Minié bettered this idea by placing a plug or cup in the shape of a steel calotte in the hollow, one of the advantages of which was that it prevented deformation of the bullet during handling.

With these solutions the rifled muzzle-loading percussion gun reached its peak, displaying its superiority over the smooth-bore weapons, its safeness in firing and good ballistic features. All these qualities were to be seen to advantage in the Crimean War.

Clash or regular French troops and Garibaldi's volunteers.

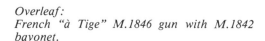

Overleaf:
French "à Tige" M.1846 gun with M.1842 bayonet.

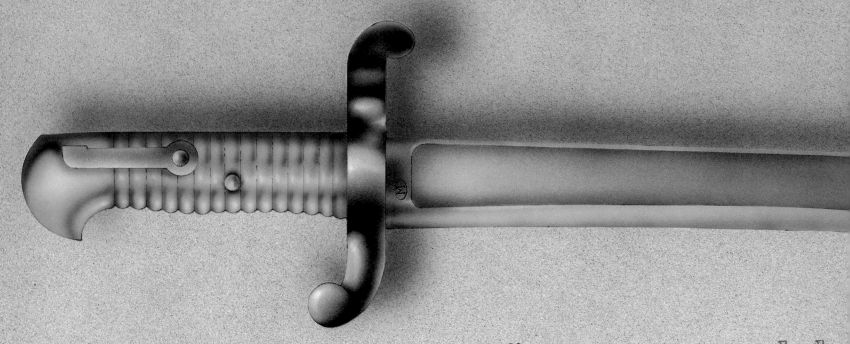

Baïonnette modèle

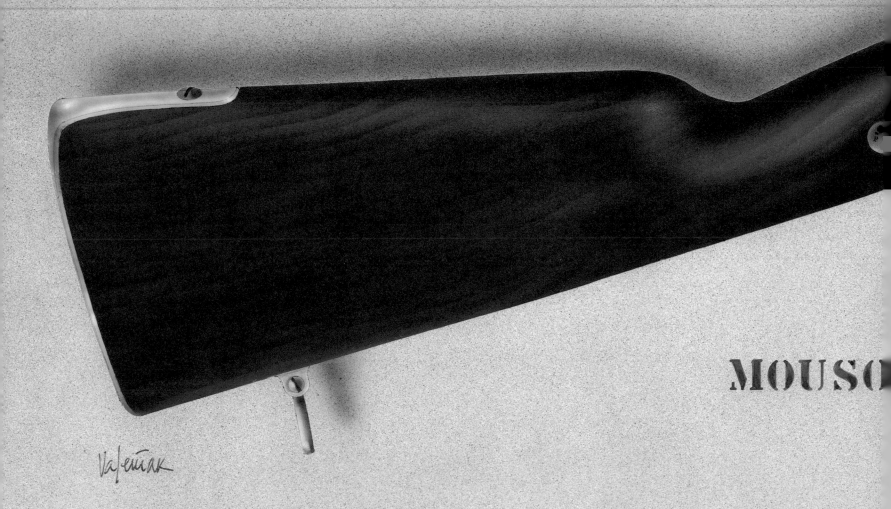

MOUSQ

Valentak

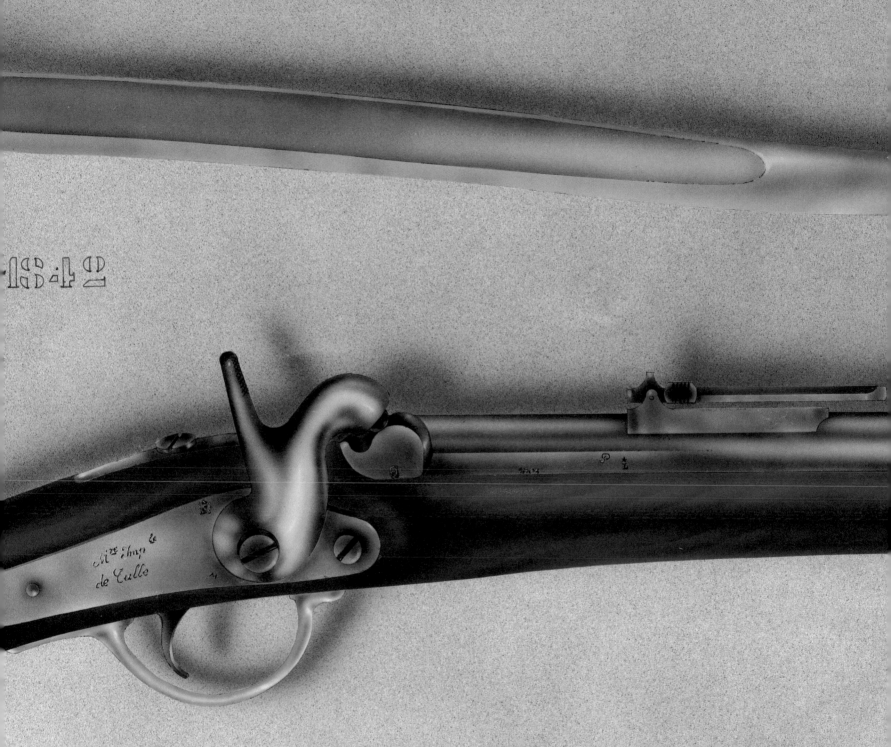

Mre Iple de Tulle

1842

ETON MODELE 1846 aTige

Russian Percussion Guns

ТУЛА

RUSSIAN M. 1849 CAVALRY CARBINE	
- Calibre	18.03 mm
- Rifling	2
- Capacity	1
- Length	807.7 mm
- Length of barrel	416.5 mm
- Weight	3,030 gr

Experiments with percussion firing began in Russia around 1827. Although certain results were achieved at that time on hunting guns and some types of military weapons, the government in St. Petersburg showed a lack of confidence in Russian constructors. In line with its Francophile orientation, in 1843 the Russian Army adopted the French percussion system M.1840/42 at the proposal of Colonel Glinky-Mavrodin. By decree of August 16, 1844, work began in the Tula, Sestroreck and Izhevsk arms factories on the adaptation of flintlocks to the new firing action. In the following year the production of a completely new percussion gun was mastered, but it retained the main features of the obsolete adapted weapon: a smooth bore and calibre of 6.9(7) linien.

Besides this relatively poor weapon, in the 1850s Russia had a negligible quantity of rifled percussion guns. The Committee for the Improvement of Armament decided as early as 1840 to equip some sharpshooter units with the so-called Lütich-stutz. Essentially this was the British M.1837 rifle designed by Captain Berner, officer of a jaeger regiment of the Brunswick Army. During 1843, the first 50,000 Stutz rifles were ordered for the Russian Army from the firm Mahlerbe in Liège. By 1849, St. Petersburg had purchased a total of 20,756 M.1843 rifles which were considerably improved in the country.

Captain Gartung, markmanship instructor to the Guards, developed the first Russian rifle from the M.1839 flintlock on the basis of the Lütich-stutz, in 1845. Six years later Staff Captain Ernrot of the Finnish Sharpshooter Batallion designed another Russian rifled gun.

These three rifles were virtually the only Russian percussion rifled guns when the Crimean War started. According to their own sources, at the outbreak of hostilities Russia had only 4.35% of such weapons. The British and French armies, equipped with the excellent Enfield M.1851 and the Thouvenin M.1842/46, inflicted devastating losses on the enemy. The view is sometimes expressed that the blame for this lay with the flintlocks, which, supposedly, accounted for a considerable part of Russian arms. This theory is completely groundless, for at that time in the whole Russian Army only 6.5% of its guns were flintlocks. Of the troops on active service in the Crimea, only two garrison half-batallions, a quarantine guard detachment and the Feodosi veterans unit had old muskets. In other words, it was the smooth bore that was exclusively to blame for the Russian

Nicholas I Romanov, Emperor of Russia (1825 – 1855).

losses. To illustrate: on the river Alma in September 1854, French and British soldiers, thanks to their rifles, moved down the Russian infantry and artillery as though on a firing range. On the left flank, they hit almost all the officers who were sitting on their cannon. The Uglitsky and Kazan Infantry regiments, who were ranged in batallions in the centre, resembled sitting ducks. Their smooth-bore percussion guns could not even reach the enemy. The whole infantry was thus forced to lie helplessly in whatever cover they could find.

Because of the devastating effect of the enemy's weapons, in 1854, while the war was still in progress, the Russians rifled some 20,000 old smooth-bore guns of M.1845 type. In the same year, they gradually began production of new rifles, the M.1854, but again with the old 7-linien calibre. Certain innovations on it were introduced by Glinky-Mavrodin, now a general, the earlier advocate of the French system.

It was not until 1856 that Russia finally abandoned the traditional 7-linien weapon and adopted the new, smaller calibre gun of 6 linien (15.24 mm). This led to the appearance of the outstanding M.1856/60 family of guns, which was the equal of the British Enfield. Unfortunately for the Russian Army, this arrived too late. Neighbouring armies were already working intensively on the more modern breech-loading systems.

Opposite:
A Cossack of the Terek Squadron of the Emperor's Escort.

Overleaf:
M.1849 Russian cavalry carbine, detail of the barrel and Czar Nikola I Romanov's initial.

ШТУЦЕР ОБРАЗЦА

Russian Cavalry: SHORT

КАВАЛЕРИЙСКИЙ КАПСЮЛЬНЫЙ

849

RIFLE MOD. 1849

Turkish and Balkan Percussion Guns

The first military reforms in the backward and decadent Ottoman Empire were undertaken in the reign of Sultan Selim III (1761 – 1808). Besides organizational changes, Selim tried to uniform the Army and equip it with standardised modern arms. After a certain interval, Turkey resumed this process, obtaining its rifles in France and Belgium. During the crisis of the 1850s, Britain also started delivering guns. Thus, at the outbreak of the Crimean War, "the sick man of the Bosphorus" had a large number of French and British guns which far surpassed the enemy's smooth-bore percussion arms in quality. During operations, Constantinople acquired some of the new British Enfield M.1853 guns. Pleased with their quality, the Turks ordered another 40,000 of them. Moreover, they switched production in Zeitin-Burun and some other smaller arsenals from French weapons to the Enfield. In the early 1860s, Turkish plans provided for the production under licence of 250,000 of these guns.

Parallel with Turkey, her (at least nominally) vassal principalities modernised their armament, in line with their liberation aspirations. Serbia certainly went the furthest in this matter.

It acquired its first considerable quantity of modern percussion rifles from Belgium. A contract was signed in 1856 with the A. Francotte company of Liège regarding the delivery of 5 to 6,000 rifles made according to the French 1846 T *"à tige"* model. There were two names for this gun in the country: from the place where it was constructed − the Vincennes rifle, and from the place where it was produced − the Belgian Stutz!

Such a small number of good guns could certainly not satisfy all of Serbia's needs. Russia, which with the defeat in the Crimea has lost its political influence in the Balkans saw its great chance: hoping to regain its earlier status, it "generously" gave Serbia 39,200 obsolete, bad quality guns discarded after the Crimean defeat. Of this number, 92% were smooth bore!

In 1859, Serbia had machines for the adaptation of flintlocks to the French percussion system in its arsenal in Kragujevac. A commission was formed in 1861 with the task of investigating the possibilities of switching to rifled barrels. Because of the large quantities of weapons with thin walls, the Commission adopted the Vincennes type of progressive grooves (the Minié-Tamisier system). All of the 32,200 Russian M.1845 guns were rifled in Kragujevac, producing weapons with groove depth of 0.5 – 0.3 mm and a calibre increased from 17.78 to 18.1 mm.

During the liberation wars of 1876/78, Serbia still had a few Russian and Belgian muzzle-loaders. This gave rise to much ridicule on the part of the Turks, who watched the Serbs turn their guns after each shot and load them with the ramrod. On the other hand, the Serbs valued the Belgian guns for their exceptional precision. A young lieutenant, Mišić, enthusiastically described a simple private, a peasant, sitting on the ramparts and calmly, as though at a shooting range, picking off the Turks who peered out of their trenches.

The arsenal in Kragujevac, Serbia, middle of 19th century.

NEW PERCUSSION MECHANISM M.1846
1. lock plate; 2. hammer; 3. mainspring; 4. sear; 5. mainspring screw; 6. side screw holes; 7. side screw holes; 8. bridle screw; 9. tumbler; 10. bridle; 11. sear screw.

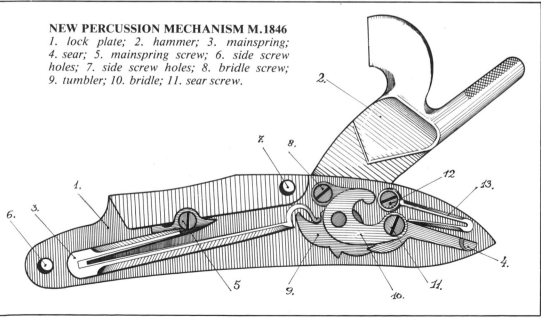

Mobilisation of the Turkish regular and irregular army.

SERBIAN M. 1845/63 INFANTRY RIFLE
- Calibre .... 17.78 – 18.1 mm
- Rifling 4
- Capacity 1
- Length .... 1,480 mm
- Length of barrel .. 1,050 mm
- Weight .... 4,270 gr

Overleaf:
Serbian M.1845/63 infantry gun, with the Kragujevac Arsenal in the background.

Тополивница

Крагујевцу.

British Percussion Guns

British soldiers with winter helmets in the Crimea, 1854.

In the early years of the 19th century, significant developments were achieved in the field of percussion arms in Great Britain. This is understandable considering the country's advanced industry and the existence of a large number of qualified personnel. It is enough to say that even such an inventor as James Watt worked on the realisation of the technical documentation for percussion mechanisms. One episode connected with British percussion guns flatters the vanity of the British because it illustrates their patriotism. Mr Forsythe, whom we have already spoken of, indignantly refused the enormous sum of 20,000 pounds which Napoleon himself offered him for his patent!

Most credit for the introduction of the percussion mechanism into the British Army should be given the Inspector of Small Arms to the Ordnance Board, a Mr. Lovell. At that time the Imperial Army was issued several new types of weapons. The first of them was the already mentioned Brunswick rifle M.1836, cal. ˙704 and the so-called Victoria carbine. Besides these unsuccessful rifled guns, Lovell also introduced the smooth-bore percussion musket, M.1838, into the Army, a weapon with all the good characteristics of the old M.1802 flintlock. A year later, wishing to reduce investments, the British started adapting existing flintlocks to the percussion system, but most of these "hybrids" (M.1839) were destroyed in the Tower fire of 1841. Military circles were thus forced to replace the loss by producing completely new weapons. But instead of immediately adopting rifled barrels, they constructed yet another smooth-bore musket, the M.1842.

In the mid-19th century, much was being done in Great Britain on the testing of grooves and bullets. It is all the more surprising, therefore, that London disregarding the many excellent English constructions, paid 20,000 pounds for the licence of the French Minié project, which was the basis for the Rifle Musket, Pattern 1851, cal. ˙702. The quality of this gun was confirmed on the continent, and the British version gave good results in action against the Kaffirs. Except for the 44th Division, the troops fighting in the Crimea were equipped with M.1851 guns. But this type of weapon was short-lived. Only two years later, the army acquired probably the best rifle of the whole of Europe of the time, the famous Enfield M.1853. Since this gun appeared during the Crimean War, it had ample opportunity to prove its worth at the siege of Sebastopol as well. One decade later the American Confederate States bought 70,980 Enfield rifles. Satisfied with their quality, the Americans started producing it themselves, but in a ˙540 calibre.

The most interesting episode relating to the Enfield rifle is connected with India. At that time Britain had only 40,000 British soldiers in India, the remaining 200,000 being local recruits, sepoys. Confident in the loyalty of these troops, the Empire issued the new M.1853 to all its soldiers without distinction. Unfortunately, the religious beliefs of the native soldiers were overlooked. Word spread among them that the Enfield bullets were greased with a mixture of pig's lard and cow's fat and, since the men ripped off the top of the cartridge with their teeth whilst loading, they could not avoid coming into direct contact with the bullet. This outraged both the Hindus, who considered the cow a holy animal, and the Moslims, for whom the pig was an anathema, and was said to have caused the bloody rebellion of the natives which resulted in heavy British losses, inflicted by those self-same Enfield rifles! However much truth there is in this story, it is certain that for years after the Indian rebellion was crushed, all rifles intended for use by native soldiers had the grooves removed by subsequent boring!

Opposite:
British Coldstream Guardsmen in the Crimea.

Overleaf:
British M.1853 Enfield rifle.

TOWER

BRITISH M. 1853 ENFIELD RIFLE	
- Calibre	14.7 mm (˙577)
- Rifling	3
- Capacity	1
- Length	1,841 mm
- Length of barrel	889 mm
- Weight	4,160 gr

Valentine

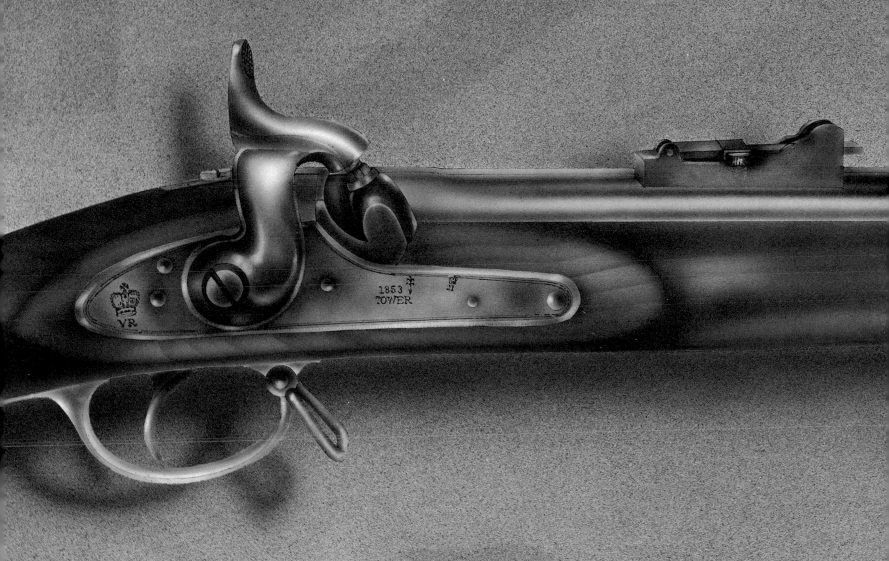

American Percussion Guns

Russia, which even as late as 1839 constructed and produced flintlocks is often cited as an example of extreme backwardness in the field of arms and armament. It is, however, frequently overlooked that other countries, too, were slow in replacing flintlocks by percussion guns. The USA, for instance, constructed its last flintlock, albeit with a grooved barrel, as late as 1842. A year earlier, the US Army adopted the first rifling percussion arms of ˙540 calibre. In memory of the German *Jäger-Stutzen,* it was called the *Yager rifle.* And as it was the weapon of the First Mississippi Regiment, it also came to be known as the *Mississippi rifle.* Following Jefferson's regulation on standardizing calibres, the M.41 had its calibre changed to ˙580.

But these rifles were just a drop in the ocean of old flintlocks. For this reason, in 1842 the Ordnance Department constructed another percussion gun, for unknown reasons with a smooth-bore barrel of ˙690 cal. Soon realising this was a mistake, the American Army took advantage of the thick walls of the M.42 and subsequently rifled it.

At the outbreak of the war with Mexico (1846–48), the number of percussion guns was still extremely low. Victory over the far weaker neighbour was attained almost exclusively with flintlocks.

On July 5, 1855, on the orders of the Secretary for War, Davis Jefferson, the

Map of the warring sides in the American Civil War.

Springfield M.1855 rifle was adopted as the model according to which the standard American military arms were to be produced. This gun had a Maynard percussion system, named after Dr. Maynard, a dentist by profession, who invented a percussion system identical to the one used today in children's toy guns. An explosive mixture was compressed at regular intervals in between two bands of paper, forming caps. The band was wound on an axis and turned mechanically, bringing the cap to the lug one by one. In 1845 the US government paid this dentist the sum of 4,000 US dollars to build his patent device into 4,000 guns. Nine years later they bought the right to use Maynard's system on all army and navy weapons for 50,000 US dollars. The Springfield construction and the Maynard percussion system together gave the M.1855 gun.

After the testing of this weapon in action, the faults of paper-band caps became obvious. Owing to frequent complaints from the troops, the Secretary for War was forced to order a new type of percussion gun, which mostly kept the Springfield design but was combined with traditional lugs and copper caps. The new musket (M.1861) was the main weapon used in the Civil War. The later, 1863 model differed only slightly from the M.1861 and Colt's special musket bearing the same designation.

Opposite and above: Confederate soldiers.

PATENT SHEET FOR MAYNARD'S PRIMING COCK No. 4208
of September 22, 1845

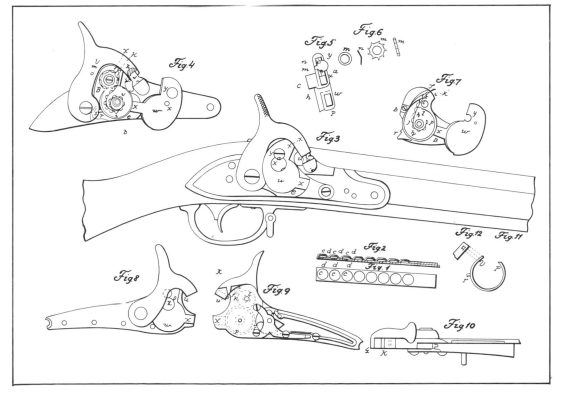

US M. 1855 SPRINGFIELD RIFLE	
- Calibre	14.73 mm ('58)
- Rifling	3
- Capacity	1
- Length	1,254 mm
- Length of barrel . . .	838 mm
- Weight	4,540 gr

Overleaf:
US M.1855 Springfield-Maynard system infantry gun.

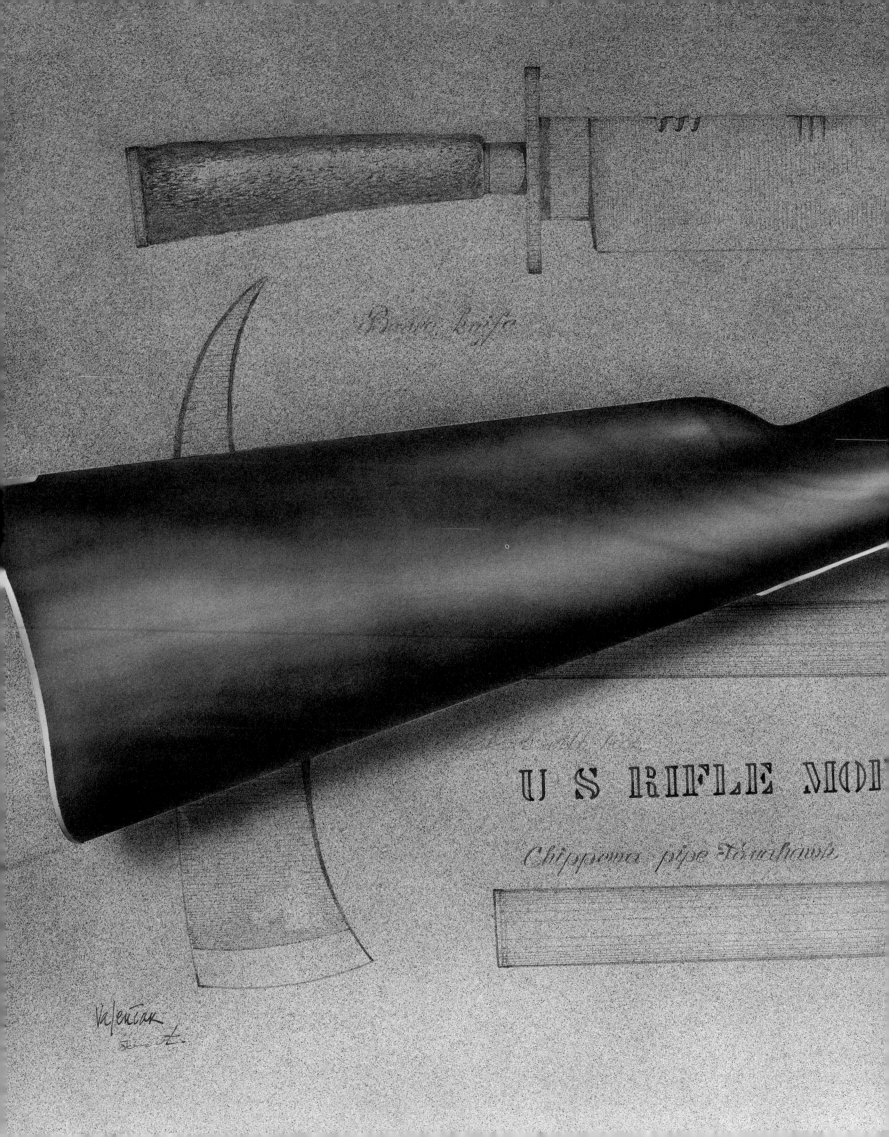

Bowie knife

U S RIFLE MOD

Chippewa pipe Tomahawk

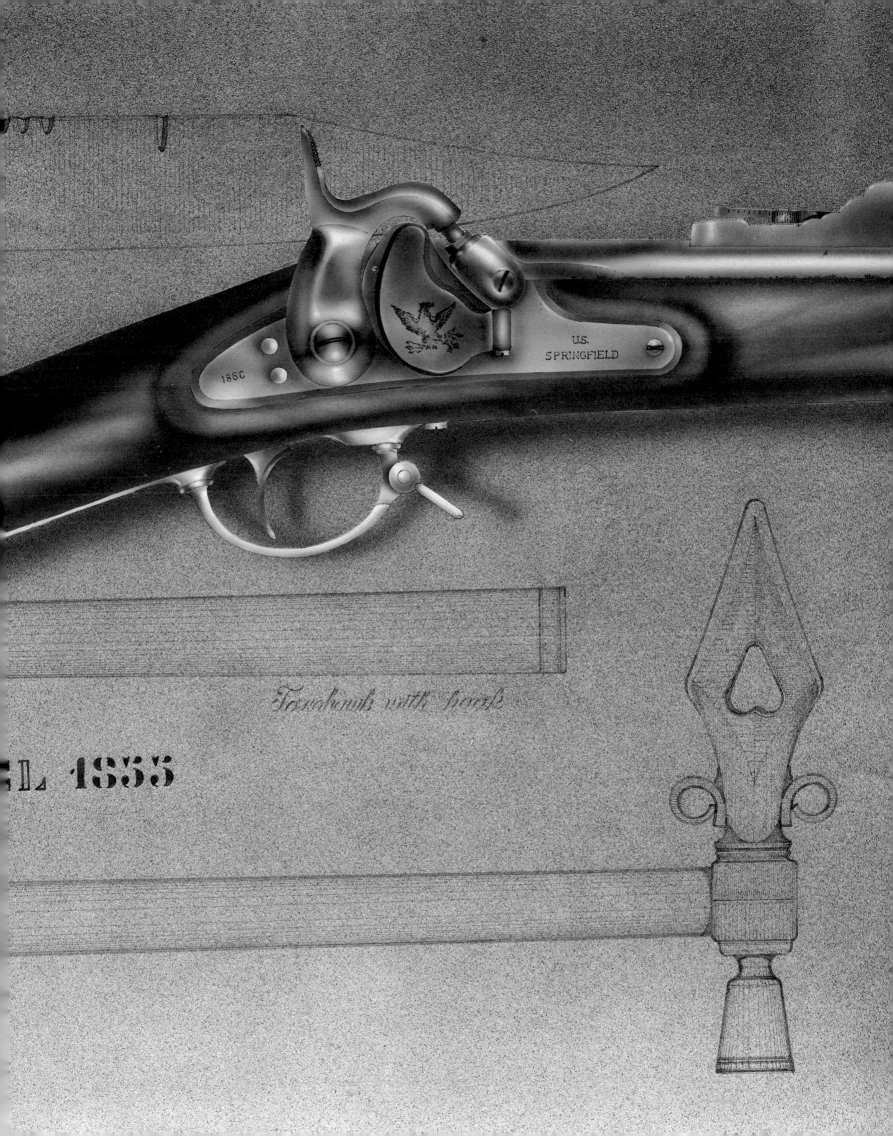

U.S.
SPRINGFIELD

1860

Tomahawk with hook

L 1855

Cavalry pistols

Like the flintlock pistols, percussion cavalry pistols merely followed the development of infantry arms. They usually incorporated smaller models of the gun mechanisms, little or no attention being paid the design and ballistics of these short arms. True, in the 19th century attempts were made to produce pistols that could, if necessary, be converted into carbines by adding a butt. This idea was well known in both Europe and America, and was to become popular again with the advent of self-loading pistols.

Austria, for example, took a similar construction over from the Norwegian cavalry in the mid-19th century. This was basically a lighter version of the M.1859/60 Lorenz pistol onto which a butt could be affixed, thus making a carbine 660 mm long! Three years later, because of the impracticality of such a hybrid, the Aus-

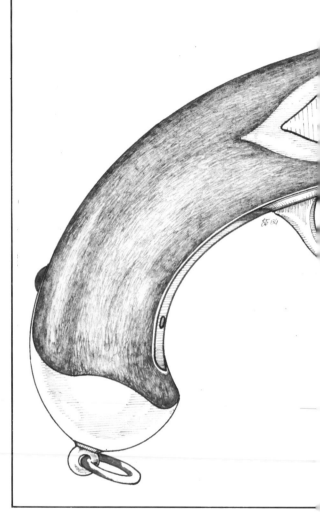

trians returned to the standard Lorenz M.1859/60 cavalry pistol.

One of the designs typical of the Europe of that time was the Russian Cossack 6-linien pistol. The frequently used Russian measurement, the *linia,* which usually denoted the calibre, was equivalent to 2.54 mm.

The Cossack 5``` pistol originated from the M.1856/60 family of Russian weapons. Its characteristics are a robust construction, a hammer with a ring, and a swivel ramrod. In view of its close similarity to the Cossack M.1860 gun, this was probably also one of the projects of A. E. Tchernolikhov, the excellent Russian constructor whose school also produced F. V. Tokarev.

French hussar, middle of 19th century.

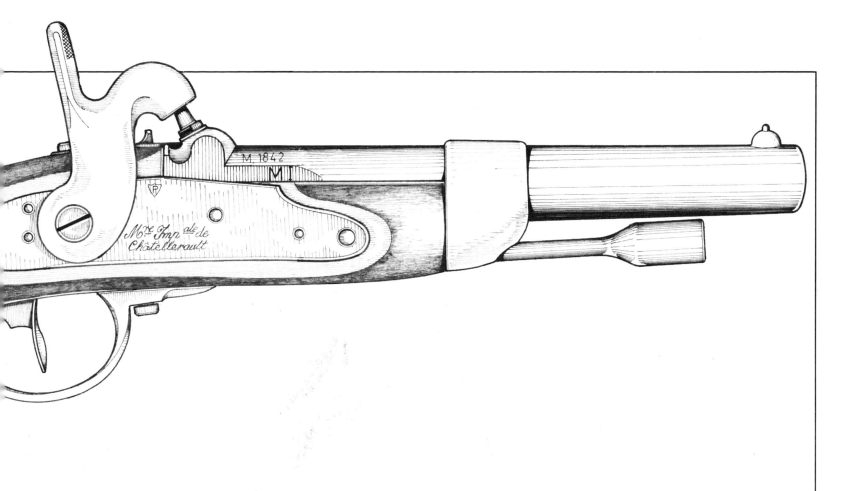

French cavalry pistol, M.1822/42.

French hussar, 1850. Drawing by A. Strassge-schwandtner.

RUSSIAN COSSACK PISTOL 6'''	
- Calibre	15.24 mm (6''')
- Rifling	4
- Capacity	1
- Length	400 mm
- Length of barrel ..	250 mm
- Weight	1,300 gr

Overleaf:
Cossack 6 linien Czernolihov pistol.

ТУЛА

Завртсю реіса цевіи

Обарога

Отруј ісіце обарога

Тоу обараіе

фиі. 5.

фиі. 9.

фиі. 4.

фиі. 4.

Задњак „Векексве" гуше са стожером, рове- ни ío идеи Тувенена у Векелској ико- ли ігугаіа. стожер је цвріну у задеке. о ову гагено са ним. у гадьи део цеви

Рис.1. Части ударн

Рис.10. Стержневой штуцерь Тувенена

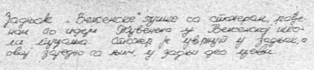

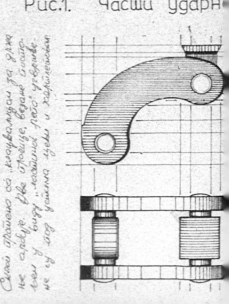

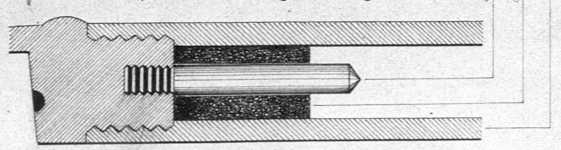

Ѕелове уріко Бранко Богановић. у Беоргу авгуй нееуг 1983 ог. Рабено ірена „Викнолову. „Оружеле и воорумене рускіг воиск..."

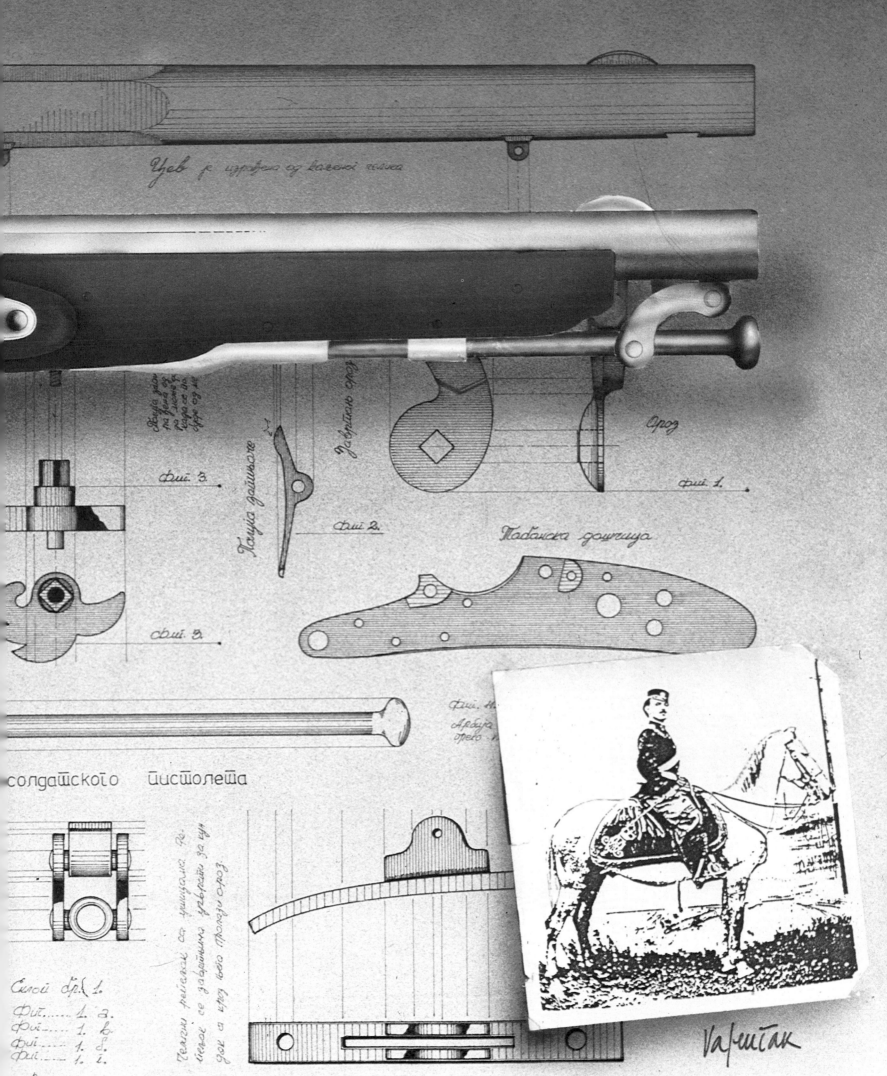

Цев ƿ израђен од каленог челика

Полуга даишаке

Завршно срог

Орог

Фиг. 3.

Фиг. 2.

Фиг. 1.

Фиг 2.

Табанска доштица

Фиг. 3.

Фиг. 4.

Арбуƺ

солдашскоƌо иисшолеша

Силой бр. 1.

Фиг...... 1. а.
Фиг...... 1. в.
Фиг...... 1. д.
Фиг...... 1. е.

Ва鉾ишак

BREECH-LOADING PERCUSSION AND SINGLE-SHOT CARTRIDGE GUNS

Prussian artillery in the battle of Leipzig, 1866.

BREECH-LOADING PERCUSSION SYSTEMS

Percussion muzzle-loaders reached their peak in the mid-19th century. From the ballistic point of view, their performance was excellent, and technically, they were quite reliable. Only one problem remained for military circles — firing speed. Faster loading by means of mechanisms at the back of the barrel had been solved from the constructional standpoint, much earlier on. However, until the middle of the last century the low level of technology and the semi-handwork methods of production did not permit wider application of these solutions. The discovery of the percussion cap and the rapid expansion of industry provided greater possibilities for the development of breech-loading systems.

The effectiveness of Prussian needle-fire weapons in the conflicts over Schleswig-Holstein (1848 – 1850) turned the attention of military experts to breech-loading guns. However, opinions were divided on this subject. One group of experts discounted the speed of breech-loaders, and even considered it harmful. This attitude was based on the theory that the soldiers would fire all their ammunition in the first moments of the battle und thus make further action impossible. This opinion was also strengthened by the great waste of ammunition on the part of the inexperienced Prussian soldiers in their battle with the Danes. Moreover, the excellent results of the Austrian Lorenz muzzle-loaders in the 1859 war only confirmed their belief that such rapidity of fire was unnecessary.

The opponents of breech-loaders were not totally convinced even by the results achieved by the new weapon in the War of Secession. The wider use of a large number of various breech-loading systems was naively explained away as the extravagance of the Americans! The Prusso-Danish (1864) and Prusso-Austrian Wars (1866) finally silenced even the most hardened conservatives and opened wide the gates for breech-loading guns.

Apart from Dreyse, most constructors of the mid-19th century based the designs for their breech-loaders on existing percussion weapons. This was primarily for financial reasons: the idea was to use the enormous number of existing muzzle-loading rifles by adapting them as easily and cheaply as possible to breech-loading systems.

Green

The American constructor James Durell Green offered one such solution. He constructed a barrel that could be turned 90° and so be loaded with a paper cartridge. The ignition of the powder was still achieved by the classic Maynard magazine with fulminating compound between the two paper strips. This solution was patented on January 2 and June 27, 1854 (US Patent No. 10,391 and 11,157). Green built his device into a cavalry carbine and at the end of the year offered the weapon to the US government. On May 24, 1855, the Chief of Ordnance bought only 200 Green carbines, for 6,000 US dollars.

The ambitious constructor, dissatisfied by the lack of attention that the USA had shown his guns, decided to move to Europe and offer his carbine to France and Britain. Whereas Paris rejected it, towards the end of 1855 Britain, somewhat hastily, bought 2,000 carbines for 11,100 pounds! The production of the weapons lasted until May 1858, when the finished carbines were finally transported across the ocean by steamship. In the meantime Britain had lost interest in Green's weapon, so that almost the whole contingent was stored in the Arsenal in the Tower. With the outbreak of Civil War in America, an absurd turnabout took place. Exploiting the need of the belligerent sides for weapons, the British sold the Americans, among other guns, the (American) Green system carbines! Thus the Yankees during this war carried weapons marked with the initials of Queen Victoria — VR! On November 17, 1857, Lieut. Colonel Green patented a new type of gun under the number 18,634. This time the constructor based his weapon on bolt-action loading, an oval bore and an interesting under-hammer firing method. The bolt was opened by the movement of a handle left and back. The cartridge was placed in the chamber and the bolt returned to its original position. The charge was still ignited by a copper cap, only now placed under the barrel.

Among the first to become interested in this solution was the US Colonel Craig, who in 1857 ordered 100 Green M.1857 guns for the needs of troop testing. The constructor refused to sign such a con-

Green, James Durell, born May 12, 1828 in Lynn, Mass., died March 21, 1902. Turned to arms construction after graduating from Harvard. During the Civil War, served as Colonel of the 5th Massachusetts Militia. Several types of breech-loading rifles produced according to his designs were adopted by the armies of Serbia and Russia. On the basis of Green's bolt-action, the French Chassepot I and the Baden M.1863 rifle were developed.

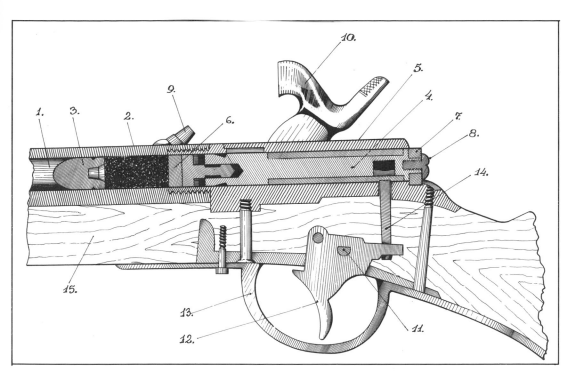

GREEN SYSTEM RIFLE M.1857

1. chamber; 2. barrel; 3. bullet; 4. bolt; 5. bolt jacket; 6. obturating washer; 7. bolt handle; 8. bolt-handle screw; 9. cap; 10. hammer; 11. sear; 12. trigger; 13. trigger-guard; 14. abzugstollen; 15. forestock.

SERBIAN M. 1867 GREEN SYSTEM RIFLE	
- Calibre	13.8 mm
- Rifling	4
- Capacity	1
- Length	1,440 mm
- Length of barrel	950 mm
- Weight	4,500 gr

tract, stating that such a small series would be unprofitable. At this time there were rumours throughout America that Russia, too, was pressing ahead in the search for a perfect breech-loading weapon. Intrigued by this, in 1859 Green personally demonstrated his gun to the chairman of the Russian Commission for the Choice of Guns, Count Levachoff. Russia showed a liking for Green's construction and for the sum of 18,000 pounds ordered 3,000 Dragoon M.1857 guns. Just when the production of the Russian weapons was in full swing, the Civil War broke out in America. The patriotic constructor immediately joined the army, but did not miss opportunity of offering the Government the Russian model of the gun as well. It is hard to say how he succeeded in obtaining an order for 900 of these guns since all tests revealed the weapon's poor performance. The Russians, too, soon realised they had struck a bad bargain with Green's weapon, and after testing it, did not introduce it into the army. The Obturateur gun, based on Green's idea, was given a similar assessment in Russia.

The experiences gained during the Civil War switched the development of arms in another direction, for it had become obvious that the future of guns lay in a metallic cartridge. The only solution left to Green was to offer his old bolt-action, intendend for a paper cartridge, for the adaptation of existing percussion arms. During 1865 he adapted the British Enfield gun to his cylindrical bolt-action loading with a gutta-percha stopper. Such

weapons operated by means of a classic hammer, cone and copper cap, and used a perforated paper cartridge (for easier firing) with Minié's bullet. Britain did not show particular interest in this unsuccessful hybrid. The Principality of Serbia, at that very time searching for the cheapest breech-loader solution, in 1867 imprudently purchased the rights to it. A certain number of Austrian Lorenz M.1854 guns, bought one year previously in Vienna, were adapted according to the Green system. Unfortunately, all the failings of such guns soon became obvious. In 1868, when the Green guns were first used to fire a salute of honour, less than 100 rifles actually fired from a whole batallion! Yet neither this experience nor the well-intentioned criticisms of the younger officers brought the Serbian command to its senses. Thus the army went to war against Turkey, in 1876, with 12,000 Green M.1867 guns. Although Serbia at that time was in possession of the largest number of weapons based on the Green system, this fact has mostly been ignored in historial sources. The explanation for this may be that after its disastrous war experiences, the government recalled *all* the Green guns and had them changed to a better system. This is the reason that not a single one has been preserved in Serbia to this very day! On page 54 of his *Handfeuerwaffen* (Volume II), J. Lugs gives a drawing of this solution, probably based on the 1864 illustration provided by Ploennies *(Neue Studien)*. The photographs on pp. 47 and 48 of M. Morin's *Le armi portatili dell' Impero Austro-Ungarico* (Firenze, 1981), are far more interesting. In this work, Morin presented a gun that he calls the Austrian experimental M.1862 Lindner system gun. Comparing this photograph with the original illustrations of the Serbian Green gun from 1879, it seems obvious that Morin, by a lucky accident, published a photograph of probably the last extant M.1867 gun!

According to some sources, J. D. Green sold 350 of his M.1857 guns to Egypt, and the French M.1865 Chassepot I system and the Badische Jägerbüchse M.1863 were constructed on the basis of his solution.

Overleaf:
Section of M.1867 Green system infantry gun.

Барут тежи 4,75 грама

Цев пушчана
од каљена челика

Куршум тежи 30 грама

Ц

Усадник дрвени
израђен је из једног дела с кундаком

В

ПеБ

Браник

Обарача с

Затињаче

Сл. 2.   Чеп затварачев

Пушица је израђена у воду Р4

Пресек пуш
ве по сло
ка Главка

61.0   31.0   54

Сл. 3.   Сандук

Сл. 4.
Ручица

164,7

20   6.7 1.8   19,8   5   24,4   3.2 6   19

Сл. 6. Лучић
Ручице

Сл. 5.   Поклопац

Војни Музеј са Шишком - Р 1/1

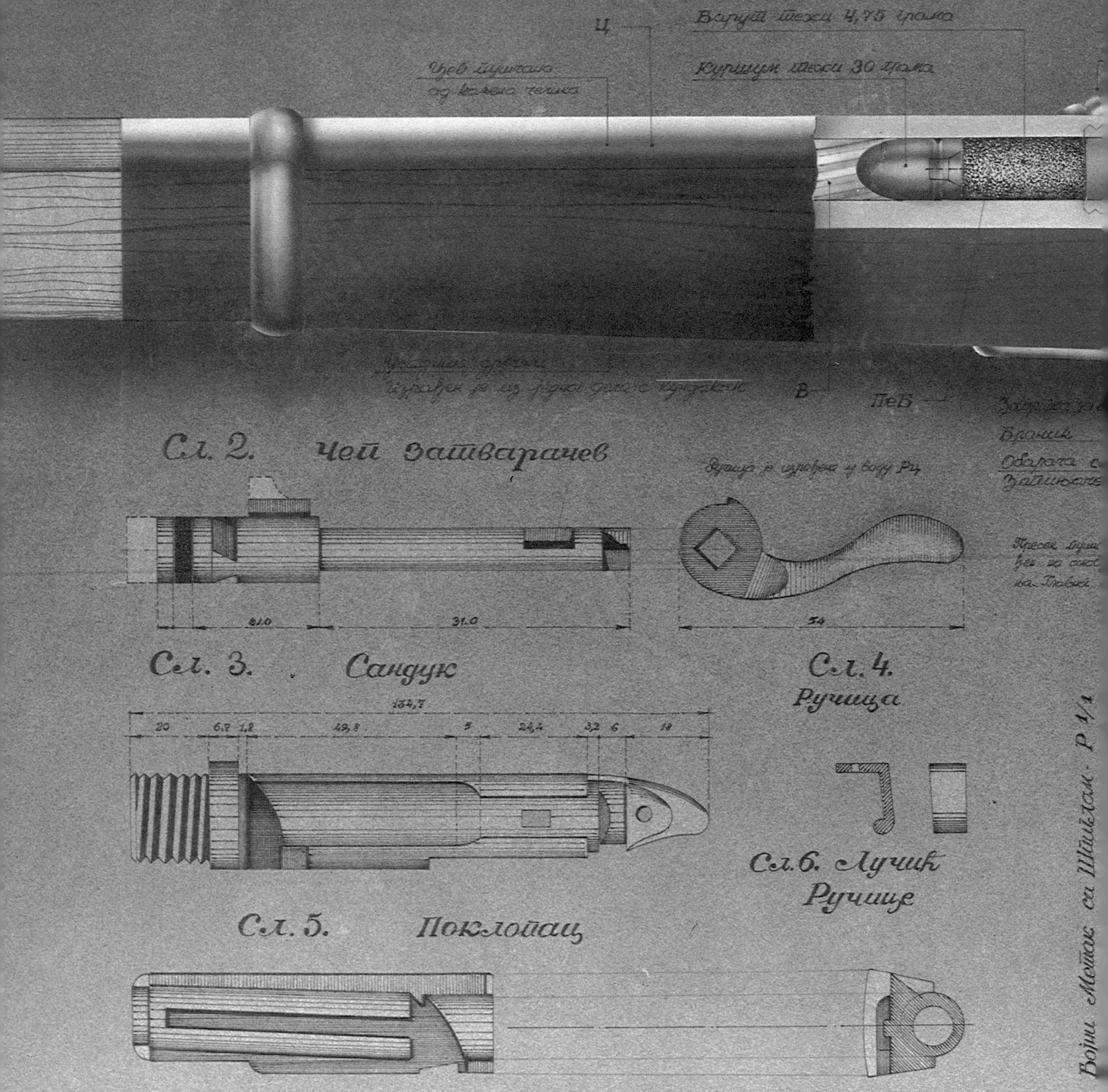

Према књизи „Артиљерија"- Слике за „Артиљерију" Косте Миловановића, Београд 1879. године
„Подметне оправке" Табла Iа-Iб, исцртао пушку Гринову Брана Бојановић, Београд 1984. год.

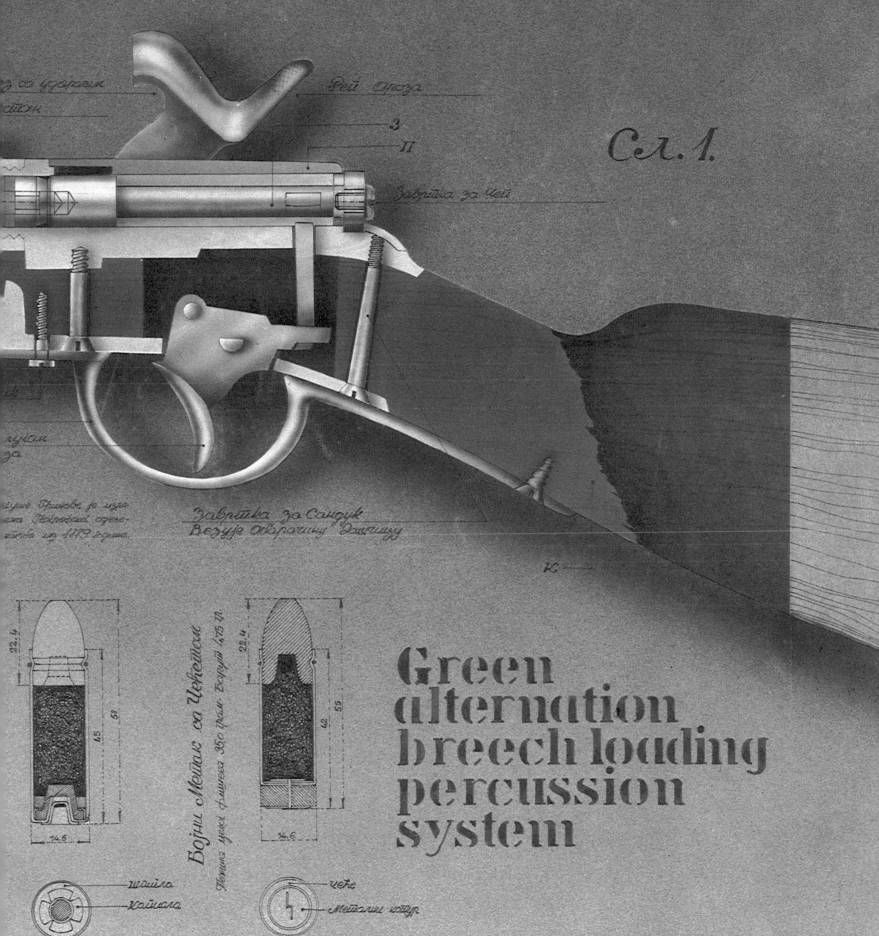

СИСТЕМА МОД. 1867

Сл. 1.

Green alternation breech loading percussion system

Valentar

Russian Gille-Trummer and Terry-Norman Guns

Searching for the best breech-loader solution, Russia tested a number of European and American weapons. In 1857 the Arms Commission also investigated the construction of a Belgian designer, Gille, which, like the Green, was based on cylindrical bolt-action loading and a paper cartridge with a separate cap. This solution displayed a number of weaknesses, which a marksmanship instructor, F. F. Trummer, was given the task of removing. Trummer finished his work in 1861, greatly improving the bolt-action mechanism and the fit of the chamber. Four new types of weapons were manufactered according to the new Gille-Trummer system: the M.1861 sharpshooter rifle and dragoon rifle, a cavalry carbine and the M.1862 military pistol. Although these prototypes showed good results in the first phase of testing, subsequent studies revealed several insuperable problems. These arms required great precision in the production of the chamber and homogeneity of the lead bullet, both of which were beyond Russian technology at that time. Further work on the Gille-Trummer solution was halted and attention was focussed on the British Terry construction.

The Terry carbine was produced by the Collisher and Terry Company of Birmingham and 28 Norfolk Street, London, founded in 1855. The mechanism, based on bolt-action firing, was patented in

Alexander II Romanov, Emperor of Russia (1855 – 1881).

1856 by the junior partner of the company, Terry. In Britain, Terry's system, called the *capping breech loader,* was considered a success. Moreover, the Confederate forces bought a large number of Terry carbines during the Civil War. In America the bolt-action of this weapon was referred to as the *door bolt,* probably

M.1866 TERRY-NORMAN SYSTEM RIFLE
1. bolt; 2. bolt handle; 3. hammer; 4. cap; 5. powder; 6. steel cup; 7. bullet; 8. trigger; 9. trigger-guard; 10. butt; 11. cleaning rod; 12. abzugstollen.

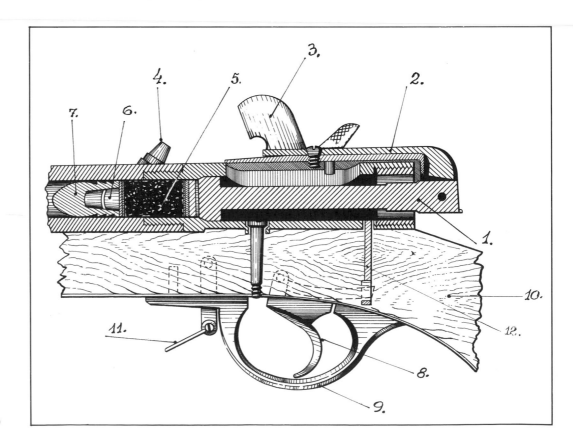

because of the unusual association. It is interesting to note that even the famous American cavalry general Jeb Stuart carried an English Terry carbine.

In Russia this solution attracted military circles by its simplicity and low production costs. The first prototypes were acquired from the British in 1865 and in February 1866 the Commission started testing them. During the first tests, a master gunsmith at the Tula works, I. G. Norman, made over 20 changes to the British original! Even this rifle based on the Terry-Norman system remained a poor weapon. Ignoring this fact, the chairman of the Arms Commission, Herzog Georg von Mecklenburg, insisted on this particular system being adopted by the Russian Army. It was von Mecklenburg who was responsible for the decree, issued on November 15, 1866, ordering the adaptation of M.1856 percussion guns to Terry-Norman system breech-loaders. I. G. Norman was honoured with the Cross of St Stanislas, 3rd class, and a 500-rouble reward!

Although this weapon was favourably assessed at the International Exhibition in Paris in 1867, the same year saw its demise. Only 67,000 M.1866 guns had been produced by then. The obvious failings of this obsolete mechanism finally left von Mecklenburg without any arguments, and adaptation to the Terry-Norman system was stopped.

Mobilisation of the Russian army before the Russo-Turkish war of 1876.

RUSSIAN M. 1866 TERRY-NORMAN SYSTEM RIFLE
- Calibre . . . . 15.24 mm (6''')
- Rifling 4
- Capacity 1
- Length . . . . 1,340 mm
- Length of barrel . . —
- Weight . . . . 4,400 gr

Overleaf:
Russian M.1866 Terry-Norman system infantry rifle with detail of barrel and bayonet.

Terry

РРИ-НОРМАНА ОБР. 1866

Norman Model 1866

Sharps

Sharps, Christian, born c. 1811 in New Jersey, died 1874 in Vernon, Conn. One of the most famous American arms constructors. In about 1830 worked in Harpers Ferry arsenal with constructor John H. Hall. From 1840 worked in Cincinnati, Ohio, where he improved Hall's breech--loading gun. In 1848 he was granted a U.S. patent, on the basis of which his well-known gun was first produced in 1850/51, in Mill Creck, Pa. Sharps's single-shot rifle was later manufactured in large quantities and several variations. Apart from its official use in the U.S. Army, especially during the Civil War, it was also popular among civilians, becoming famous as the favourite weapon of buffalo hunters. Among Sharps's other constructions the best known is his four--barrelled pistol with a rotating firing-pin, produced in England (Tipping and Lawden, Birmingham) and Austria (Grünbaum, Vienna) as well as in the U.S.

An American constructor, Christian Sharps, worked on a breech-block mechanism very different from Green's. On September 17, 1848, he patented the so-called *sloping breech,* applied on a carbine on which the hammer was placed on the inside of the frame (US Patent No. 5763). The lock plate of this weapon carried the already mentioned Maynard primer device. The breech-block of the carbine opened downwards by means of the trigger guard, freeing the chamber into which the cartridge was loaded. In Sharps' first version, the cartridge was made of paper, but it was later changed to a better solution: a linen cartridge with a paper base. When the chamber was closed, the breech-block tore the paper part of the cartridge and thus freed the powder charge.

Somewhat later, Sharps modernised this first carbine by moving the hammer to the outer side of the frame. The third type of Sharps carbines was created by removing Maynard's magazine, and was fired by a classic cap on the cone. After 1859, this weapon had a new magazine with caps built into it, in the form of a brass tube with waterproof primer discs, developed by Sharps and a gunsmith by the name of *R. S. Lowrence.*

The fifth, final and most popular Sharps carbine had many of the characteristics of its predecessors. The greatest difference was the now vertical breech-block placed perpendicularly to the barrel.

This last weapon had iron furniture, far cheaper than the previous brass. Some of these carbines, instead of the usual patch box, had coffee mills built in! Sharps guns were certainly very popular in America in the 19th century. Colonel Wrights' forces, equipped with Sharps carbines, pacified large groups of rebellious Indians on

US SHARPS SYSTEM CARBINE	
- Calibre	13.2 mm ('52)
- Rifling	6
- Capacity	1
- Length	952.5 mm
- Length of barrel	546 mm
- Weight	3,630 gr

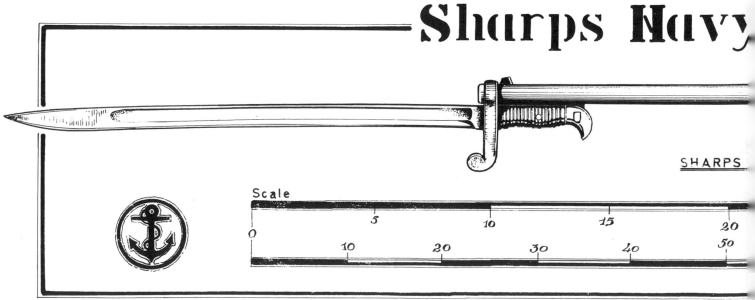

Sharps Navy

SHARPS

Scale

the western frontier with almost no losses. This success was all the greater in that Colonel Steptoes' troops, armed with muzzle-loaders, had tried to do so unsuccessfully for several years.

The weapon's popularity rose sharply also after the death of the legendary John Brown, hero of the Glory marching song, who fought with a Sharps carbine. After evangelist Henry Ward Beecher declared that in the slave question, the Sharps carbine had a moral power stronger than that of a hundred Bibles, this gun was popularly named *Beecher's Bible!*

Sharps' weapons were produced in the form of infantry rifles and cavalry and naval carbines as well. During the Civil War, the army bought 9,141 rifle and 80,512 carbines. A large number of these were adapted for metal cartridges with rim or central firing.

The quality of Sharps' weapons attracted the attention of the British as well, who fared much better with them than they had with Green's solution. In July 1855, they signed a contract for 1,000 Sharps carbines, and on August 17 increased the order to 6,000.

Men of the 6th Maine Infantry.

Overleaf:
American Sharps system cavalry carbine.

Rifle M.1855

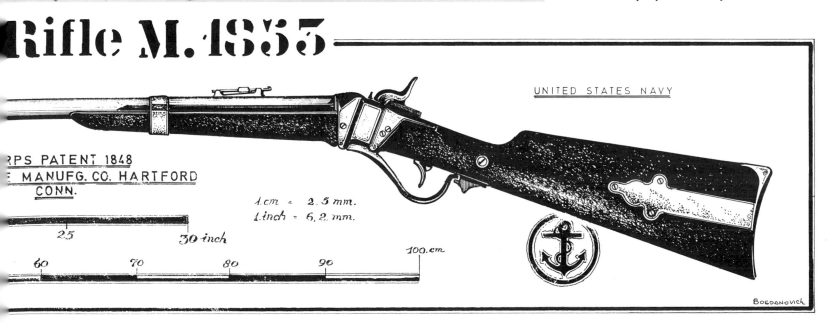

UNITED STATES NAVY

RPS PATENT 1848
E MANUFG. CO. HARTFORD
CONN.

1 cm = 2.5 mm.
1 inch = 6.2 mm.

25   30 inch

60   70   80   90   100 cm

BOGDANOVICH

SHARPS BREECH LOADING

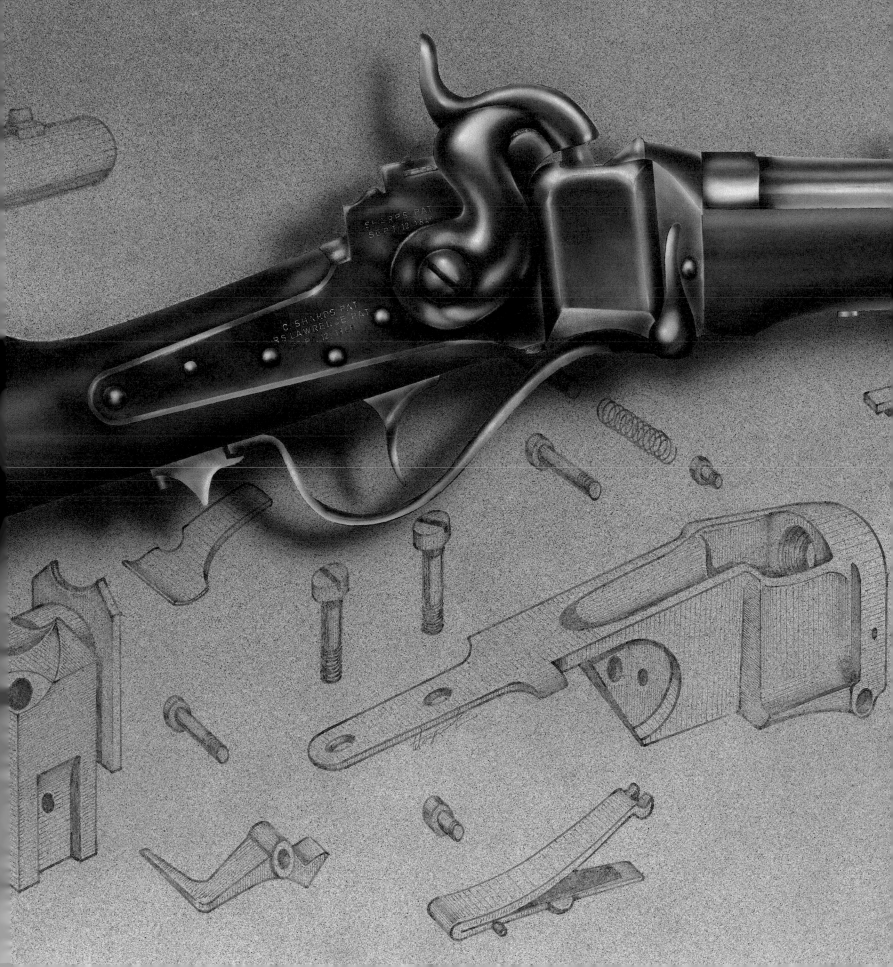

SINGLE-SHOT CARTRIDGE RIFLES

Dreyse

Dreyse, Johann Nikolaus von, born November 20, 1787, in Sommerda near Erfurt, died December 15, 1867, in Sommerda. Worked in Paris for a time in the gunsmith's works of the famous constructor Oauly. Took over his father's workshop on returning to Sommerda, and drawing on experience acquired in France, started constructing his own weapons. From these projects his first breech-loading needle-gun developed (1835).

One of the first constructors to come to the idea of combining the paper cartridge with the cap was a mechanic from Sommerda, Johann Nikolaus Dreyse. The firing of such a bullet was achieved by a long steel pin which set off the ignition of the explosive mixture. Legend has it that Dreyse came upon this idea in the early 1820s when he accidentally caused the detonation of a cap while filling it with the mixture by means of a pin.

The first Dreyse gun offered to the Prussian Ministry of War did not arouse much interest. This attitude on the part of military circles did not deter the constructor. Protecting his patent for eight years, he diligently worked on improving it. It is interesting that support of the imperial family was instrumental in getting Dreyse's weapon adopted by the Prussian Army. Conscious of the conservatism of higher military circles, Nikolaus Dreyse made a very smart move: he personally presented Crown Prince Wilhelm with a sporting carbine based on his own bolt-action. Delighted with the weapon, Wilhelm supported the ingenious mechanic, and this led to the speeding up of the military testing of needle-firing guns, started as far back as 1836. Finally, by imperial decree of December 4, 1840, the Dreyse gun was adopted for use by the Prussian Army.

According to the contract, Dreyse personally delivered 60,000 M.1841 guns to the army, further production being left to the state arsenal in Spandau. The Prussian Army was thus the first in the world to be completely equipped with breech-loading arms. The Dreyse needle-firing gun with bolt-action laid the foundations of all later modern rifles.

It seems that the Germanic spirit was even then obsessed by secret weapons, for Berlin wished the so-called *Zündnadelgewehr* to remain a strict military secret. But then, as now, no weapon could be kept for long from inquisitive eyes. During the turbulent May in Dresden in 1849, the needle-gun was used in street fighting. Finally, one got as far as England, where it was submitted to stringent testing.

The basic principle of the Dreyse bolt-action was that, by turning the bolt left and pulling it back, the chamber was opened and the long steel pin cocked. A paper cartridge consisting of an egg-shaped lead bullet, a papier-mâché *sabot* (the so-called *Spiegel*) and a powder charge, was then loaded into the chamber. The flattened end of the bullet leant against the *Spiegel,* in which the primer cap was placed on the other side. The pin, when released, penetrated the paper cover and powder charge before igniting the cap.

For two decades, over ten different models of the Dreyse *Zündnadelgewehr* were developed on the same principle. These guns played a significant role not only in the history of arms but also in the development of tactics. We have already mentioned that breech-loading arms long had to combat conservative attitudes. Its

BREECH-BOLT SYSTEM DREYSE
1. receiver; 2. nadelrohr; 3. breech-bolt; 4. chamber; 5. trigger-spring; 6. needle; 7. messingschaft; 8. abzugsnase; 9. and 13. trigger-lever; 10. and 14. schnapper; 11. schlosshülse; 12. feder mit der ledernen Einlage.

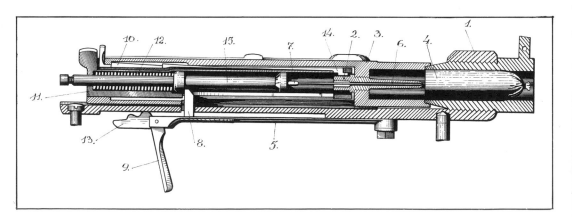

opponents used a number of arguments apart from the great waste of ammunition. For example, it was said that the great penetrative power of the Dreyse rifle was not good, because a soldier when hit would not immediately fall down! Furthermore, fighting from the lying position — first possible with the advent of breech-loaders — was considered unworthy (sic!) of soldiers. Finally the importance of cover and the reduced target offered by a prone soldier was also ignored.

The experiences of the 1866 war finally changed the opinion of these "experts". In the euphoria that followed the news of the Austrians' heavy losses, people went so far as to ascribe all credit for the victory exclusively to the Dreyse gun. It should not be forgotten, however, that the Prussians also knew how to use this weapon correctly: they introduced flexible firing units developed from company and even platoon lines. At the same time, the Austrians stubbornly insisted on assault tactics with massed attacks in dense lines. Their officers were incapable of making use of the really excellent ballistic performance of the Lorenz guns. These massed ranks of infantry were an ideal target for the Prussian needle-guns. It is hardly surprising, then, that at the famous battle of Königgratz, in the fight-

Prussian hussars enter Paris, March 1st, 1871.

ing around the hill of Chlum, the Austrian Graf Leiningen Brigade was reduced, in only 20 minutes, to one third of its size! The total number of men lost was 8,894 Prussian and 23,598 Austrian soldiers! Not realising the importance of the new tactics, Vienna unfairly blamed the commander of the Northern Army, Bendek, and the Lorenz rifle for the defeat in the Seven Weeks' War!

The war against France 1870/71 was the swan-song of the Dreyse needle-gun. Despite the fact that the enemy was in possession of a somewhat more modern Chassepot needle-gun, the Prussian rifle still emerged triumphant.

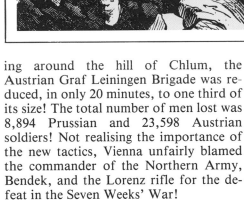

DREYSE SYSTEM M. 1865
ZÜNDNADELBÜCHSE

- Calibre	15.43 mm
- Rifling	4
- Capacity	1
- Length	1,230 mm
- Length of barrel	768 mm
- Weight	4,375 gr

ERFURT

Overleaf:
German Dreyse system Jägerbüchse M.1865 and paper cartridge.

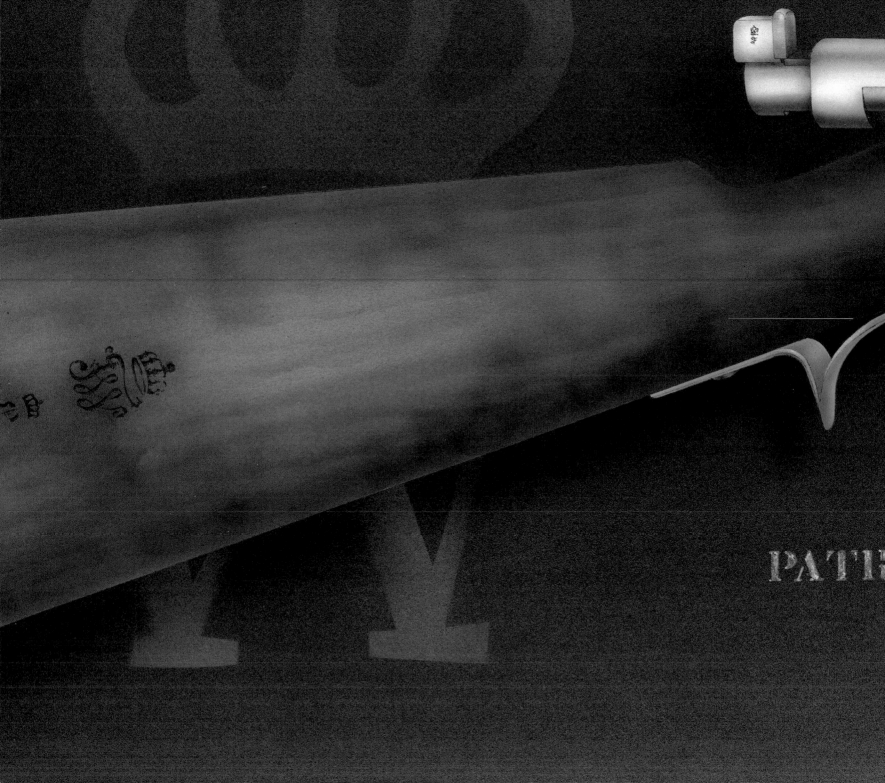

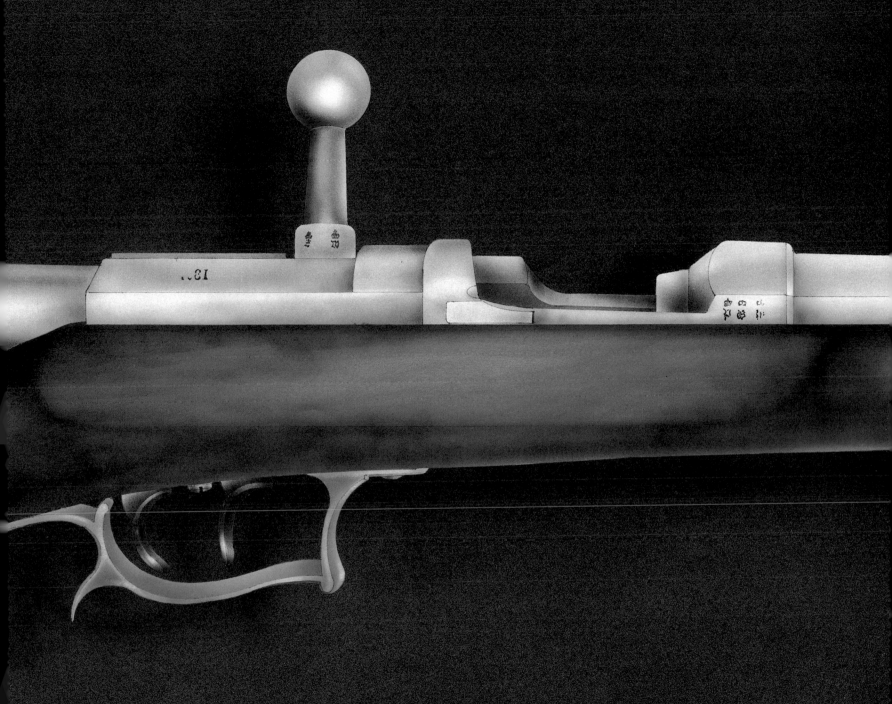

DREYSE M 1865

NE M.1865

Chassepot

France anxiously watched the rapid improvement and development of infantry arms in Prussia. The dissatisfaction of the higher circles in Paris increased drastically after several unfortunate campaigns by Napoleon III's army. On the other hand, Prussian weapons had recorded some brilliant victories, threatening "with iron and blood" to create a powerful and united German state on the borders of the French Empire. Like other European countries, France ascribed the success of the Prussian army to the Dreyse needle-guns alone. Because of this, enormous efforts were made to create a weapon that could parry those of the menacing neighbour. In 1865, the supervisor of the French Artillery Arsenal, Antoine Alphonse Chassepot, came up with a solu-

washer was mounted on the front part of the rifle's bolt.

During the first shots it really did prevent the escape of gasses better than the Prussian conical steel bolt-action and cartridge chamber assembly, but after prolonged firing this washer became so deformed that it lost its original function.

The next year, the French intended yet another breech-loading gun for their army, the so-called *"à tabatière"* M.1867, created by adapting an old percussion model from 1857. The changes consisted in cutting the breech and installing a breech-block, hinged on the right-hand side, carrying a firing pin, which swung open to load and extract: thus the name "snuff-box".

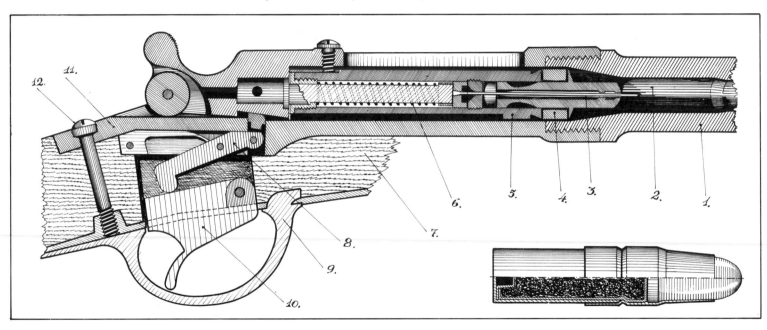

tion of the breech-loader with bolt-action based almost completely on the already-mentioned Green construction. However, French military circles, aware of the failings of the two-piece cartridge, insisted on a needle-gun. To meet their demands, one year later, Chassepot completed an improved gun, a challenge to the Dreyse. The French constructor adopted a smaller calibre barrel (11 mm) and better internal organization, resulting in a ballistic performance superior to that of the Prussian weapon. Furthermore, the French *Fusil Mle.1866* used paper and linen cartridges with the cap placed in the central part of the base. Such organization of the ammunition permitted the pin to be much shorter. But one of the greatest advantages of the Chassepot, at least to start with, was thought to be the sealing of the chamber whereby an india-rubber

RIFLE SYSTEM CHASSEPOT M.1866
1. barrel; 2. chamber; 3. needle; 4. obturating washer; 5. breech-bolt; 6. spring; 7. forestock; 8. abzughebel; 9. trigger-guard; 10. trigger; 11. breech-tang; 12. breech-tang screw.

PAPER CARTRIDGE SYSTEM CHASSEPOT

Pleased with the results achieved, but also overrating the significance of the new weapon, the French were impatient to find a good opportunity to show it off. Finally, they used the claim of Prince Leopold von Hohenzollern-Sigmaringen to the vacated Spanish throne as a pretext to declare war.

The German states were aware of the shortcomings of their outdated needle-guns even before war broke out. By Wilhelm I's decree of March 10, modernization of the Dreyse gun was started in May 1870, according to the project of an em-

---

FRENCH M. 1866 CHASSEPOT SYSTEM RIFLE

- Calibre .... 11 mm
- Rifling 4
- Capacity 1
- Length .... 1,300 mm
- Length of barrel .... 825 mm
- Weight .... 4,150 gr

ployee of the Arsenal in Spandau, Ludwig Beck. The declaration of war on July 19 of the same year stopped the work, and the Prussian Army found itself in the position of having to face the modern Chassepot rifles with nothing but their old-fashioned weapons. Regardless of this, the war ended in a German victory that gave them Alsace and Lorraine and war reparations of five thousand million francs!

True, Germany paid dearly for its victory. For example, of the 109,200 German infantrymen who took part in the battle at Gravelotte, the Chassepot gun eliminated 19.96%. The 1st batallion of the 2nd Guards regiment alone lost 55.5% of its men in this battle.

The victors adapted a large quantity of the captured Chassepot guns by shortening them into carbines intended for their own cavalry. With the introduction of the metal cartridge, this weapon was further adapted for use with the new ammunition, resulting in the Prussian M.1871 carbine and Saxony M.1873 Bremer-Einhorn system carbine.

On the other hand, the French too followed this example. After 1874, and the introduction of the modern Gras gun, they adapted all the remaining Chassepot weapons to the new metal ammunition.

Attack of the German Jäger-Battallion no. 5 on a French battery. War between France and Germany, 1871.

Overleaf:
French M.1866 Chassepot system infantry rifle, paper cartridge and markings: the original French and the subsequent German.

MANUFACTURE IMPERIALE   M^{LE} 1866

Mutzig

FW

D 72629

FUSIL CHASSEPOT

MODELE 1866

Carle

The Russians soon realised all the failings of their percussion breech-loading rifles. The only weapon based on this principle to remain in use in the army until the late 1870s was the M.1863 Gille-Trummer system officers' pistol. The cruel lessons of the Franco-Prussian War reminded St. Petersburg circles of needle-guns, known in Russia since 1835. Accordingly, the Commission for the Choice of Guns encouraged local and foreign constructors to work on similar solutions. In mid-1866 a gunsmith by the name of Carle (also Karle, Karl, Carl) entered the public competition and, through his representative, Zons, submitted his own needle-gun construction.

A certain amount of confusion surrounds this inventor today. Whereas Russian literature gives him as a Briton by ori-

der chamber mechanism. The greatest problem was posed by the paper ammunition. Russia had adopted the cartridge of the chairman of the Arms Commission of the Sestroreck Colonel Weltischtschew, the most important element of which was the classic Minié bullet. Unfortunately, it later emerged that the Weltischtschew-system cartridge had a number of shortcomings, was expensive and complicated to make in the troops. Despite these failings, on March 28, 1867, the improved Carle-system weapon was adopted for use by the Russian Army. At first it was planned to adapt the Cossack Chernolikhov-system M.1860 rifle to this system, but during 1868 it was discovered that the needle-gun was not suitable for use by the Cossacks. Finally, the old infantry M.1856 percussion guns were adapted to it.

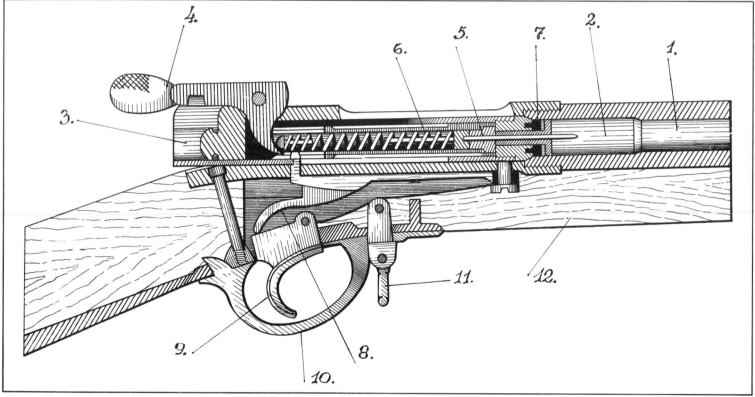

RIFLE SYSTEM CARLE M.1867
1. barrel; 2. chamber; 3. breech bolt; 4. bolt-handle; 5. needle; 6. spring; 7. washer; 8. abzugstollen; 9. trigger; 10. trigger guard; 11. sling swivel; 12. forestock.

RUSSIAN M. 1867 CARLE SYSTEM RIFLE	
- Calibre	15.24 mm (6''')
- Rifling	4
- Capacity	1
- Length	1,340 mm
- Length of barrel ..	852 mm
- Weight	4,900 gr

gin, living in Hamburg, other authors claim him to be a German gunsmith from Suhl. In any case, his solution aroused the interest of the Russian Commission, which left the testing of the Carle weapon to a team headed by master gunsmith Chagin.

Carle's construction comprised a bolt-action breech which was cocked by a lever placed on the upper rear side. The sealing of the chamber was achieved by a leather ring, and the ignition of the cap by a steel pin.

Chagin made a number of modifications to this weapon, mostly in the pow-

As early as 1867 there were plans to adapt or produce 785,295 Carle guns, but by 1874, "only" 215,500 M.1867 guns had been turned out. These were issued to the troops of the Caucasian, Turkestan, Orenburg and Siberian districts (line infantry, not Cossacks, as D. Venner stated). In the war of 1877/78, these forces succeeded, despite the many faults of the Carle weapons, in capturing a number of towns held by the Turks in the Crimea.

By this time, the rest of the world had switched to metal cartridges, so that the Russo-Turkish War was the last in which guns with paper cartridges were used.

Albini-Brändlin, Baranow

The invention of the metallic cartridge (with a metal case) gave a great impulse to the development of breech-loading guns. The first such cartridge was patented by Samuel Johannes Pauly back in 1812. Two decades later, the French gunsmith, Lefaucheux, constructed a pin-fire cartridge. From this moment on, there was rapid progress in infantry ammunition, which moved into three directions. One group was made up of constructions on Lefaucheux's principles, with a radially placed pin. The French gunsmith Flobert was the founder of the second family of ammunition with the so-called rim-fire. With these cartridges, the initial mixture was placed in a rim on the broadened base of the metal case.

Finally, the best quality group of cartridges comprised constructions with a priming cap placed in the centre of the base of the case. M. Pottet is considered to have been the first to invent central-firing cartridges. On the basis of his work, Boxer and Berdan developed far better ammunition which allowed the arms constructors free scope for their ideas.

Belgian constructor, Brändlin, and at a competition in Woolwich carried off first prize with the new gun. Roused by this foreign approval, the Italian Navy finally decided on the Albini-Brändlin rifle for its use in 1866. The armed forces of Belgium, Bavaria, Württenberg and some British colonies followed suit.

Unlike the Italians, the Russian Admiralty paid Albini's solution due attention in 1865. A young official of the Naval Museum of St Petersburg, Lieutenant Baranow undertook the testing of this weapon and greatly improved Albini's gun by making more than ten changes on its construction.

The navy was satisfied with the simplicity of this new breech-block and the low production costs. True, this solution did have some faults, to which the army drew attention: at an elevation of over 45 – 50° the breech-block opened of its own accord uncontrollably; cleaning the weapon from the back was almost impossible; and the case was not automatically ejected but had to be removed manually.

Brändlin, F. A., English arms-factory owner in Birmingham. In 1863, improved the Mont-Storm percussion breech-loader, which provided the basis for the adaptation of muzzle-loading Enfield guns in the British Army. In 1866/67, patented a breech-loading mechanism for the adaptation of muzzle-loaders, together with the Italian Naval Captain, Augusto Albini. Finally, together with A. Sommerville, produced Galand-type revolvers according to the 1868 patent.

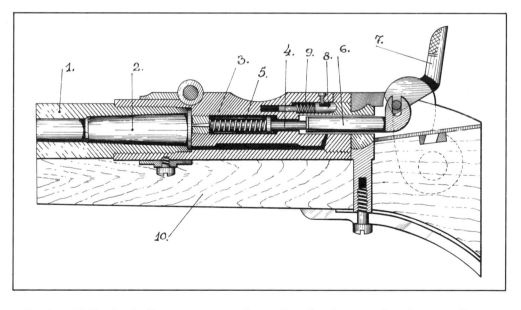

RIFLE SYSTEM BARANOW
1. barrel; 2. chamber; 3. breech-block; 4. firing pin; 5. firing pin spring; 6. striker; 7. hammer; 8. locking pin; 9. locking pin spring; 10. forestock.

RUSSIAN M. 1869 BARANOW SYSTEM RIFLE	
- Calibre	15.24 mm (6''')
- Rifling	4
- Capacity	1
- Length	1,340 mm
- Length of barrel . .	851.2 mm
- Weight	4,500 gr

During 1865, the Italian inventor and naval officer, Augusto Albini, patented his gun with the rising breech-block. Its body was opened by an upward movement in the direction of the mouth of the barrel. Because of its similarity to the lid of a box, this solution was also, like the French M.1867, sometimes calles *"a tabacchiera"*. The firing pin, triggered by a traditional hammer, passed through the breech-block.

The Italian Army and Navy did not, at first show much interest in their compatriot's device. Because of this, Albini improved his solution together with a

Despite these weak points, on January 24, 1869 the Admiralty adopted the Baranow-system gun for the use of its fleet. The contract for the production of these weapons was given to the Putilov works in St Petersburg, and for the production of the ammunition to the naval workshop in the same city. A total of 10,000 old muzzle-loading guns were adapted to the Baranow system for the needs of the Russian Mediterranean and Pacific fleets.

Overleaf:
Russian M.1869 Baranow system infantry rifle, based on Albini-Brändlin system guns.

КАЗНОЗАРЯДНАЯ ВИНТОВКА

(Russian M.1869 Ba

Вскоре вопрос о казнозарядной винтовке для флота был поставлен на реальную почву. В 1865. года лейтенант Н. М. Баранов, нагольник Морского Музея в Петербурге, предложил свою систему для переделки винтовок. Н. М. Баранов начал работу над конструированием ручного огнестрельного оружия с 1854. г., когда ему едва исполнилось 18. лет, и начал с "приложения" своей системы к охотничьему ружью."

"Винтовка Баранова имела откидной зашвор, от... Бранд-лин-Альбини. По отзыв... что было пл...

...саном за ...кого суждения бар... ...что обстоятельство, что ...хлинском заводе еще в. 1865. г. металлические гильзы изготовляли без особых затруднений так что можно было надеяться на дальнейший успех в этом деле. И успех пришел. Вслед за Ох-

Рис. 2

Знак .с

Vahentak, Andpet

ИСТЕМЫ БАРАНОВА ОБР. 1869

now System Rifle)

Д. 1324

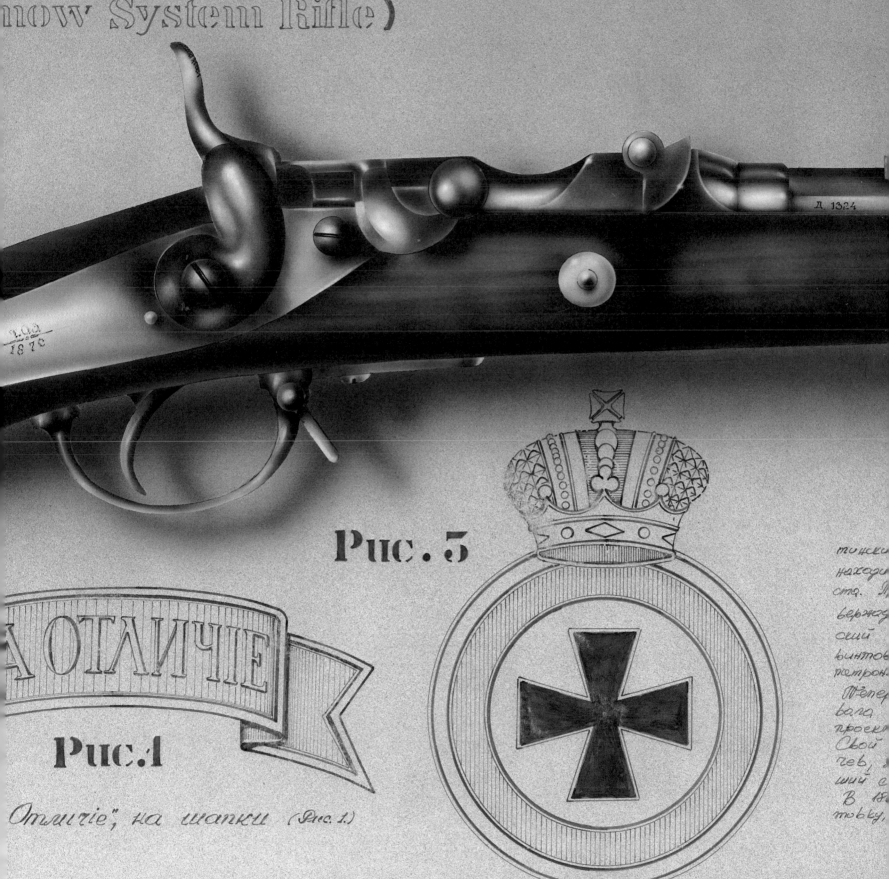

Рис. 5

Рис. 1

ОТЛИЧИЕ

Otличie", на шапки (Рис. 1)

тонск

находи

ста.

бержа

сий

винтов

петрон

Теперь

вала

проекь

Свой

чев,

ший

В 18

товку

Krnka

Krnka, Karel, born April 6, 1858, in Velký Varadín, died February 25, 1926, in Prague. Son of the famous Czech (Bohemian) constructor Sylvestr Krnka. Served in the Austro-Hungarian Army as an infantry officer, but later turned completely to the construction of arms. First worked on improving Werndl's rifle, later on the repeating rifle (together with his father). His greatest success was the adoption of his self-loading pistol by the Austrian Army – *Repetierpistole M.07*.

MONTENEGRIN M. 1855/66 KRNKA SYSTEM RIFLE

- Calibre .... 14.8 mm
- Rifling 4
- Capacity 1
- Length .... 1,220 mm
- Length of barrel .... 850 mm
- Weight .... 4,730 gr

In mid-1867, a colonel of the lancer Guards regiment, T. F. Gan, brought with him from Vienna to Russia the prototype of a breech-loader of the Czech constructor Sylvestr Krnka. This was shown to the Arms Commission, which decided that the construction in question was identical to that of a certain Kornich, already known in the country. The Krnka gun was nevertheless tested in the Volkov plain near St Petersburg and on that occasion given some bad marks.

In July 1867, the Russian military attaché to France, Colonel Witgenschtein, informed St Petersburg that Baron Hohenbruck's rifle, which had attracted the attention of French military circles and guns-

With him he brought a rifle signed *KRNKA*. It is interesting that Russian documents indicate that Krnka and the Baron Hohenbruck were one and the same person. Czech sources, on the other hand, state that Krnka worked on the prototype together with a Baron E. von Hohenbruck, and that therefore two different persons were involved. In any case, the Arms Commission once again compared the construction of the gun brought from Vienna by Gan with the drawings sent by Witgenschtein from France and the prototype brought by Krnka himself, and reached the conclusion that in all three cases, the same construction was in question. After this the Main Artillery Direc-

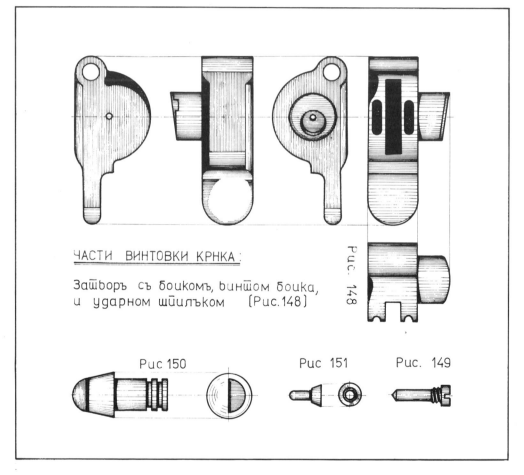

ЧАСТИ ВИНТОВКИ КРНКА:

Заѿворъ съ боикомъ, винѿом боика, и ударном шѿилъком [Рис. 148]

Рис. 148

Рис 150   Рис. 151   Рис. 149

miths by its simplicity and low production costs, was to be tested at the range of the sharpshooter school in Vincennes. Drawings of this weapon, which Witgenschtein enclosed with his report, showed the Arms Commission that the construction in question was actually the one brought from Vienna by T. F. Gan.

The opinions of the excellent French experts influenced the Russians. In the autumn of the same year, Sylvestr Krnka, alias Baron Hohenbruck, an Austrian subject, was invited to St. Petersburg.

DETAIL OF BREECH-BLOCK SYSTEM KRNKA
Fig. 148: breech-block; Fig. 149: breech-block screw; Fig. 150: striker; Fig. 151: firing pin.

tion gave the order to start serious testing of Krnka's weapon parallel with Baranow's. The managers of private and state-owned arms works — members of the Arms-testing Board — announced that adaptation of old guns to the Krnka system would be 1.5 roubles cheaper per weapon than adaptation to the Baranow system and that, in the same length of time, almost 200,000 more Krnka guns could be produced.

It would seem that financial reasons carried the day. By his decree of March 18, 1869, Czar Alexander II authorised the adaptation of muzzle-loaders, and of August 8, of the poorer Terry-Norman breech-loaders as well, all to the Krnka system. Already in that same year a part of the Russian Army was issued the newly--adapted gun. It was then that some of

the faults of the extractor came to light, but these were speedily removed by local constructors.

By January 1, 1877, Russia had turned out 613,287 improved Krnka guns, with which 26 to 27 divisions were armed in the 1877/78 war.

Wishing to strengthen the newly formed Principality of Bulgaria, in the course of 1878 Russia delivered 61,700 Krnka rifles to Bulgarian soldiers, and in the next year as many as 150,450 — almost a third of its available weapons!

Krnka's M.1869 solution was based on the classic breech-block placed in a massive bronze frame. The breech was opened to the left, vertical to the barrel. A firing-pin, triggered by the somewhat modified hammer of earlier percussion guns, passed through the breech-body.

Death of Russian Major Gartalow. Russo--Turkish war, 1876 – 1878.

Krnka's M.1855/66 rifle, intended for use by the army of the little Balkan Principality of Montenegro, was based on a similar solution. Prince Nikola of Montenegro personally ordered 2,500 breech--loaders of this system from Krnka in February 1869. By 1875, Montenegro had bought another 4,500 infantry rifles of the Krnka system from the Thomas Sederl factory in Vienna.

Overleaf:
M.1856/69 Krnka system infantry rifle with the insignia of the Montenegrin Army.

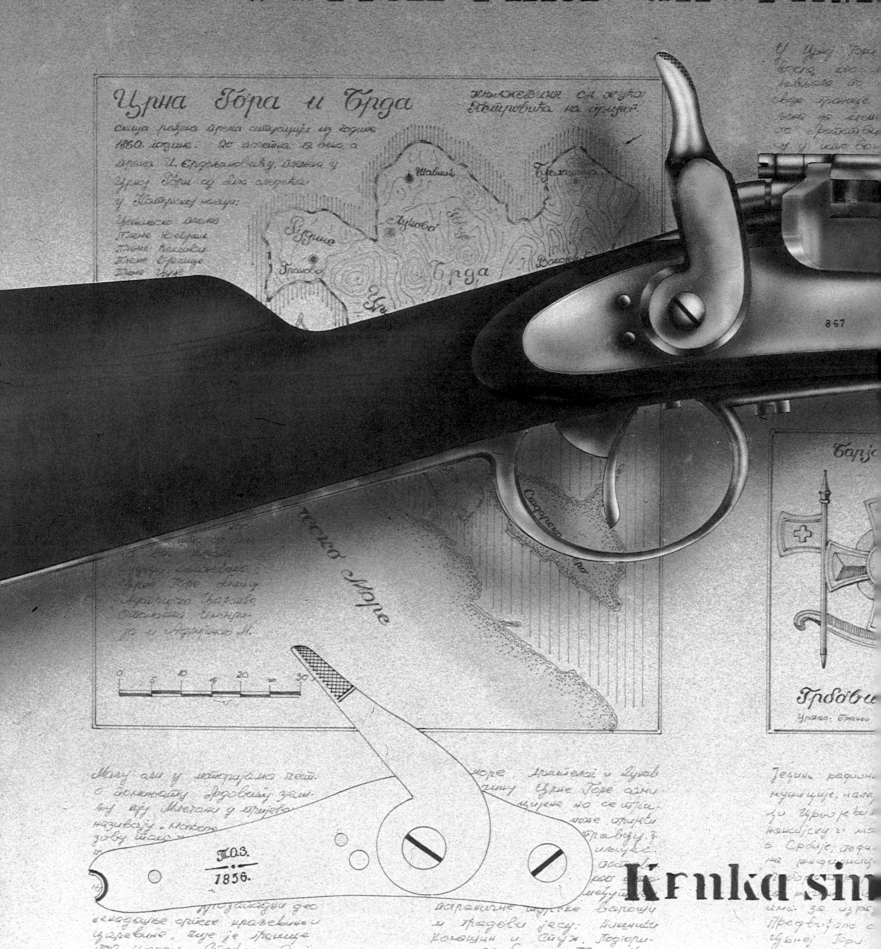

Водник   Десетар

Чепна застава, 1876 година

Ратни барјак, 1876. године (1)

le shot cartridge rifle

Wänzl, Werndl-Holub

Werndl, Josef, born February 26, 1831 in Steyr, died April 29, 1889 in Steyr. Born to a well known family of gunsmiths. During his youth worked in Prague, Vienna and Thüringen. Acquired most of his experience of modern technology in the USA, working for the Colt and Remington companies. In 1853 he returned to Steyr where he inherited the family works after his father's death. At about this time he also started collaborating with the talented constructor Karl Holub, together with whom he designed the Austrian M.67 rifle. After Holub's return from his specialization in Hartford, USA, the two partners founded an arms factory in 1864. Five years later, this factory became a stock company with J. Werndl as Chairman of the Board.

Realization of the importance of breech-loading guns of modern warfare came to Austria in an exceedingly painful manner. Defeat in the 1866 war called for urgent re-orientation in the arming of its forces. Already in 1865 the Ministry of War in Vienna had started testing breech-loaders and examined 52 different breech solutions in the first ten months of their work.

It was not until June 1866 that the Ministry founded a board for the selection of a breech, headed by two energetic and capable men: Erzherzog Wilhelm and 29-year-old Lieutenant-Colonel A. Kroppaczek. At the same time, the Artillery Committee, under Artur Graf Bylandt-Rheydt, was given the duty of examining and testing the barrels and ammunition, that is to say, the ballistics of the weapon submitted. The guns tested were divided into two basic groups: the first made up of models created by the adaptation of muzzle-loading guns, the second of models of new rifles. The first group was then subdivided into systems with paper cartridge, needle-firing guns and systems with metallic cartridges.

After six months of work, the board and the committee submitted a joint report to the Ministry of War. By the final decision of Emperor Franz-Joseph I of January 5, 1867, the Ministry issued Regulation no. 92, Article 7, by which the Wänzl-system breech-block was adopted for the adaptation of muzzle-loading to breech-loading guns.

Wänzl, owner of a gunsmith's workshop in the Vienna suburb of St Margareten, had actually perfected the Swiss Millbank-Amsler-system breech-block. The body of Wänzl's breech-block was opened upwards, towards the mouth of the barrel. A stem, connected to the hammer by a system of levers automatically blocked the breech-block when the hammer was released. The firing-pin was still triggered by the hammer, and the gun used rim-fire ammunition.

In Austria, Wänzl's rifle was rightly accepted as merely a temporary solution. The Ministry of War continued searching for a high-quality weapon that would be manufactured in its entirety. One of the most serious claimants to the title of the new Austrian gun was the Remington. But in 1867, the Commission of the K.u.k. Artillery Committee was presented with the Werndl-Holub system gun.

Josef Werndl worked as constructor in all the major Austrian works for the production and repair of weapons, and for a while even in the Colt and Remington factories in the USA. In America

Clash of Austrian and Prussian Infantry. War of 1866.

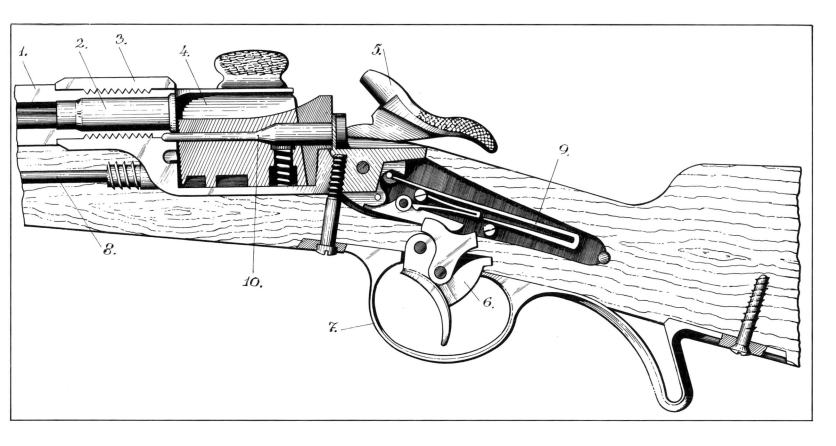

he became acquainted with the modern method of serial production and applied this knowledge in his factory, founded in 1864 in Steyr (later called the *Österreichische Waffenfabrik Gesellschaft* — ÖEWG). With his collaborator, the Czech Karel Holub, Werndl produced the prototype of a breech-block which he offered the Austrian Commission.

The Werndl-Holub breech-block was of massive cylindrical shape, with its axis somewhat under that of the barrel. The bolt-action was opened by pressing a leaf--shaped handle rightwards. The firing--pin, which passed diagonally through the body of the breech-block, was initiated by the hammer placed on the outer side of the lock plate. With this type of breech--block, the Commission suggested a new type of ammunition, barrel and butt. The weapon created in this way was adopted for the whole Austrian army in 1867.

As early as February 10, 1874, the M.1867 was replaced in the army by the improved Werndl M.1873. The body of the breech-bolt was reinforced, a fixed axis was built in, and the safety device improved. The hammer was moved to the inside of the lock-plate and the furniture was changed. Only four years later Austrian weapons underwent yet another change. This time the ammunition was modified and reinforced, which led to the modification of the rifles as well.

AUSTRIAN M. 1877 WERNDL-HOLUB SYSTEM RIFLE	
- Calibre	11 mm
- Rifling	6
- Capacity	1
- Length	1,281 mm
- Length of barrel	843 mm
- Weight	4,500 gr

But the best part of the story is the fact that the Austrians had no opportunity to use Werndl guns in any conflict in the 19th century. True, they were used during the occupation of Bosnia-Herzegovina, but never entered the main European stage. It seemed that this gun would be forgotten in some dark and dusty arsenal, but in the difficult moments of the First World War, the conflict of the then most modern weapons of the 20th century, Austria remembered these museum pieces and issued them to its final category of conscripts. There was even more of an anachronism in the Kingdom of Yugoslavia — Werndl guns were jealously kept in the military reserves right up until World War II!

RIFLE SYSTEM WERNDL-HOLUB M.1877
1. barrel; 2. chamber; 3. receiver; 4. breech--block; 5. hammer; 6. trigger; 7. trigger-guard; 8. cleaning rod; 9. main spring; 10. axis pin.

Overleaf:
M.1877 Werndl-Holub system infantry rifle.

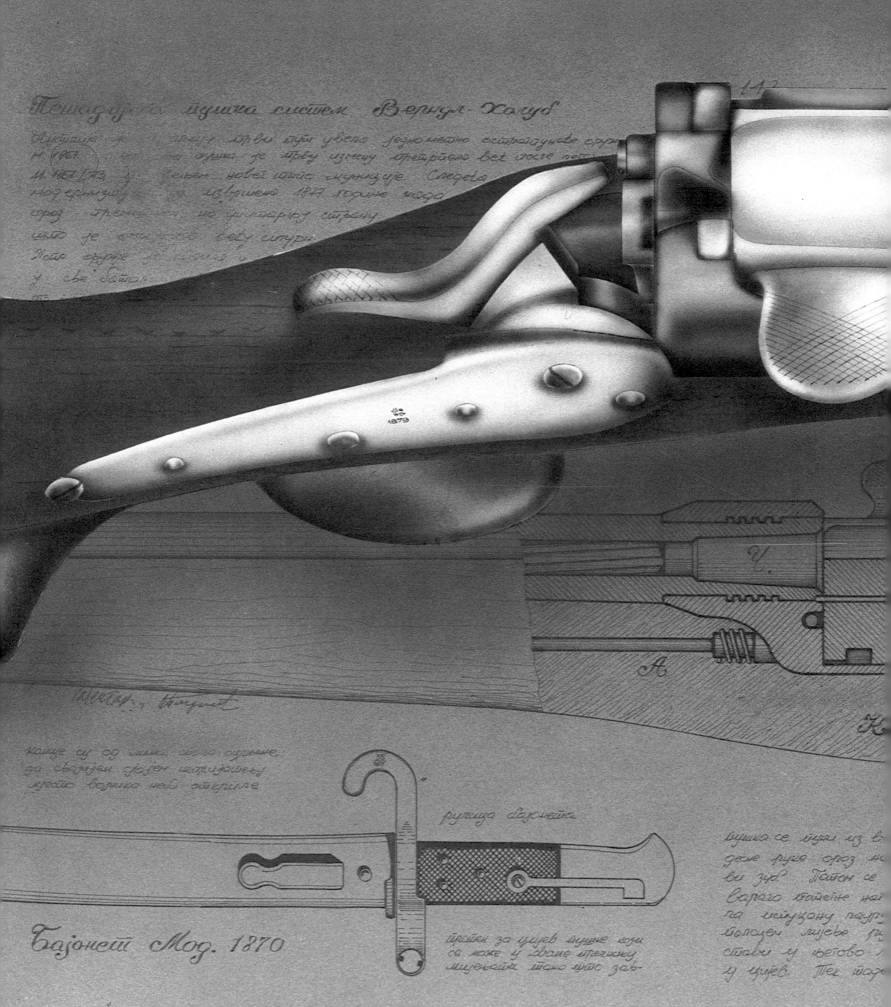

Пешадијска пушка систем Вердл-Холуб

Бајонет Мод. 1870

ручица бајонета

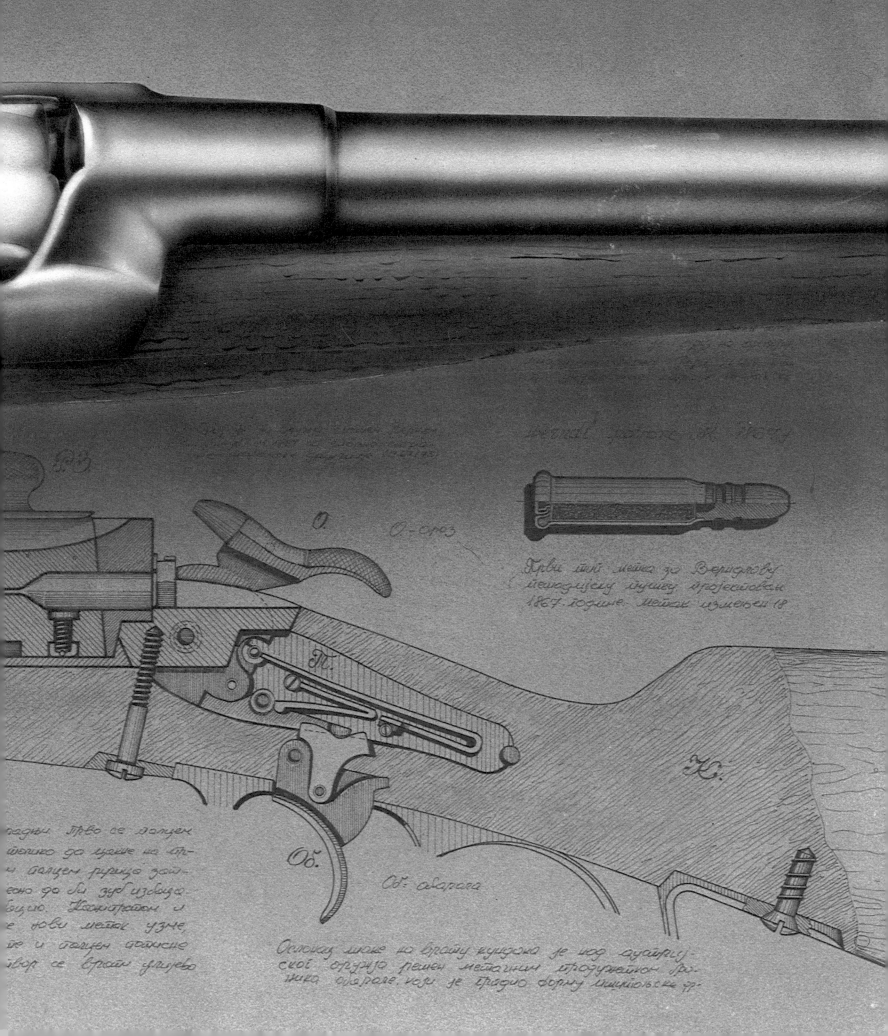

Springfield

The USA is the country in which probably the greatest number of breech constructions were invented during the 19th century. The Civil War was an ideal testing range in which these solutions could prove themselves or fail and be forgotten. Thus at the end of the War the army had a large choice of proven models from which they had to choose one.

At about this time, the Master Armorer of the Springfield Armory, Erskine S. Allin, patented his breech-block project. Towards the end of 1865, work started on adapting the old percussion M.1861 – 63 guns to this system.

The Allin conversion system used a rising breech-block hinged at the front, which when raised by unlatching a thumb piece, exposed the breech for loading the chamber with a short, calibre ·58 rim-fire cartridge.

In the course of the next year, 1866, the Allin rifle was somewhat modified in accordance with the experience gained during troop testing of the M.1865 gun. Among other things, the calibre was adapted to central-fire ·50 ammunition and the firing-pin was given a spring. Whereas only 5,000 had been adapted to the previous model, as many as 25,000 muzzle-loading rifles left over from the Civil War were altered to the new system.

Two years later, in January 1868, the Board of Officers approved the production of a completely new barrel that suited the Springfield breech-block. It was precisely in 1868 that Allin's construction first started to be called after the factory in which it originated. It is possible that this change was prompted by the fact that the authorship of this construction was dis-

Major General George Armstrong Custer, U.S.A.

puted by a factory supervisor. Namely, Hiram Berdan also had a patent for an almost identical breech-block construction. Although it has never been cleared up whether one stole this solution from the other, or whether both constructions really were original, Berdan's heirs received an allowance from the American government for the use of his patent.

It is certain, however, that copyright did not particularly interest the market in which the Springfield gun enjoyed wide popularity. It acquired ever greater number of supporters among the military which, eight years after the Civil War, had still not chosen a uniform breech-loading gun.

Finally, by an act of Congress of June 6, 1872, a new Board of Officers was formed, with General A. H. Terry as chairman, and given the task of finally settling the dilemma. The Board set to work in New York City on September 3 of the same year. After six months of diligent work, during which more than 100 diffe-

---

AMERICAN M. 1868 SPRINGFIELD RIFLE

- Calibre	12.7 mm (·50)
- Rifling	3
- Capacity	1
- Length	1,321 mm
- Length of barrel	914 mm
- Weight	4,200 gr

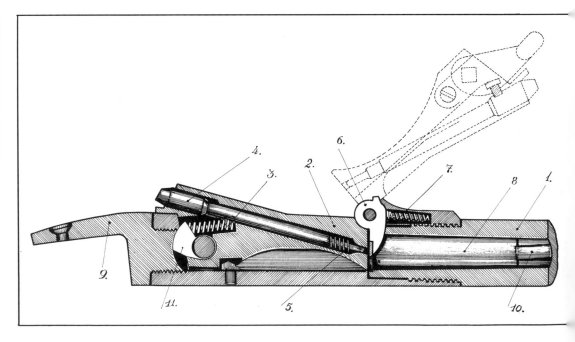

SPRINGFIELD SYSTEM BREECH-BLOCK
1. barrel; 2. breech-block; 3. riegelstück feder; 4. firing pin; 5. firing pin spring; 6. extractor; 7. extractor spring; 8. chamber; 9. breech-tang; 10. grooves; 11. riegelstück.

rent guns were examined, the M.1873 system Springfield rifle was adopted for the US Army. At the same time, the calibre of guns was made uniform ('45). Springfield carbines and rifles thus entered American history, and stayed there, through many famous episodes, for fully thirty years.

Today probably every child knows the story of the victory of the Sioux chieftain, Tatanka Yotanka, alias Sitting Bull, at Little Big Horn. On that legendary June 25, 1876, troopers of the 7th Cavalry regiment of General George Armstrong Custer fought to the last man — with Springfield M.73 carbines.

In the following two decades, the same arms underwent a number of changes which nevertheless did not undermine Allin's basic concept. Ironically enough the modified Springfield, too, had its baptism of fire in a clash with the unfortunate Indians. In one of the darkest episodes of American history, the massacre of Indians at Wounded Knee in 1890, white soldiers were still using single-shot weapons of the Springfield system. Moreover, during the intervention on Cuba in 1898, American volunteer regiments fought against the modern Spanish Mauser M.1893 rifles with their old Springfield!

Rifles of Union soldiers stacked near the railroad station, Petersburg.

Remington

The famous Remington factory, Ilion, New York, turned out the popular type of breech-block which in a short time became widespread throughout the world and retained its position for a considerable period, despite later competition from more modern repeating arms.

Basically, Samuel Remington made use of Leonard Geiger's solution, patented on January 27, 1863, which Joseph Rider improved and, on December 8 of the same year, protected under a new patent, no. 40,887. The main construction of this weapon was based on the so-called split breech, which envolved into the still popular rolling-block type of breech-block.

The Remington rolling-block action was loaded by cocking the hammer and swinging the breech-block backward by the pressure of the thumb on the thumb piece.

1871, another 1,008 infantry rolling-block rifles were troop tested, but this was more the duty of General A. H. Terry's Commission, which was working at the time on the choice of a uniform breech-block, than a sign of any particular interest. On the other hand, the US Navy adopted a quite different position. On October 24, 1865, the Navy Department bought 5,000 Remington carbines of '50 calibre, taking a cup-anvil, for the needs of the fleet. Five years later, the Navy ordered 22,000 so--called *US Navy Rifle Model 1870-Remington,* but on production only took 12,000. The rest was put on the open market.

Dissatisfied with the commercial results achieved in the USA, already in the 1860s Samuel Remington turned to other customers. One of the first international successes of his company was in Sweden,

REMINGTON SYSTEM ROLLING-BLOCK
1. barrel; 2. breech-block; 3. hammer-block; 4. extractor; 5. hammer; 6. mainspring; 7. breech-tang; 8. trigger; 9. trigger-guard; 10. cleaning rod; 11. forestock.

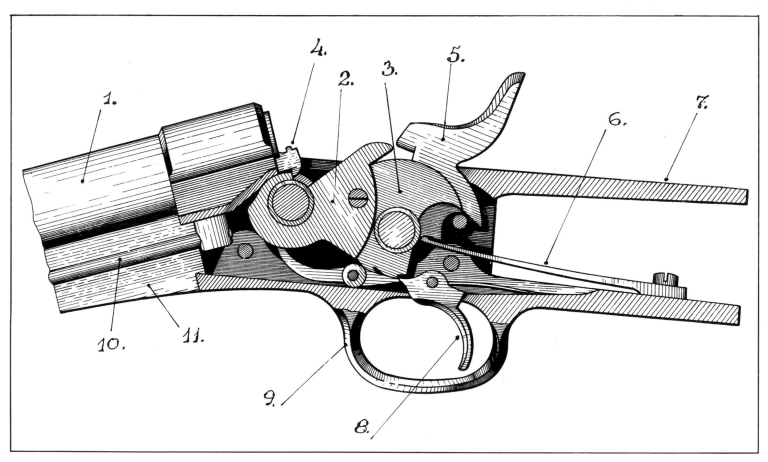

AMERICAN M. 1871 REMINGTON SYSTEM RIFLE	
- Calibre	12.7 mm ('50)
- Rifling	3
- Capacity	1
- Length	1,314 mm
- Length of barrel	914 mm
- Weight	4,100 gr

The US Government signed a contract with the producer on October 24, 1864, for the delivery of 14,999 carbines of the same system, calibre '56 – 50 rim-fire. The following year the contract was extended to another 5,000 carbines, but in the new calibre of '46 rim-fire. With the purchase of these cavalry weapons, the US Army more or less lost interest in the Remington system. True, during May

Norway and Denmark. The joint Swedish-Norwegian commission for the choice of a breech-loading system, founded on October 5, 1866, decided on the Remington rolling-block following twelve months of diligent work. After the Scandinavian countries, this type of weapon gained acceptance in Greece, Egypt and Spain. During 1876, Mexico bought 10,000 Spanish-model Remingtons, and

Brigadier General O.B. Willcox, U.S.A., and staff.

on September 7 of the following year ordered, through contract no. 115, another 3,000 rifles and 1,000 carbines, again in the Spanish calibre of '43.33. Two decades later, not wishing to relinquish this excellent weapon, the Mexicans adapted it to their new 7 × 57 mm ammunition.

It should be added that Remington almost managed to "conquer" the Austrian Army. The chairman of the commission for the choice of breech-loading weapons, Erzherzog Wilhelm, in a letter dated February 9, 1867, personally informed Samuel Remington that his rifle had shown the best results among the weapons tested by November 18 of the previous year. As we know, Vienna eventually chose a local solution, and the Austrian version of the Remington has become a real collector's piece and museum rarity.

Weapons with the rolling-block were used for a very long time. The French even possessed a single-shot Remington M.1914, 8 mm cal., during World War I.

The same type of breech-block achieved great popularity not only through its application to military weapons, but also because of its use in pistols and excellent shooting and hunting rifles.

Overleaf:
Remington system infantry rifle with the state markings.

115

REMINGTON BREECH-LOADING

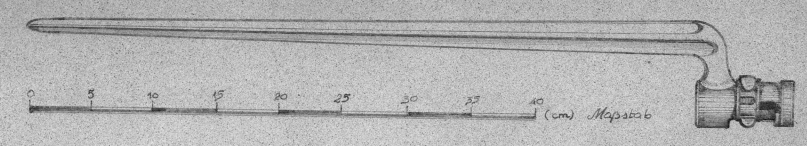

Schwedisches Dillenbajonett M. 1867 für Remington Gewehr

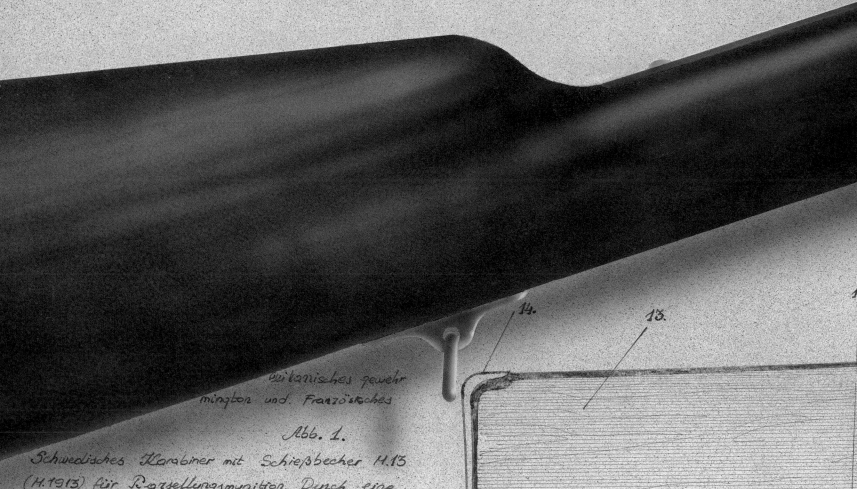

britanisches Gewehr
mington und Französisches

Abb. 1.

Schwedisches Karabiner mit Schießbecher M.13 (M.1913) für Darstellungsmunition. Durch eine Platzpatrone 12,17 mm wurde ein Projektil abgefeuert, das die Detonation einer Granate simulierte.

Abb. 2.

Schwedisches Schützengewehr nach Art des M. 1867. Zu beachten das nichtmilitärische Visier.

Vajačak

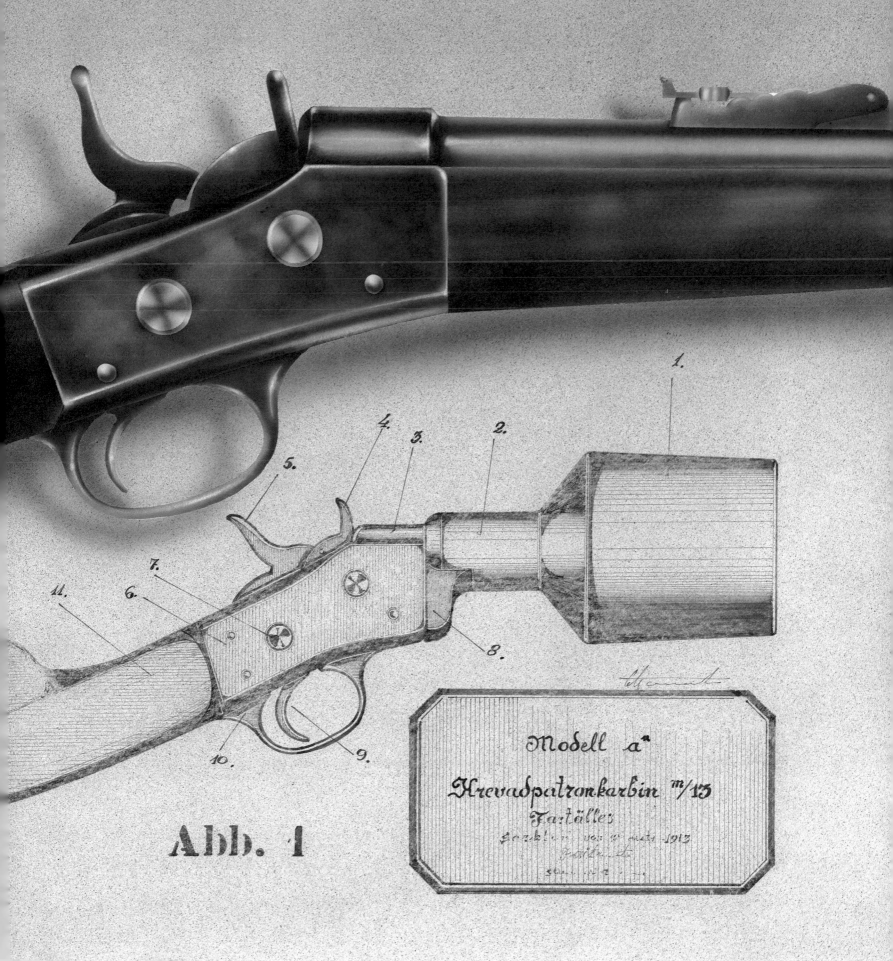

Abb. 1

Modell "a"

Krevadpatronkarbin m/13

Faställes

Snider

In July 1864, a Select Committee was set up in Great Britain, with the duty of choosing a reliable and pracitcal type of breech-block which could be used to modernize percussion muzzle-loading Enfield M.1853 weapons.

Over fifty constructors and arms producers entered the open competition. That number was soon reduced, by selection, to eight, and then five entrants. Finally, the construction of Jacob Snider of New York received the highest number of votes.

Snider's breech was closed by a block which was hinged laterally on the right, and fitted into a recess behind the barrel. To open the breech, a thumb piece was pressed which caused the block to swing over to the right.

The Ottoman imperial government, of which Egypt was a vassal at this time, was surprised by the simplicity and low production cost of the Snider breech-loaders. Accordingly, Turkey ordered a large consignment of these weapons from its protector, Great Britain. The guns intended for Turkey were produced in two different ways: by adapting Springfield M.53 rifles, and by manufacturing completely new weapons according to the Snider principle. Moreover, in its Zeitin Burun workshop Turkey organized the adaptation to the Snider system of existing British percussion arms. Thus, despite heavy losses of military equipment in the war with Russia (1876/78), in the early 1880s Turkey possessed an enormous potential of 400,000 Snider M.1866 guns!

Clash of British troops with warriors from the Zulu tribe. Ginginlow, East Nathal, 1879.

At first these weapons used paper Enfield ammunition with a separate cap. This anachronism was "justified" by the wish to use up the large amount of left-over ammunition as well as the old percussion guns. It soon became obvious that this was a mistake, so the weapons were adapted to the metallic central-fire cartridge. The final choice of ammunition for the Snider rifles was made in 1867 when Colonel Boxer's cartridge was adopted. The issue of these weapons to the British Army was begun in 1865. One of the first countries to follow the English in this choice was Denmark. Next, Egypt too opted for the Snider system, but ordered its rifles in 1866 from the USA. The contract was signed with the Colt Company, which had adapted 12,000 old Springfield M.1861 muzzle-loaded rifles to this system.

Opposite:
Equipment of Turkish infantry: 1. Snider rifle with bayonet; 2. Henry-Martini rifle with bayonet; 3. Cartridge box; 4. Water bottle; 5. Belt pin; 6. Fez.

Overleaf:
Turkish M.1869 Snider system infantry rifle.

TURKISH M. 1866 SNIDER SYSTEM RIFLE	
- Calibre	14.7 mm
- Rifling	3
- Capacity	1
- Length	1,372 mm
- Length of barrel	930 mm
- Weight	4,140 gr

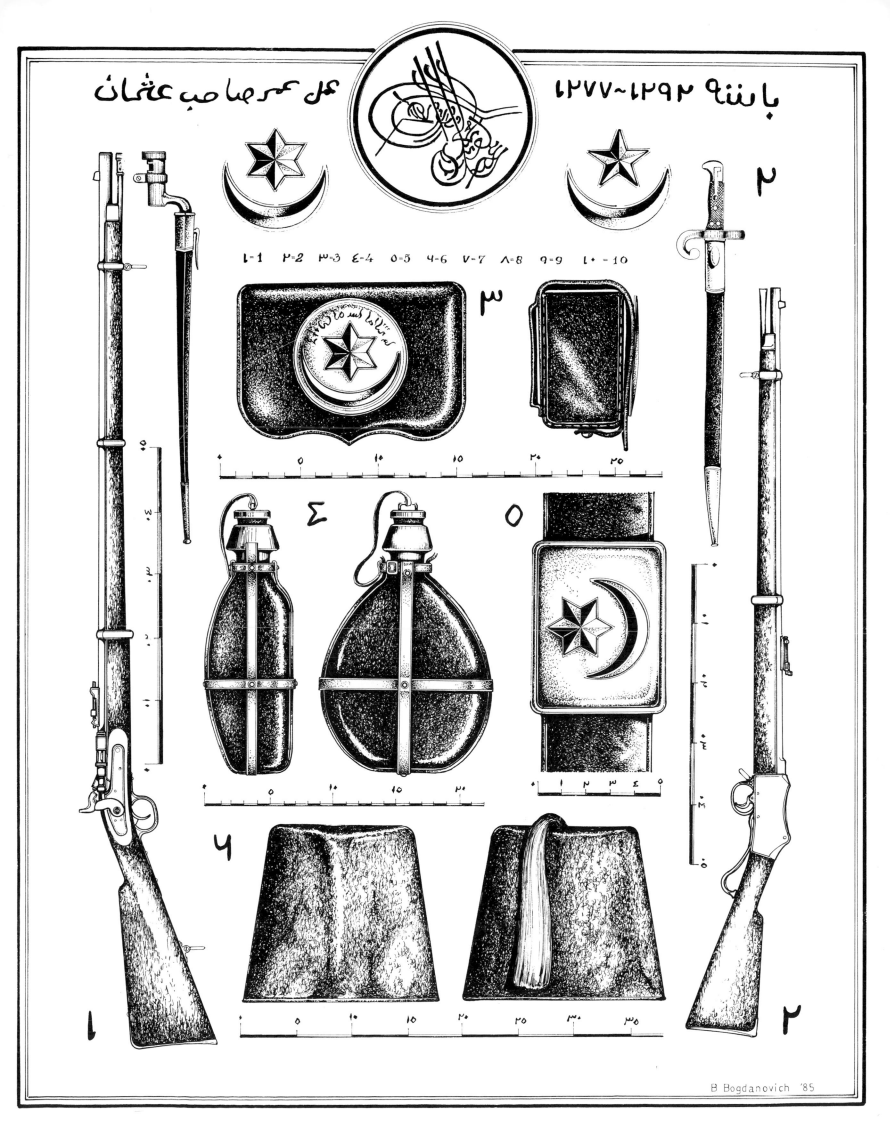

١٢٧٧-١٢٩٣ بانناق

عمل محمد صاحب عثمان

١=1 ٢=2 ٣=3 ٤=4 ٥=5 ٦=6 ٧=7 ٨=8 ٩=9 ١٠=10

B Bogdanovich '85

SNIDER BR

Tugra:ABDÜL

Vafenar, Stewart

ECH LOADING RIFLE

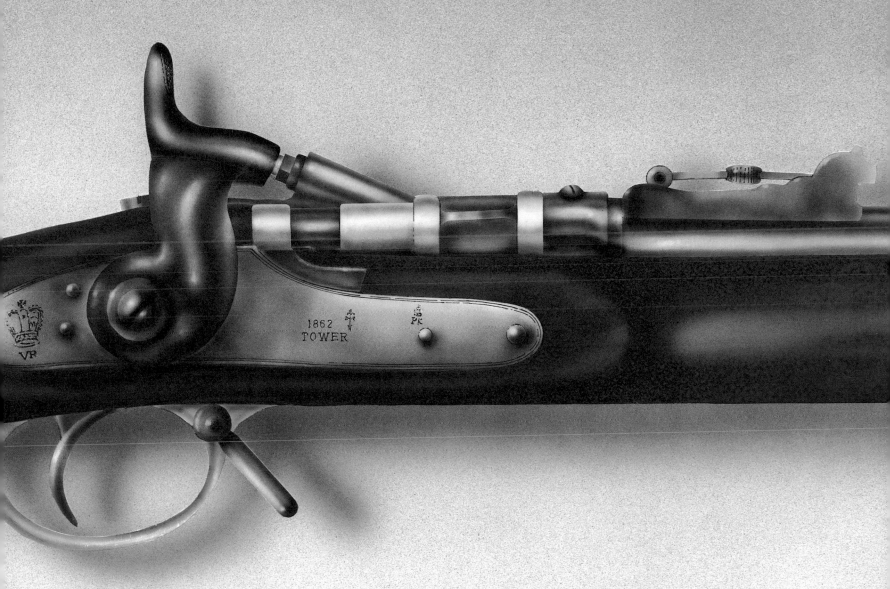

1862
TOWER

VR
PK

ASIS IBN MAHMUD (1277-1292)

Peabody, Roberts

On July 22, 1862, Henry O. Peabody of Boston, Mass., patented (US Patent no. 35,947) a type of breech-block which rivalled the Remington in popularity. The original solution of the Peabody breech-block was intended for the adaptation of old muzzle-loaders to breech-loading guns. Alternations according to this system were started during the Civil War in the Providence Tool Company factory. In later years, Peabody considerably improved his breech-block and re-issued his new project on March 13, 1866, and December 10, 1867. The factory in Providence undertook production of the new weapon, selling it successfully on both home and foreign markets. In a short while, Turkey, Canada, Switzerland, Romania, France, Spain, Denmark and some other countries decided to adopt the Peabody system. Between 1870 and 1872, Mexico, too, bought 8,500 Peabody rifles which the Spanish Army had used on Cuba in battles with Carlos Manuel de Sespedes' rebels.

In 1866, a Serbian engineering officer, M. Jankovich, was the first to describe Peabody's weapon — with unconcealed approval — and its history in the USA in a military magazine in the Balkans.

Among other things, this partial author also mentioned that the representative of the Providence Tool Company in Europe was J. R. MK. Donaldo and Co. of Hamburg.

It would seem that in Serbia Janković was not a lone supporter of Peabody's weapons. After debacle with the Green gun, on May 14, 1869, the Serbian government decided, as a temorary solution, on a loan necessary to adapt 55,000 old Austrian Lorenz rifles to Peabody-system breech-loaders. The work of adaptation was entrusted to the Austrian manufacturer Thomas Sederl, who within a year had managed to procure the necessary machines and mount them in Belgrade fortress. The production of the new weapons officially started in mid-1871.

Contemporary reference works mention this weapon but, in doing so, persist in calling it the Peabody-Roberts system. We do not know how Roberts found himself in this combination, but can only assume that modern authors have been mislead by a certain similarity and the same producer (Providence Tool Company) of both breech-block solutions.

On February 27, 1866, US General Benjamin S. Roberts patented (no. 52,883) his

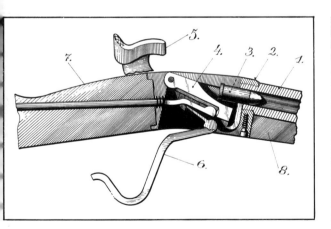

DETAIL OF BREECH-BLOCK SYSTEM PEABODY
1. barrel; 2. receiver; 3. chamber; 4. breech-block; 5. hammer; 6. ladehebel; 7. small of the stock; 8. forestock.

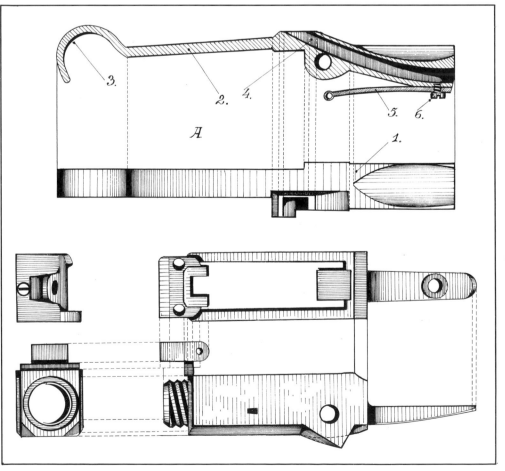

PEABODY SYSTEM BREECH-BLOCK M.1870
A. BREECH-BLOCK
1. breech-block; 2. lever; 3. hook; 4. firing pin; 5. breech-block spring; 6. breech-block spring screw.

Serbian infantry, Serbo-Turkish war, 1876 – 1878.

conversion breech-loading cartridge system. Its main characteristic was a short lever in the rear of the breech-block which, when raised, opened the cartridge chamber. By an 1867 decree of the State Ordnance Board, such weapons were produced by the Providence Tool Company exclusively for the needs of the State of New York.

On the other hand, on the improved Peabody rifle with the characteristic two--piece stock, the mechanism was operated by pulling the trigger guard downward, which opened the breech for loading in the top of the breech-block. This solution was adopted in the USA and all the mentioned countries and has remained well known to this very day because of its distinctive appearance.

Serbia was the only county in the world

that had bought the licence for the original Peabody conversion breech-loading cartridge system, which did, in fact, bear a resemblance to that of Roberts. In his book on US muskets, rifles and carbines, A. Gluckman gives a detailed description of this rifle and says: "... The breech was opened by lifting with the forefinger the loop of tailpiece projecting over the breech tang, which opened the breech for the insertion of a rim-fire cartridge. Lifting the tailpiece also operated the extractor."

Unlike the original, Serbian weapons used central-fire ammunition and were also made in two versions: with breech--blocks and frames in bronze or steel. Because of the strange association of the breech-block with cutlery, Serbian soldiers also called these "spoon-rifles".

SERBIAN M. 1870 PEABODY SYSTEM RIFLE	
- Calibre	13.9 mm
- Rifling	4
- Capacity	1
- Length	1,430 mm
- Length of barrel	863 mm
- Weight	4,450 gr

Overleaf:
M.1870 Peabody-Conversion system infantry rifle.

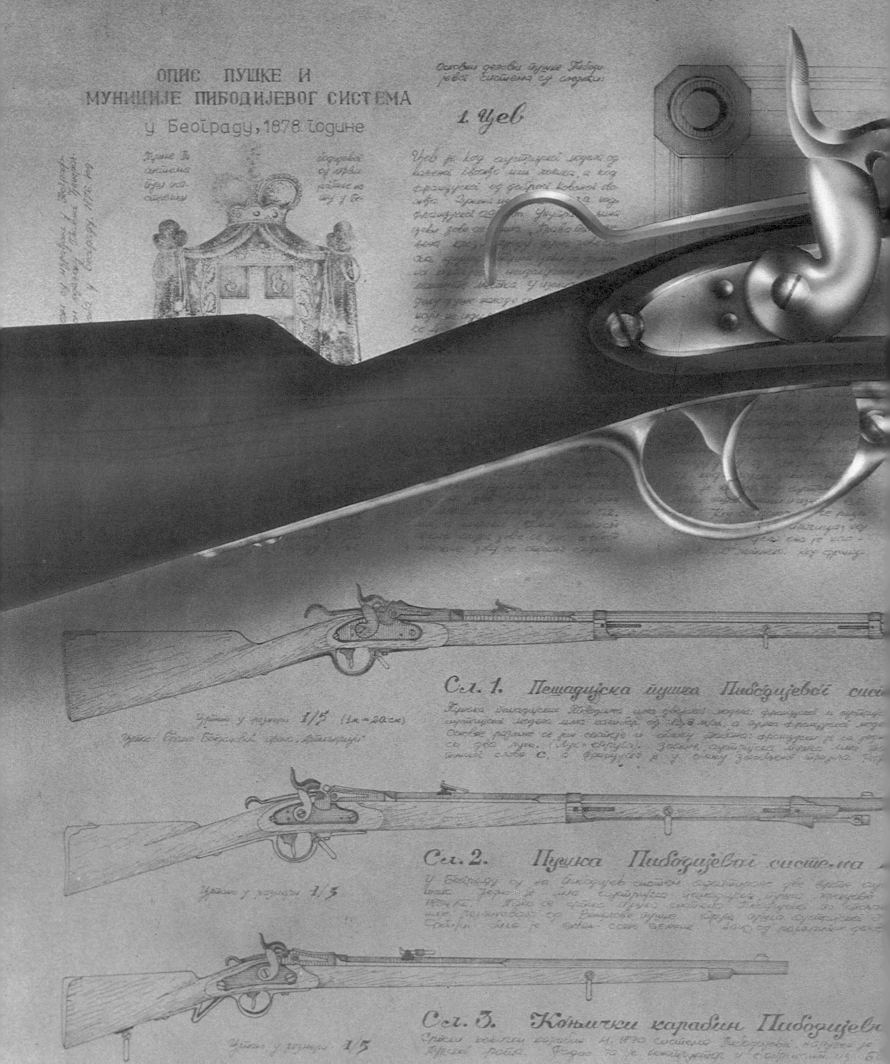

ОПИС ПУШКЕ И
МУНИЦИЈЕ ПИБОДИЈЕВОГ СИСТЕМА
У Београду, 1878 Године

1. Цев

Сл. 1. Пешадијска пушка Пибодијевог сис...

Цртано у размери 1/5 (1м=20см)

Сл. 2. Пушка Пибодијевог система

Цртано у размери 1/5

Сл. 3. Коњички карабин Пибодијев

Цртано у размери 1/5

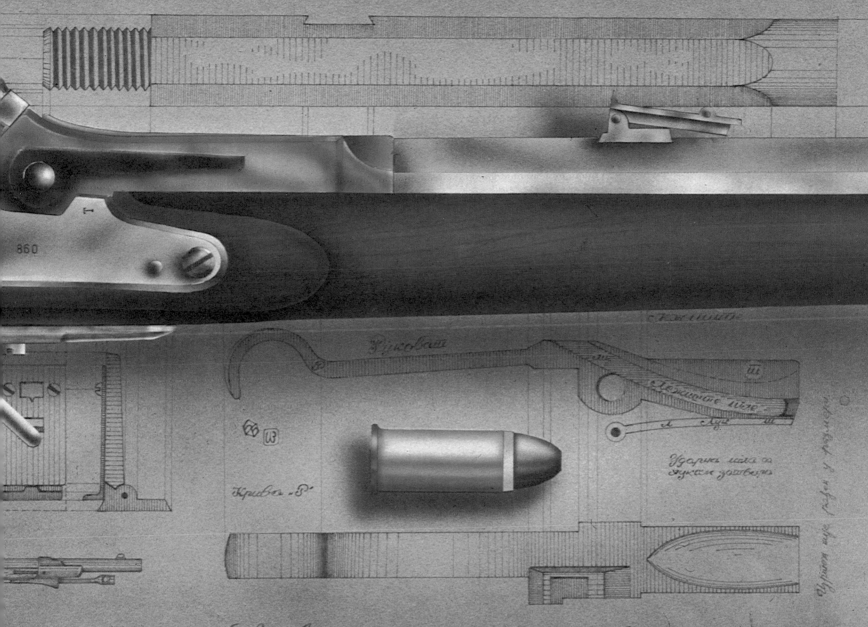

М.1869/70.

6. Затварач у изгледу озго и у пресеку са стране

M.1869/70-II

Peabody conversion
breech-loading
cartridge
system
model 1870

Henry-Martini

Henry, Alexander, born 1817 in Edinburgh, died 1895. Worked for the famous gunsmith Mortimer, later founded his own workshop in Edinburgh, Scotland. Produced exceptionally precise sports and match rifles. Patented a single-shot rifle with a falling-block which he offered the British Army. The gun was not accepted, but Henry's rifled barrel and Martini's breech-block were.

Martini, Friedrich von, born 1832, died 1897, Swiss gunsmith of Hungarian origin, modified the American breech-loading Peabody mechanism and in 1865 offered it to the Swiss Army. It was later adopted by the British, Turkish, Romanian and some other armed forces.

TURKISH M. 1871
HENRY-MARTINI SYSTEM RIFLE
- Calibre . . . . .11.43 mm (·45)
- Rifling 7
- Capacity 1
- Length . . . . .1,231 mm
- Length of barrel . . . . .825 mm
- Weight . . . . .3,950 gr

Peabody's solution of the breech-block continued to live an independant life under another name and in a different form.

Friedrich von Martini (1832–1897), an eminent engineer of Hungarian origin, considerably improved Peabody's breech-block in his workshop in Frauenfeld and patented it under the joint name of Peabody-Martini. The distinctive features of the new construction were a concealed hammer placed inside the frame and a long lever for opening which extended beyond the trigger guard. This type of breech-block showed excellent results on hunting and sporting weapons, and at first satisfied military experts as well.

In the 1860s an Edinburgh gunsmith, Alexander Henry (1817–1895), patented a new type of barrel with 7 grooves, based on ·450 calibre central-fire ammunition.

At a competition organized in Britain in order to find a weapon to replace the Snider-Enfield, first prize went to a gun of the Martini system, second to Henry. By this time, Martini had dropped the Peabody from the name of the rifle and presented it under his own.

The Britons found the Solomon-like solution, a way to use both the first- and second-placed weapons. By taking Martini's breech-block and Henry's barrel, they came up with a new rifle which was immediately given to the troops for testing.

Satisfied by the results achieved during 1871/72, London issued the first Martini-Henry Mark I (M.1871) to the army in 1874. The Mark I rifle cost the British Army two pounds, eighteen shillings and ninepence. This was certainly a good deal more expensive than the former Snider guns, acquired at the price of only one pound, but the quality of the new weapon was far higher.

During 1876 and 1879, the M.1871 underwent some minor changes on the basis of which Mark II and Mark III were made. The real failings of the Henry-Martini came to light during the 1882 Egyptian campaign. This gun gave excellent results under ideal conditions, but on desert battlefields, Martini's breech-block frequently locked because of the sand. On the other hand, Henry's grooves of the rifling, deep and square cut, provided a lot of resistance to the bullet, causing a strong recoil when fired. In 1886, the military commission intended to produce a better rifle on the basis of experiences of the Egyptian campaign, the Mark IV, with a ·402 calibre. But the appearance of the more modern repeating rifles was a good enough reason to abandon this idea,

so that the last Henry-Martini model retained all its old faults.

Apart from the British Army, Romania, Turkey and some other European countries decided on the Henry-Peabody-Martini M.1871. After the liberation war of 1876/78, Romania formed a new army of eight regular infantry regiments, 30 regiments of territorials and a certain number of militia regiments. During 1880, the British Royal Ordnance Factory at Enfield contracted to produce the Henry-Martini "Perfextionne" (Mark II and III) for the regular and territorial infantry and cavalry.

Turkey, however, decided in 1872 on the Mark I M.1871. It is interesting to note that Constantinople gave the contract to the Americans, i.e. the Providence Tool Company. By the outbreak of war in 1876, the Turkish Army was in possession of an imposing number of Henry-Martini rifles – 650,000! The Turkish weapons had only the name of the factory written in the Latin script on the frame. All serial numbers, and the Imperial monogram, *Tura,* were in Arabic script in Turkish. Although these weapons proved far more powerful than the Russian Krnka and Serbian Peabody guns, the Porte lost almost half of its arms in this war. Serbia captured 5,937 Henry-Martini rifles which it immediately used to arm part of its regular infantry.

Turkey augmented its Henry-Martini rifles by signing a contract, in 1881, for another 100,000. In 1911 after the Army changed to the Mauser system, a certain number of these weapons were adapted to 7.65 mm calibre.

The popularity of such hybrids in Turkey was immense, so that private workshops in the Balkans started copying them. Gunsmiths smuggled Mauser barrels from Austria and Serbia and mounted them on locally-made Martini breech-blocks. For commercial reasons, original British patent inscriptions were clumsily faked on them.

This weapon, more dangerous for the owner than the enemy, was not popular in Turkey, and was thus placed almost exclusively on the Albanian market.

Opposite:
Turkish irregular cavalry, about 1870.

Overleaf:
M.1871 Peabody-Henry-Martini system infantry rifle; Turkish Army uniforms from the 1877/78 war.

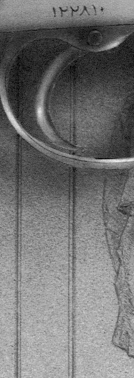
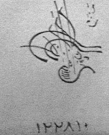

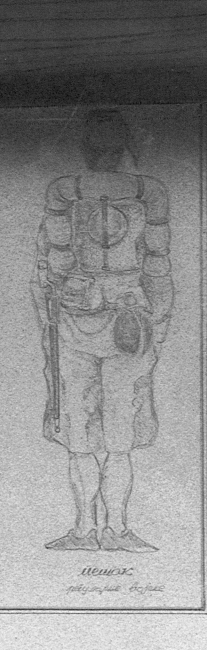

редиф

пешак
рашчне воjске

коњик пешак
прва Срб. иорджане инвета

коњик

коњик

Berdan I and II

Berdan, Hiram, US Colonel. During the Civil War commanded Sharpshooters regiments. In 1864 he left the Army and turned to the construction of arms. His first significant success was his central-fire cartridge with brass case, patented in 1865. He patented several rifle constructions, of which the most famous is the Russian Berdan No. 2. He died in 1893.

The Americans' experiences of the Civil War caused the Army Ministry of imperial Russia to send two officers to the USA – Colonel A. P. Gorlov, and Captain K. I. Gunius, their duty being to select and present their government with the best among the multitude of breech-loading rifles of the American system.

In 1866 Gorlov decided to submit the greatest possible number of American guns to serious analyses. The following year this excellent gunsmith met, in New York, a member of the Technical Committee, Captain Gunius, who was already engaged on a similar project.

After much work and deliberation, the Russian officers came to the conclusion that only the solutions of Hiram Berdan from 1866 and 1867 deserved closer attention. Berdan had first patented this already mentioned breech-block on January 10, 1865 (US Pat. no. 45,899). Gunius and Gorlov started testing this classic model in which the breech-block lifted up and forwards. The firing-pin was set off by a traditional hammer, placed on the outer side of the lock-plate. Spain had already decided on Berdan's weapon, and Britain was negotiating for 50,000 guns. But the Russian officers found a number of faults with Berdan's construction. First of all, they considered the ˙420 calibre bullet to have far better ballistic characteristics than the standard American ˙450. Furthermore, they criticised the exterior hammer, the organization of the breech-block which, at greater elevation of the rifle, made loading impossible, and the complicated and expensive production.

Accordingly, Gorlov and Gunius started adapting and reconstructing the rifle. First of all, in 1868 they designed a new bullet, calibre ˙420, with a bottle-shaped case. Furthermore, they made twenty-five changes on the weapon itself, of which the most important the absence of a hammer. A firing-pin was placed in the breech-block with a spiral firing-pin lever which was cocked by means of a thumb-piece on the upper side. The newly-devised gun thus lost almost all the external features of the original Berdan solution.

Satisfied with the weapon, Czar Alexander II decreed on October 28, 1868, that the Gorlov-Gunius gun was to be used in sharpshooters' batallions. A contract for 30,000 guns was signed with the American Colt company, and 7.5 million corresponding bullets were ordered from the works in Bridgeport.

In America, the same gun was known under the name of the Russian Musket. The US market soon accepted the Russian type of breech-block which, combined with barrels of ˙50 and ˙45/70 calibre, was used on sporting and hunting weapons.

In Russia, this new gun was officially named the *Sharpshooters Rifle M.1868,* but was better known as the old system Berdan and Berdan No. 1. In time the Russian constructors were unfairly forgotten, and only the name Berdan No. 1 M.1868 was left.

Hiram Berdan cam to St Petersburg personally in 1869 to offer the imperial army his new bolt-action construction. At the same time, Russia was also offered the Bavarian Werder-system gun. In May 1869 a commission was formed, with General Hotbek as chairman, in order to test the new rifles. In 1870, after a series of tests, the Commission adopted Berdan's bolt-action construction for use by the whole army. The infantry Berdan No. 2 was made on the basis of this solution, and on August 31, a carbine of the same name. Provision was made for Dragoon and Cossack guns by a decree of September 26, 1870, but the Cossack weapon required a completely new design, which Colonel Safonov undertook. The Cossack Berdan No. 2 rifle, finished in 1873, was the last Berdan-type to be introduced into the Russian Army.

However, Russian industry was not able to turn over to the production of this modern weapon. As an example, in the Tula works alone, one steam-powered machine, three turbines and 1,118 lathes had to be installed! Accordingly, a contract for the delivery of the necessary machinery was signed with the Greenwood and Batley Company of Leeds, and the installation work was entrusted to an Englishman, James Burton. In the meantime, the British NA and A Co. Ltd. of Birmingham undertook the production of Berdan No. 2 weapons. The Tula, Sestroreck and Izhevsk works were adapted by 1874, so that arms production was completely transfered to the home industry. By the Russo-Turkish War, in 1876, the military forces had 253,152 infantry and 2,352 Dragoon rifles of the Berdan No. 2 system.

After the introduction of Mosin-Nagant repeating arms, Russia placed the obsolete Berdan rifles into store, but reactivated them during WWI and the October Revolution.

In addition, large quantities of these weapons were sold or given to friendly states. In 1890, Serbia bought from St Petersburg 75,000 Berdan No. 2 guns. Five years later, the little Principality of Montenegro received 30,000 infantry rifles and 500 cavalry carbines as a gift from Russia.

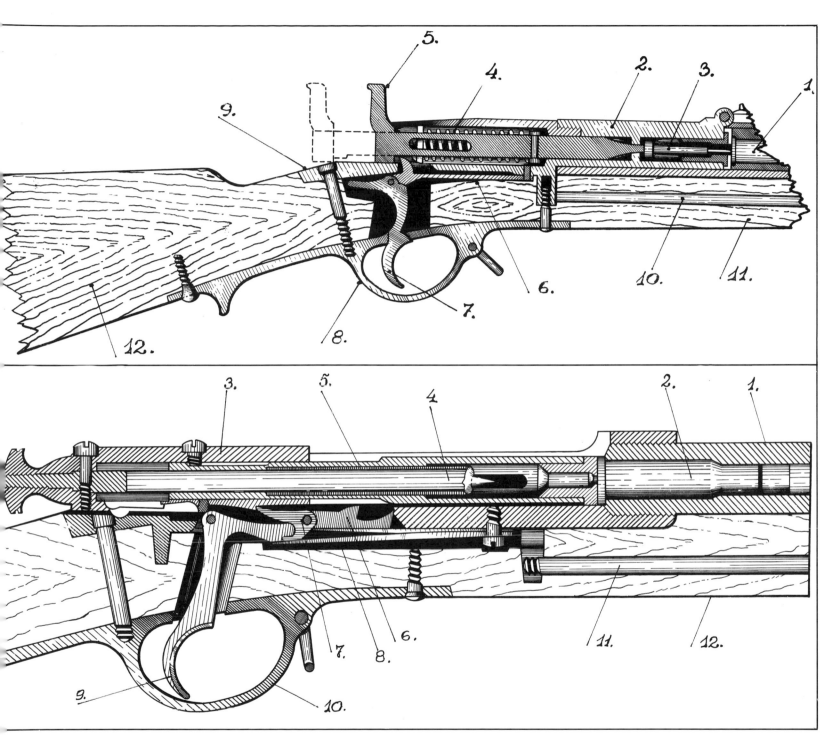

RUSSIAN M. 1870 BERDAN II SYSTEM RIFLE	
- Calibre	10.67 mm (·42)
- Rifling	6
- Capacity	1
- Length	1,350 mm
- Length of barrel	830 mm
- Weight	4,400 gr

RIFLE SYSTEM BERDAN No. 1

1. chamber; 2. breech-block; 3. firing pin; 4. firing pin spring; 5. bolt-handle; 6. abzug-stollen und abzughebel; 7. trigger; 8. trigger-guard; 9. breech-tang; 10. cleaning rod; 11. forestock; 12. butt.

RIFLE SYSTEM BERDAN No. 2

1. barrel; 2. chamber; 3. breech-bolt; 4. firing pin; 5. firing pin spring; 6. abzughebel, sicherheitsstollen und auswerfer; 7. abzug-stollen; 8. trigger-spring; 9. trigger; 10. trigger-guard; 11. cleaning rod; 12. fore-stock.

Overleaf:
Russian Cossack M.1873 Berdan No. 2 system rifle.

Ш.54: COSSACK

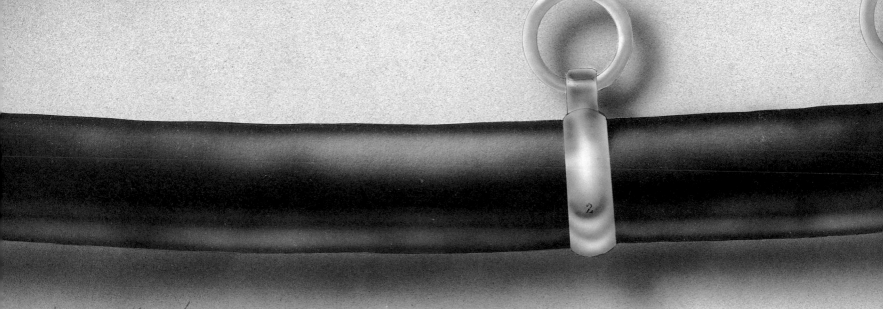

ШАШКА КАЗАЧЬЯ СОЛДАТС
(cossack shashka, soldi

Valencak, th....

RIFLE, BERDAN №2)

КАЯ ОБРАЗЦА 1859 ГОДА
1859 pattern)

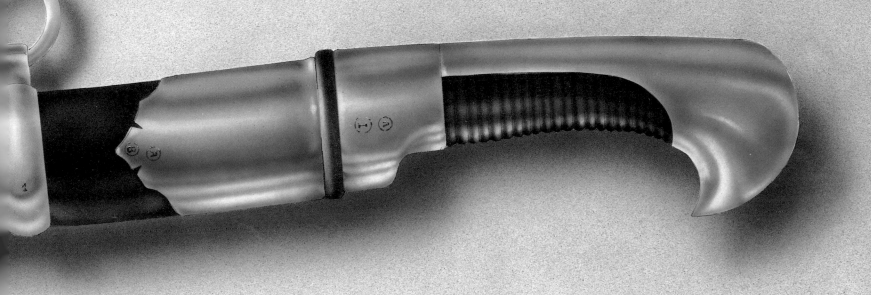

Mauser-Norris

Mauser, Peter Paul, born June 27, 1838, died May 29, 1914 and his brother **Mauser, Wilhelm,** born May 2, 1834, died January 13, 1892, Oberndorf/Neckar (Germany). Started their careers as gunsmiths of the Royal Würrtenberger Arms Factory. In the second half of the 1860s, constructed a breech-loading gun mechanism of excellent characteristics, adopted by the German Army as model 1871. In 1872/73, founded an arms factory in Obendorf which produced a large number of rifles for the German and foreign armies, and revolvers. After 1880, the single-shot Mauser rifles were joined by guns with box-magazines which c. 1900 were considered ideal modern military rifles. The Mauser factory developed and started producing the first successful semi-automatic (self-loading) pistol, the "Construction 1896" (C 96).

In the late 1860s, the higher military echelons became more and more aware that the future of firearms lay in the bolt-action breech. Dreyse laid the foundations of this construction, which was soon accepted in France (Chassepot, Gras), Russia (Berdan), Italy (Carcano) and many other countries. Realizing this fact, a then still unknown official of the Württenberg State Arsenal, Peter Paul Mauser, constructed his own rifle based on the Dreyse breech-block and offered the patent to the army. But the Minié rifled musket was still firmly established in the Württenberg of that time and could not be ousted by some new gun that easily. This did not dishearten Mauser. On the contrary, he adapted his gun to the latest ammunition with a metal case and in 1867 offered it to Prussia and Austria. It seems that Mauser was ahead of this time. Prussia was just then in a state of elation over the success of its needle-guns in the 1866 war, and Austria chose the Wänzl breech-block. However, the far-sighted chairman of the Austrian Commission for the choice of arms, Artur Graf Bylandt-Rheidt, showed Peter Paul Mauser's construction to Samuel Norris, the European representative of Eliphalet Remington and Sons. This astute merchant, with excellent connections all over the continent, was perceptive enough to recognize the potential of Mauser's solution. Accordingly, he used his private contacts in France which, at that time, was desperately looking for an answer to the German weapons, and pointed out to the French all the qualities of the Mauser construction. Relying on the favourable opinions of military circles in Paris as strong arguments for negotiations, Norris

approached the Mauser brothers. Thanks to mutual interests, this contact was crowned by an agreement on a joint venture. While Norris believed that he would easily earn high profits collaborating with these two "peasant-gunsmiths", the Mauser brothers, for their part, counted on exploiting the international connections this merchant had built up, and elbowing their way onto foreign markets.

Time showed that the Mauser brothers were right. Although the Mauser-Norris C.67/69 weapons did not bring financial profit almost anywhere, they did, nevertheless, arouse the interest of military circles in a number of countries.

The impatient Norris soon withdrew from the project, leaving the Mauser brothers to continue their penetration of other markets alone. As early as 1870, the Prussian Army started testing their gun in the *Militär-Schieß-Schule*. After a number of improvements, by an imperial decree of March 22, 1872, Prussia adopted the Mauser's *Infanterie-Gewehr Modell 1871*. Most of the machinery necessary for the local production of these weapons was delivered by the Pratt and Whitney Company of Hartford, Conn.

From the one million Mauser M.71 rifles manufactured the Austrian ÖEWG Company delivered 474,622, as well as 60,000 carbines. The rest were produced by a number of German state and private works.

Thus the German Army was equipped with one of the most advanced guns of the period. True, the barrel was an imitation of the Chassepot solution, but Mauser's breech-bolt became the foundation on which all later bolt-action types of modern rifle were developed.

GERMAN M. 1871 MAUSER SYSTEM RIFLE
- Calibre .... 11 mm
- Rifling 4
- Capacity 1
- Length .... 1,345 mm
- Length of barrel .... 855 mm
- Weight .... 4,500 gr

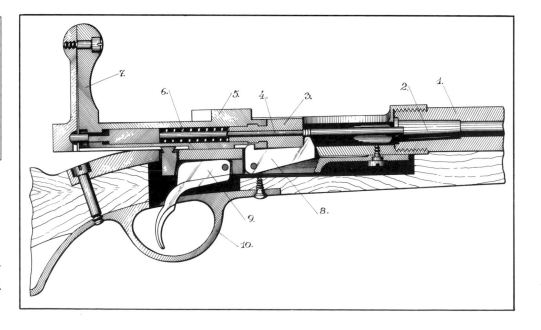

RIFLE SYSTEM MAUSER-NORRIS
1. barrel; 2. chamber; 3. bolt-head; 4. firing-pin; 5. breech-bolt; 6. firing pin spring; 7. bolt-handle; 8. abzugstollen und auswerfer; 9. trigger; 10. trigger-guard.

Mauser-Koka

**Milovanović-
-Koka, Kosta,**
born June 8, 1847
in Belgrade, died
May 6, 1905.
Serbian general,
talented con-
structor in the
field of infantry arms. During 1873 completed the Artillery Engineering school in
Berlin. Long-time professor of the Military Academy in Belgrade, author of
several works on the theory of armament.
Developed the Serbian Mauser system
M.1880 rifle.

**SERBIAN M. 1880 MAUSER-KOKA
SYSTEM RIFLE**
- Calibre . . . . 10.15 mm
- Rifling 4
- Capacity 1
- Length . . . . 1,295 mm
- Length of barrel . . . . 801 mm
- Weight . . . . 4,500 gr

Apart from the countries of the German Empire, the Mauser rifle started its conquest of foreign markets in – China! This country purchased 26,000 M.1871 rifles and carbines in 1876.

Particularly interesting, however, was the Mauser's connection with Serbia, which produced a rifle that had the best ballistic characteristics of the 1880s, and was later to serve as the basis for the development of Mauser's repeating arms.

On the basis of an order issued by the War Ministry on December 25, 1878, the Artillery Committee drew up a programme for the choice of a new single-shot rifle. The first step was to set up a Commission, headed by Major Kosta-Koka Milovanović.

Dozens of producers and designers submitted entries for the open competition, from which the Commission accepted 29 rifle systems for testing. Amongst others, the Mauser, Winchester, SIG, Lee, Dreyse, Francotte and Werndl (ÖEWG) rifles were present.

By process of elimination, by the end of 1879 several rifles were selected for the short list, including the original Mauser M.1871 and its improved version from 1878. Interested by the amount of work and the development of the situation, Wilhelm Mauser came to Belgrade in June 1879. But the chairman of the Commission was dissatisfied with the ballistic characteristics of the German gun. For this reason he left his post in the Commission and independently started work on improving the 1878 weapon. First of all, Koka adopted the Swedish 10.15 mm calibre. He then concentrated his efforts in two directions: towards a weapon with classic, concentric grooves, and one with progressive, square ones which narrowed towards the muzzle.

In March 1880, only the Austrian repeating Kropaczek, the original Mauser M.1871 and both of Major Milovanović's versions were left in the running. In its report, the Commission spoke most highly of the Mauser-Koka construction with progressive grooves. Accordingly, on October 21, 1880, the Artillery Committee for Armament of the Serbian Army adopted the Mauser-Koka M.1880 system rifle. Thus Wilhelm Mauser, who had spent all this time in Belgrade, had his patience rewarded. The Serbian Minister of War signed a contract with him for the delivery of 100,000 rifles of the same name.

In accordance with the terms of the contract, the Commission for the acceptance of weapons travelled to Oberndorf on August 4 of the same year. The German producer was set rigorous conditions. In order to ensure the quality, the barrels were made by the famous Simson and Luck Company of Suhl; the butt was made exclusively from walnut trees felled in 1871; all the steel parts were blued by sevenfold greasing, and the bayonets were delivered by the Weyersberg and Co. factory of Solingen. The last of the 100,000 rifles reached Serbia in 1884. At the same time, the necessary ammunition, filled with special SGP powder *(Serbisches-Gewehr-Pulver),* was ordered from Belgium.

The new weapon proved to be excellent. Its maximum range was 3,250 m, when the lead bullet still penetrated the ground 200 m. Muzzle velocity of the cartridge, when filled with SGP powder, was 512 m/s, and with home-made powder, 460 m/s. This latter was still faster than the speed of the German M.1871, which attained 430 m/s. It was achieved primarily because of the smaller calibre and the construction of the grooves: the German barrel of 11 mm calibre was rifled concentrically, with 4 grooves 0.3 mm deep and 4.5 mm wide, one turn in 550 mm, an a pitch of 3° 36'. In contrast, the barrel of the M.1880, 10.15 mm was rifled progressively, with 4 grooves, 0.15 mm deep and 4.6 – 4 mm wide, one turn in 550 mm and a pitch of 3° 19' 5''.

Unfortunately, this excellent synthesis of two talented constructors was created too late to be competitive on the world market. The 1880s already belonged to magazine and repeating guns.

Overleaf:
M.1880 Mauser-Koka system infantry rifle inscribed in Cyrillic.

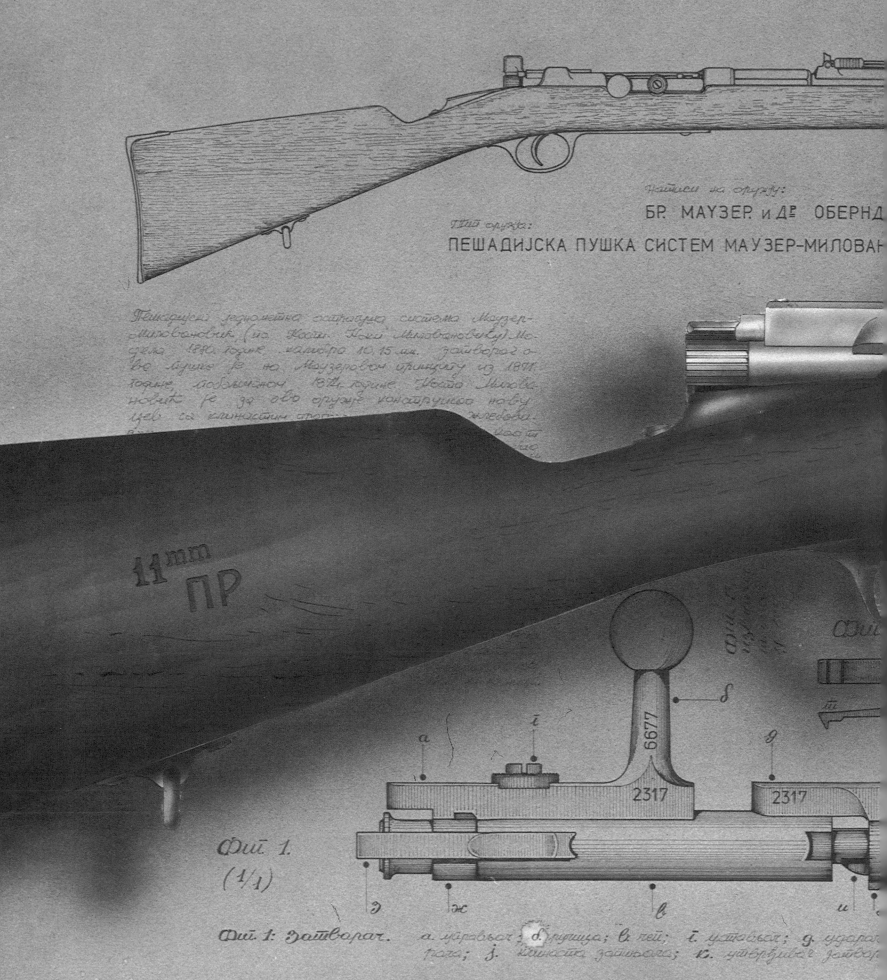

Натписи на оружју:

БР. МАУЗЕР. и Д? ОБЕРНД

Тип оружја:

ПЕШАДИЈСКА ПУШКА СИСТЕМ МАУЗЕР-МИЛОВАН

Пешадијска једнометка острагруша система Маузер-Миловановић (по Кости Којм Миловановићу) Модела 1880. годин. камбра 10,15 мм. затворог о ве пушке је на Маузеровом принципу из 1871. године побољшаном 1911 године. Коста Милановић је за ово оружје конструисао нову цев са клинастим про... жлебова.

11mm
ПР

Фиг. 1.
(1/1)

6677
2317   2317

a *i* *б* *g*

з *ж* *в* *и*

Фиг 1: Затварач.   а. управљач б. рушца; в. пет; г. устобуч; д. удала рога; з. клинаста затвода; к. утврдивач затвор

Valentčak

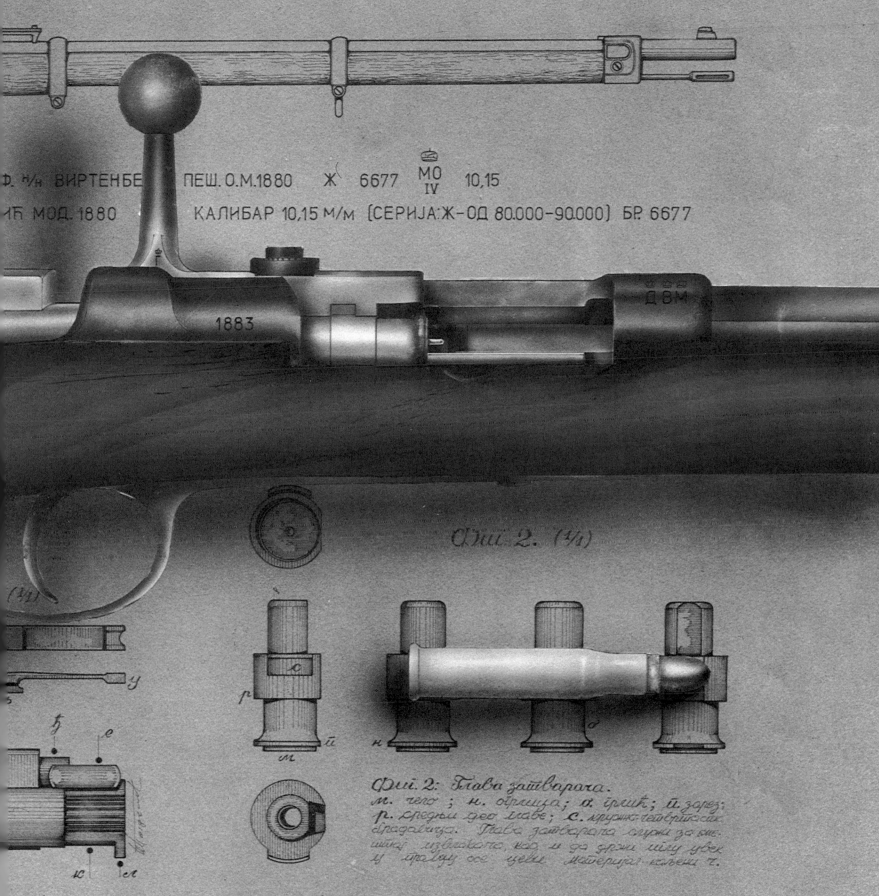

Ф. н/н ВИРТЕНБЕ   ПЕШ. О.М.1880   Ж 6677   MO IV   10,15

ИБ МОД. 1880   КАЛИБАР 10,15 М/м (СЕРИЈА: Ж–ОД 80.000–90.000) БР. 6677

1883

ДВМ

Фиг. 2. (½)

Фиг. 2: Глава затварача.
м. чело ; н. отлица; о. грлик; п. зарез;
р. средњи део главе; с. кружно четвртасто
прадавица. Глава затварача служи за ме.
шину извлакача, као и да држи шину увек
у правцу осе цеви материјал калени т.

обина кућице; с. кућица; ж. глава затварача; з. извлакач; и. книжаст зубуу уда.
л. брадавица четврдивоста.

SINGLE-SHOT CARTRIDGE PISTOLS

Werndl, Martini, Deringer

The appearance of breech-loading systems prompted constructors to work on their application to pistols.

J. N. Dreyse played a pioneer role in this field as well. His first needle-pistol project was created in the 1830s in cooperation with Collenbusch. Two decades later, Dreyse applied his needle-bolt action to pistols. This weapon equipped with a dismantling butt, was offered the Prussian Army as M.1856, but Prussia took only 200 pistols necessary for troop testing. In fact, military circles were not happy with such short weapons, believing the carbine to be far better suited to the needs of the calvary.

The attempt to introduce breech-loading single-shot pistols into the Austrian cavalry suffered a similar fate. In 1867, Josef Werndl built his excentric breech-block into a pistol which in its external form bore an unusual resemblance to the Lorenz M.1859. But in view of the contemporary tactical role of the cavalry, this short gun lost all significance.

Austria thus gave the carbine primacy, considering the revolver, which had by that time found its place in the world of firearms, to be better for the personal defence of the rider, should the worst come to the worst.

In contrast to the military forces, the civilian market accepted single-shot pistols with great enthusiasm. There were several reasons for this: its small size and simplicity of handling were well suited to citizens who wished to carry arms under their elegant clothes or in their handbags. In a very short time, production of pistols for the open market was flourishing. In this field most fame was attained, at least in name, by Henry Deringer Junior.

In 1843, Deringer started production of small muzzle-loading pistols in the family factory in Philadelphia. These weapons soon became popular, above all in California and the southern states. Two decades later, in 1863, Deringer started the manufacture of breech-loading pistols as well. The commercial success of his

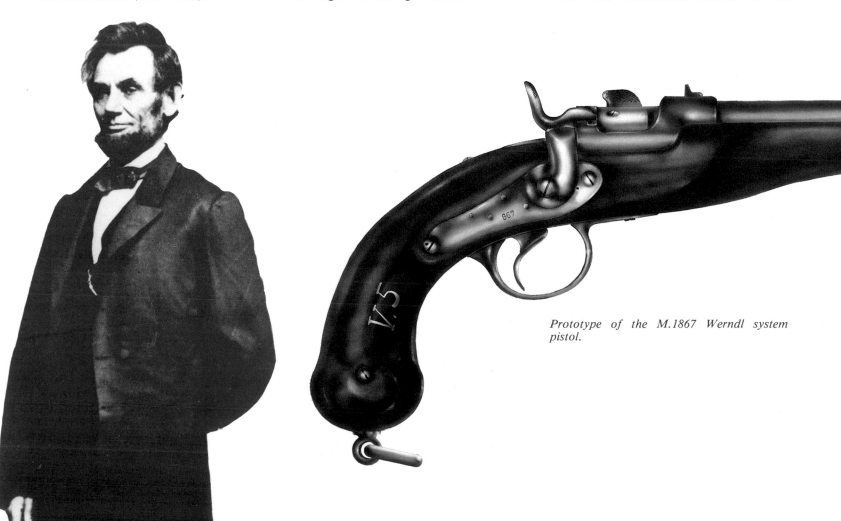

Abraham Lincoln (1809 – 1865).

Prototype of the M.1867 Werndl system pistol.

Remington-Deringer system pistol.

SINGLE-SHOT REMINGTON-DERINGER PISTOL	
- Calibre	10.4 mm (·410)
- Rifling	5
- Capacity	1
- Length	121 mm
- Length of barrel	61 mm
- Weight	210 gr

weapons intrigued almost all the leading American producers and constructors, who started to make their own, based on similar solutions. But for commercial reasons, all these manufacturers added to their own brand name the synonym for this kind of weapon — Deringer. After the death of Henry Junior in 1868, his name was carried on through the Sharps--Deringer, Colt-Deringer, Remington-Deringer and many other pocket pistols.

One original percussion Deringer has gone down in the history of the USA: it was the weapon with which the actor J. W. Booth, on April 15, 1865, shot down and killed the 16th President of the USA — Abraham Lincoln.

Because of the film industry, it is thought today that the Deringer was mainly a gamblers' pistol. True, even Doc Holiday carried this miniature weapon with him, but it should not be forgotten that one of the first owners of a Remington-Deringer was the famous buffalo hunter, later circus-owner, W. Cody, alias Buffalo Bill!

In consequence of the uncontrolled trade and mass production of single-shot pistols, the so-called Khyber-Pass pistol originated on the territories of the British colonies and in parts of the Turkish Empire. This weapon was basically a synthesis of the Henry-Peabody-Martini type breech-block and hand-made ·450 calibre barrels. Because of their appalling quality, these pistols were low-priced and intended for the lowest category of buyer.

139

REPEATING ARMS

Austrian border patrol, end of 19th century.

141

PERCUSSION REVOLVERS

Colt, Samuel, born July 10, 1814, died January 10, 1862 in Hartford, Conn. Considered the inventor of the modern revolver (his 1835/36 patent), but also deserved credit as the organizer of modern arms production in Colt's Patent Fire Arms Co. in Hartford. Aggressive and modern in his approach to sales and promotion of his arms. Even after his death, Colt's company continued to develop and has remained one of the world's leading producers of hand firearms.

AUSTRIAN M. 1849 COLT SYSTEM NAVY REVOLVER

- Calibre	9.3 mm
- Rifling	10
- Capacity	6
- Length	290 mm
- Length of barrel	135 mm
- Weight	—

The organization of large armies based on general mobilization and great changes in strategy and tactics, coupled with the rapid expansion of the modern industry, brought about a dynamic development of military technology in the second half of the 19th century. The use of open formation ranks, of camp and permanent fortified military installations and the frequent movement of troops called for ever faster firing speed which, at the cost of precision, would ensure greater density of shot. Despite the fact that the breeches of breech-loading arms had by that time reached a high degree of development, single shots no longer satisfied the given conditions. The new demands presented a great challenge to many innovators.

However, two serious obstacles had first to be surmounted. The great expense involved and the shortcomings of the initial solutions, as well as the temporary inability of industry to start mass production of more complicated weapons, was the first problem, but also the simpler. The conservatism of the higher military circles was much more difficult to overcome: most military experts in America and Europe were, at first, bitterly opposed to repeating weapons. In their view, these could only lead to pointless waste of ammunition and the loss of firing discipline. Furthermore, the conservatives considered that there would be a point to repeating arms only if every enemy soldier had to be killed several times over (sic!), and invented the slogan: "Shoot slow but sure". The Russian military theoretician, General Dragomirov, even paraphrased Suvorovlev's old saying: "Stupid is the bullet — and brave the bayonet", claiming that if repeating arms were introduced the "bullet may become somewhat cleverer, but never braver".

Although some of the advantages of repeating arms became obvious during the Civil War, they were still technically so imperfect that they could not seriously endanger the primacy of single-shot breech-loading guns. It was to take the experiences of the Russo-Turkish War (1877/78) and a number of colonial and South American wars for the military experts to be finally persuaded of the necessity fot pre-orientation to repeating guns.

The basic idea of increasing firing speed developed in two directions: on the one hand, the adaptation of existing single-fire weapons by the introduction of various kinds of disassembling magazines, and on the other the production of completely new weapons with in-built multi-shot magazines. When financial and technical analyses proved the second solution to be the only one justified, numerous constructors came up with ideas as rational and ingenious as they were fantastic. All these solutions should be classified in four basic groups:

- weapons on the revolver principle, i. e. a cylinder-shaped magazine turned by the pulling of the trigger or releasing of the hammer, bringing a bullet into the barrel;
- guns with the magazine in the butt;
- guns with a tubular magazine in the forestock;
- guns with a box magazine situated in the central part of the butt, in the breech zone.

Colt's constructions

It is difficult today to say anything about Samuel Colt that is not already known even to laymen. In fact, the name of this American has become a synonym for all kinds of revolvers.

There are a number of stories about Colt's youth and the origin of his constructions, but one thing is fairly clear: the basic principles of the revolver were not new, nor were they purely Colt's idea. This type of weapon was known as far back as the 17th century. More significant, however, is the fact that towards the end of the first decade of the 19th century, the gunsmith Elisha Hayden Collier from Boston, Massachusetts, designed the highest quality flint-lock revolver to date. When he moved to Great Britain, Collier opened shop at 45, The Strand, London, and sold part of his stock to the East India Company. It would seem that one of these flintlock revolvers played a decisive role in shaping Colt's career.

COLT DRAGOON MODEL 49

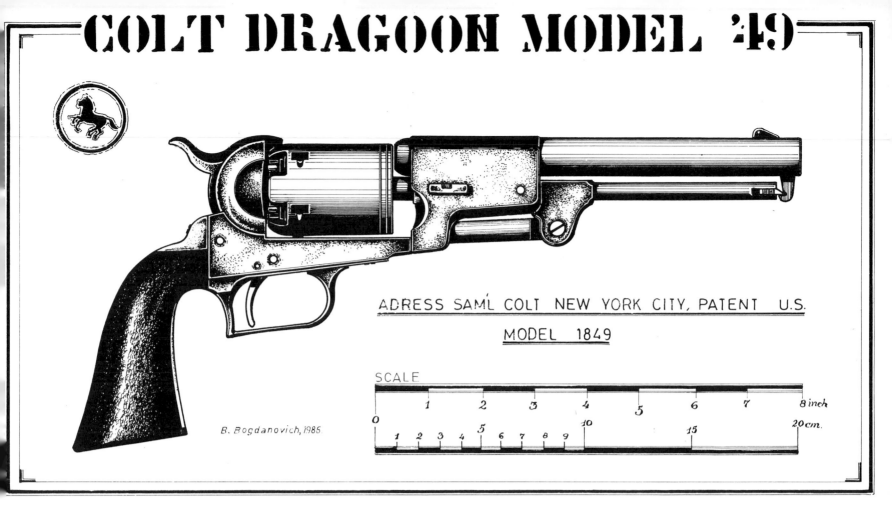

ADRESS SAML COLT NEW YORK CITY, PATENT U.S.

MODEL 1849

SCALE

B. Bogdanovich, 1985.

In his youth, Colt joined the merchant fleet as a seaman. According to some indications, the future constructor went to sea because he wished to become a lecturer! During one cruise, Colt got as far as Calcutta where, it is thought, he may have seen one of the East India Company revolvers. According to Colt, however, he got the idea for his weapon from the ship's wheel! In any case, during the long voyage the young seaman carved a wooden model of his own revolver incorporating the then new and popular percussion firing.

On his return to the USA, Colt left the production of the prototype according to the model to Anton Chase of Hartford. This is when all the faults of the original conception came to light. Colt had started from the idea of placing a plate in front of the cylinder, to prevent the balls from falling out of the chamber. This plate, however, had the disadvantage that a lateral flame leak from the firing chamber was liable to be deflected by it to another chamber, resulting in a chain of explosions in all the remaining chambers in the cylinder. This fault ruined the constructor's attempt to produce the weapon jointly with the gunsmith Pearson.

Only when he had removed the unfortunate plate and introduced the loading lever did Colt get a reasonably safe weapon. Aware of this fact, the inventor patented his solution first in Britain, and on February 25, 1836, in the USA as well.

Despite, their simplicity and practicality, Colt's first revolvers made in his own Patent Arms Manufacturing Company in Paterson, New Jersey, were not very popular in the still very conservative atmosphere of the time. Consequently, in 1840/41 Colt went bankrupt and was left with no money to continue production.

Five years later, during the war with Mexico, he struck a lucky streak. Captain Walker, who had become familiar with Colt's weapon during battles with the Seminole Indians, arranged for the Secretary of War to order 1,000 revolvers for the US Army. In order to take advantage of this opportunity, Colt persuaded Eli Whitney Junior to take on the production of the American military revolver. In the meantime, the inventor managed to open a new factory of his own in Hartford, which started turning out the famous Hartford-Dragoon.

Colt's best known muzzle-loading revolver, the famous Colt Navy, '36 calibre, was made in 1848. This light and simple weapon worked on the single-action principle, or rather, it was cocked by the thumb, and showed Colt's basic idea to full advantage. The cylinder was loaded from the front with paper cartridges. The compression of the charge in the chambers was effected by a loading lever located under the barrel. Copper caps were placed on the nipples on the front of the cylinder, thereby completing the loading. The cocking of the hammer with the thumb

turned the cylinder 60°, bringing chamber after chamber into the axis of the barrel. By pulling the trigger, the hammer was released and set off the cap by percussion.

Colt's real breakthrough onto the world market came after the Great Exhibition in London in 1851. The Colt Navy, shown in the Crystal Palace in Hyde Park, caused a real sensation. Britain, Russia, Turkey and many other countries purchased the new weapon. Belgium started its own production under licence, and the Austrian company of J. Peterlongo of Innsbruck did likewise. Almost all the world's navies were thus equipped with the same guns — Colt's revolver.

It would be unfair not to mention two very important factors of Colt's success on the market. The first, and certainly the more important, was the intelligent application of mass production by machine. In addition, Elisha King Root, the technical director of Colt's factory in Hartford, played no small role in modernizing the machinery and also in work on the construction of weapons.

Overleaf:
Austrian M.1849 Colt system navy revolver with powder-flash.

Valentian

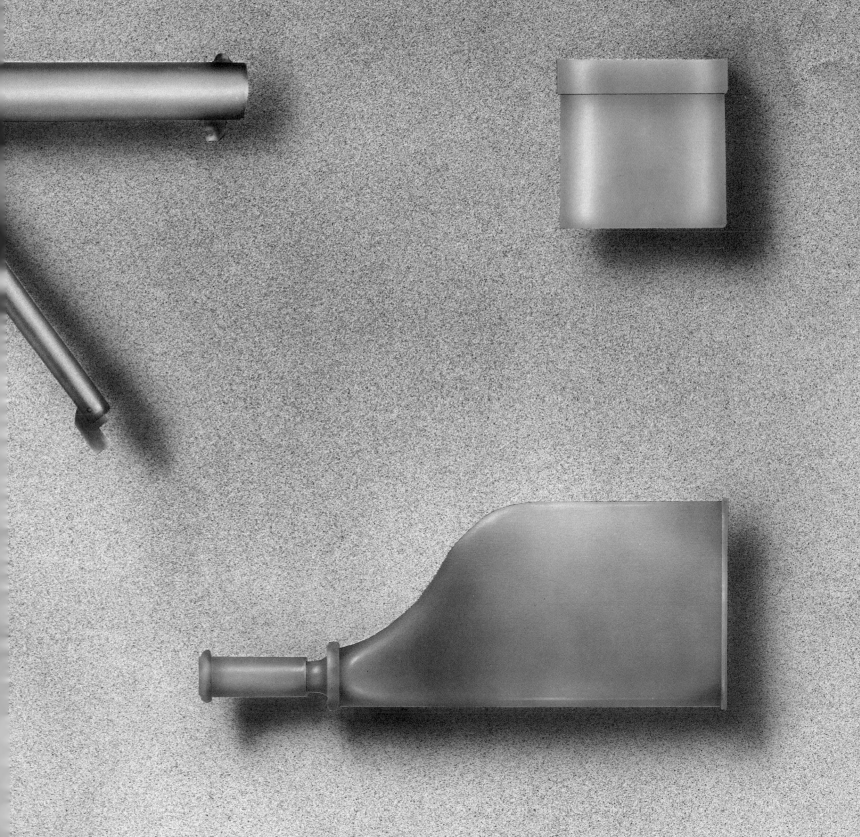

Adams

Adams, Robert, born c. December 31, 1809, at Compton near Paignton, Devon, died September 13 at Forest Hill. Partner in the Deane, Adams and Deane company which exhibited a new revolver of his construction at the Great Exhibition in London in 1851. Thanks to its construction, Adams's 1851 revolver was the strongest challenger to the Colt of that time. The improved Beaumont-Adams was a service weapon in Great Britain and some other countries.

The Great Exhibition in London in 1851 releaved that Samuel Colt had a worthy opponent in Europe. In the Crystal Palace in Hyde Park, Robert Adams of Britain caused a sensation with his percussion revolver construction. Unlike the inventive American, who had years' experience in revolver construction, Adams kept his weapon secret until the very opening night of the Exhibition. In consequence, he did not patent the revolver project until February 1851.

Adam's construction was certainly a novelty in comparison with the already stereotype Colt weapons. He applied a self-cocking system to the revolver, whereby a pull on the trigger first cocked the hammer, and then set off all the other firing actions. Essentially, this, like Colt's "thumb-cocking system", was only a *"single-action"* system. However, in modern writings the term "double-action" has been adopted for Adam's weapons, although it is generally used only for the combined firing principle: self-cocking and thumb-cocking.

Adam's solution had certain advantages on the battlefield, since the user

REVOLVER SYSTEM ADAMS
1. cylinder; 2. nipple; 3. frame; 4. hammer; 5. safety device; 6. trigger; 7. trigger guard.

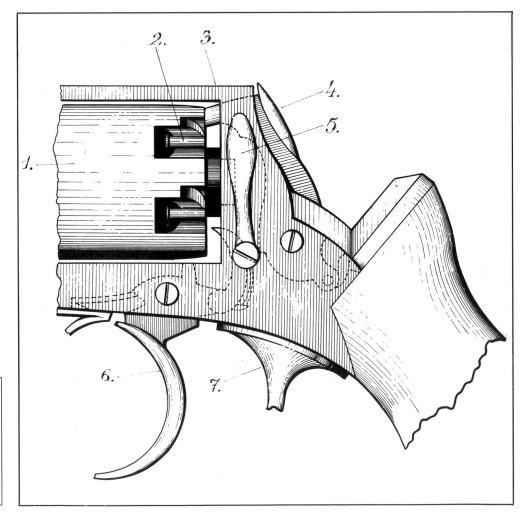

ADAMS POCKET REVOLVER
- Calibre . . . . **8.1 mm ('32)**
- Rifling **3**
- Capacity **5**
- Length . . . . **229 mm**
- Length of barrel . . . . . **114 mm**
- Weight . . . . **570 gr**

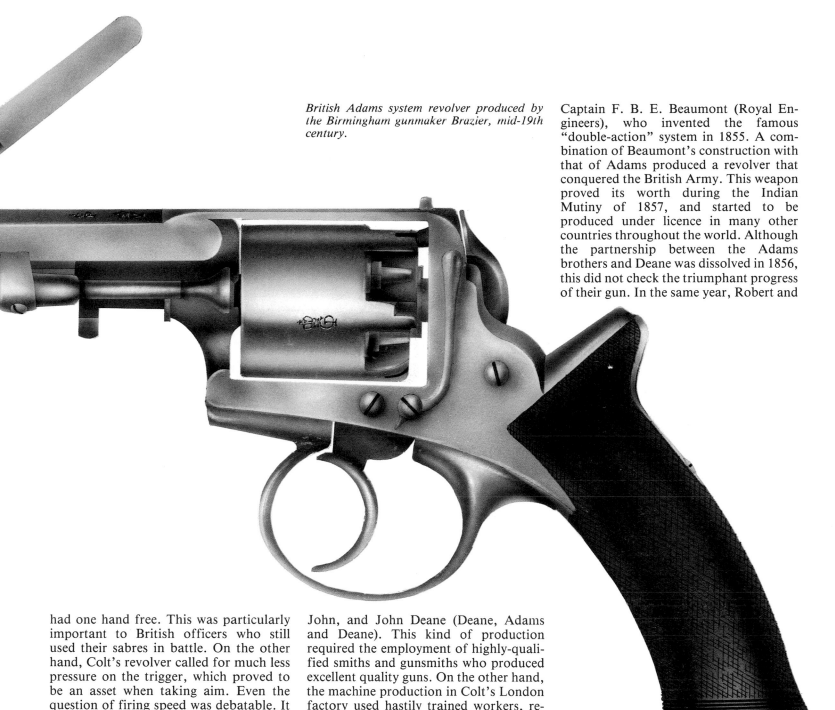

British Adams system revolver produced by the Birmingham gunmaker Brazier, mid-19th century.

Captain F. B. E. Beaumont (Royal Engineers), who invented the famous "double-action" system in 1855. A combination of Beaumont's construction with that of Adams produced a revolver that conquered the British Army. This weapon proved its worth during the Indian Mutiny of 1857, and started to be produced under licence in many other countries throughout the world. Although the partnership between the Adams brothers and Deane was dissolved in 1856, this did not check the triumphant progress of their gun. In the same year, Robert and

had one hand free. This was particularly important to British officers who still used their sabres in battle. On the other hand, Colt's revolver called for much less pressure on the trigger, which proved to be an asset when taking aim. Even the question of firing speed was debatable. It is certain that the self-cocking system had an advantage over Colt's thumb-cocking revolver, but Colt could also act by "fanning" the hammer. The trigger would be held in firing position, and the hammer cocked continuously by the flat of the free hand. In this way, all six bullets could be expelled in only three seconds! It must be admitted though, that this spectacular firing system left the Britons cold, since they did not possess the adventurous spirit of American gunslingers.

The European and American revolver solutions differed in some other details as well. Adams based his weapon on five-shot guns, whilst Colt's preference for six chambers has even become a synonym for revolvers – the *"six-gun"*. Furthermore, Adams still produced his weapons in semi-handcraft conditions in the company he had founded with his brother

John, and John Deane (Deane, Adams and Deane). This kind of production required the employment of highly-qualified smiths and gunsmiths who produced excellent quality guns. On the other hand, the machine production in Colt's London factory used hastily trained workers, replying in quantity to Adam's quality. Finally, Adam's revolver had a solid frame construction, far safer than Colt's lower frame.

It seems obvious that both weapons had an equal number of faults and advantages, so that the rivalry reached a stalemate. The Select Committee on Small Arms, founded by the British government in 1854, came to a similar conclusion, while giving Adams, an Englishman after all, a slight advantage in its reports. This did not, it seems, pull much weight with the Royal Navy which "unpatriotically" bought a large number of Colt-Navy revolvers for its own needs. In the Crimean War, all the parties, including the British, mostly used this American-made weapon.

Colt's position in Britain was finally overturned by Adam's cooperation with

John Adams, with the aid of John Kerr, founded a new workshop, the London Armoury, to which all patent rights of the Adam brothers were transferred.

In the face of such competition, in 1857 Samuel Colt was forced to close down his London Pimlico factory and send the American mechanics and experts back home.

CARTRIDGE REVOLVERS

Lefaucheux, Francotte

Lefaucheux, Casimir (1802 – 1852). Gunsmith from Paris. In 1832, produced the one-part pin-fire cartridge, as well as the corresponding breech-loading rifle, mostly used for hunting. His pistols, rifles and ammunition achieved a degree of success at the Great Exhibition in London in 1851.

Lefaucheux, Eugène Gabriel (1820 – 1871). Son of Casimir. In 1854, patented a revolver using metallic pin-fire cartridges which was adopted in 1858 by the French Navy, and later in Italy, Norway, Romania and Sweden. In the last quarter of the 19th century, Lefaucheux-type pin-fire revolvers, intended for the civilian market were produced in Belgium, in 5 – 15 mm calibres and considerable quantities.

In the mid-19th century, a large number of other, independant percussion revolver systems were constructed apart from Colt's and Adam's weapons. All these nevertheless had one big drawback: because of the increased number of cartridges, loading the gun from the front of the cylinder took a great deal of time. In view of this, constructors welcomed with relief the appearance of the one-piece cartridge with a metal case.

In 1846, the talented Parisian gunsmith, Casimir Lefaucheux, patented a "pepperbox", a special weapon with several barrels, constructed for his metal pin-fire cartridge. At the already legendary exhibition of 1851, Lefaucheux displayed a large assortment of his products based on just this type of ammunition. The acclamation in Hyde Park induced Casimir's son, Eugène Gabriel, to patent the pin-fire principle revolver as well, in 1853. Lefaucheux's new weapon was loaded from the back end of the cylinder by means of a special loading gate. At first, this revolver had the single-action firing system, but later versions were made with the double-action system. Eugène found a very simple solution for the ejection of empty cases: a sliding rod affixed on the right-hand side of the barrel.

The French Navy was the first to show interest in the new construction, adopting in 1856 the M.1855 system Lefaucheux (cal. 12 mm) single-action revolver. Two years later, Italy took the same step, followed by Sweden, Norway, Spain and Romania.

Lefaucheux's revolver gained a high level of popularity in Europe, primarily because of its simplicity and low production costs. Numerous Belgian companies started producing it for the civilian market, and similar commercial versions were produced in Germany and Austria (Gasser). Thus by 1867, about 400,000 Lefaucheux revolvers had been produced in Europe!

The USA, on the other hand, never adopted its own process of pin-fire revolver production, though both parties in the Civil War used imported Lefaucheux weapons in large quantities. As an example, the Union alone imported 12,000 of these revolvers in the period between 1861 and 1865!

At a moment when the appearance of the more modern central-fire cartridge threatened to discredit French weapons the French adapted the Lefaucheux guns to the new ammunition, simply by adding a firing-pin.

REVOLVER SYSTEM LEFAUCHEUX
1. barrel; 2. receiver; 3. chamber; 4. cylinder; 5. ejector rod; 6. hammer; 7. loading gate; 8. main spring; 9. frame; 10. trigger; 11. pin.

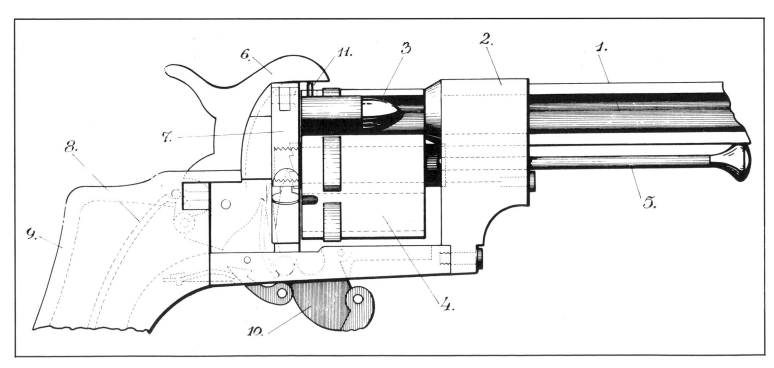

The famous Belgian company in Liège, A. Francotte, developed its own revolver construction on the basis of the modernized Lefaucheux. In 1871, this Francotte weapon was introduced into the Swedish cavalry. A similar type of revolver (M.1871, cal. 11 mm) was bought by Serbia for its army. Nevertheless, Francotte achieved far greater success on the commercial, civilian market. At one moment in time, this firm had a range of 156 different types of revolvers!

FRANCOTTE SYSTEM M. 1871 REVOLVER
- Calibre .... 11 mm
- Rifling 6
- Capacity 6
- Length .... 215 mm
- Length of barrel .... 120 mm
- Weight .... 1,170 gr

French seamen at revolver-shooting practice. End of 19th century.

Overleaf:
M.1871 Francotte system revolver.

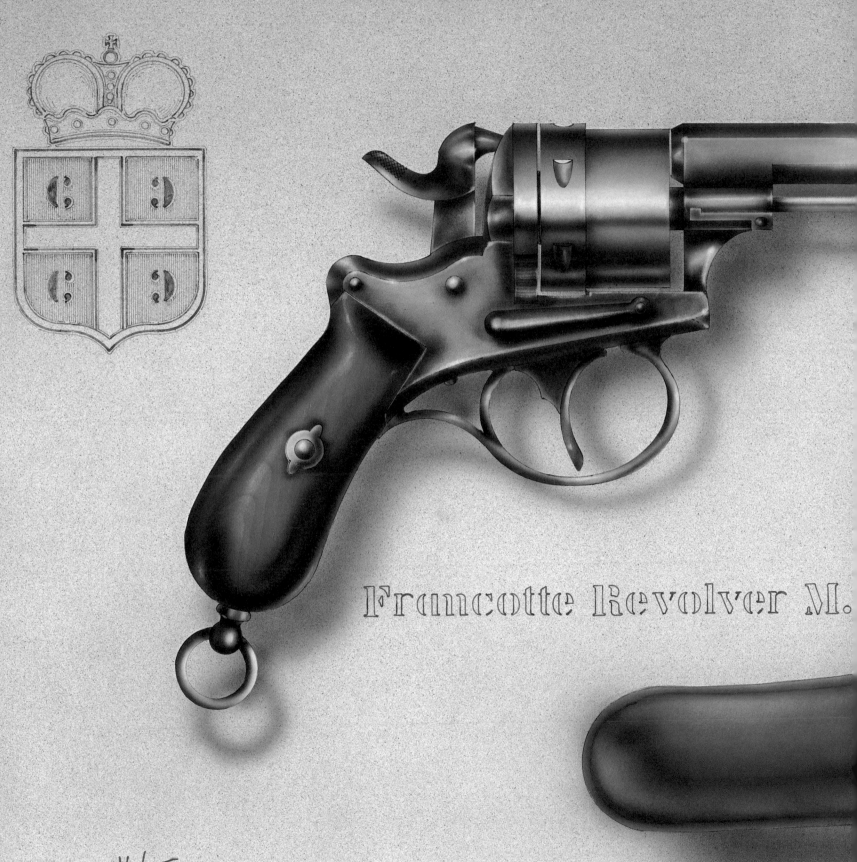

РЕВОЛВЕР СИСТЕМ ФР

Francotte Revolver M.

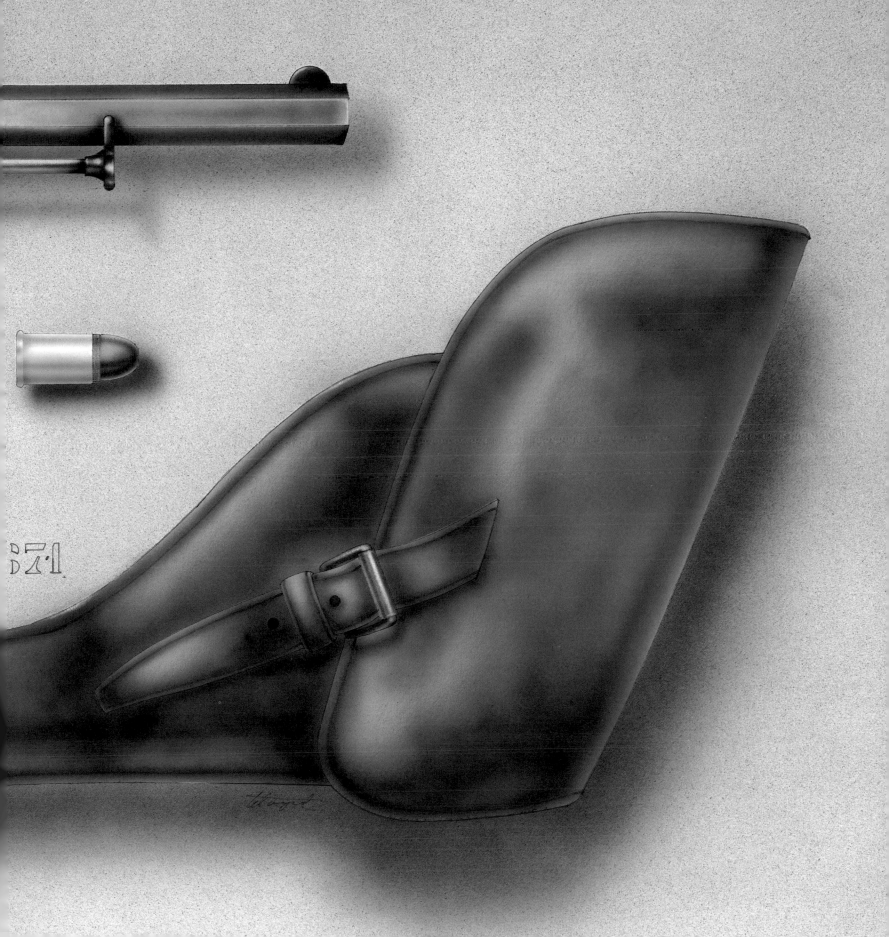

Smith and Wesson

Smith, Horace, born October 28, 1808, in Cheshire, Mass., died January 14, 1893. In 1824, started work for the Springfield Armory, where he stayed for 18 years, inventing several machines for arms production. Subsequently worked for several private arms companies, at which time he met Wesson.

Wesson, Daniel B., born May 18, 1825, in Worchester, Mass., died August 4, 1906. During their lengthy collaboration, the two talented constructors, Smith and Wesson, got into contact with Rollin White, and with the aid of his patent, started production of revolvers.

American breech-loading revolvers had a somewhat different development from their European counterparts. In the first place, they were based on rim-fire ammunition.

The then little known Horace Smith and Daniel B. Wesson started their careers by producing Volcanic repeating pistols in coproduction with O. Winchester. Since Winchester showed no interest in revolvers, Smith and Wesson dissolved the partnership and started work on weapons with a cylinder. At the beginning of 1855 Wesson finished work on his own construction of a revolver loaded from the back by a one-piece cartridge. However, when he arrived in Washington wishing to patent his invention, he found that a similar solution had already been entered in the records on April 3 of the same year by a certain Rollin A. White. The young and talented White had immediately offered his invention to Colt who, intoxicated by the commercial success of percussion revolvers, showed no interest in this technical innovation. Smith and Wesson made use of Colt's mistake, contacted White and, after prolonged negotiations, signed an agreement to begin joint arms production. In the course of 1857/58, the first model of new generation of S and W revolvers was produced. The new weapon, calibre ˙22 rim-fire, was loaded in an unusual manner: the octagonal barrel was hinged to the front of the top frame, with a retaining catch holding it to the lower frame. When the catch was pushed upward, the barrel could be raised and the cylinder removed, the empty cases being pushed out by means of a pin below the barrel.

One decade later, Smith and Wesson produced the first type of the second generation of their revolvers, on the basis of patents held by W. C. Dodge (from 1865) and C. A. King (1869). Dogc's and King's idea was based on a star-shaped extractor. Smith and Wesson contructed a new revolver of the bottom-hinged, break-open type with a system of simultaneous extraction. This was the famous six-cartridge Smith and Wesson, No.3 M.1869, with single-action firing.

The Russian general A. Gorlov, military attaché to the USA, signed a contract with the Smith and Wesson firm on May 1, 1871, regarding the delivery of 20,014 ˙44 calibre revolvers of the same name, at a price of 13.02 dollars per gun. General Gorlov and Captain K. Ordinec, who stayed at the Massachusetts factory as supervisor, somewhat modified the revolver ammunition: the weight of the bullet was raised from 14.12 to 15.95 gr, and the powder charge reduced from 1.62 to 1.42 gr. In this way they achieved a muzzle velocity of 230 m/s and $E_o = 43$ kpm. With these amended characteristics, the weapon was designated: *Revolver Smita i Vesona Obrasec No. 1.* An interesting episode is connected with the first Russian order for revolvers. On December 6, 1871, the Russian Grand Prince Alexei (later Czar Alexander III) visited Springfield. In honour of this occasion, and in keeping with American advertizing flair, the hosts organized a buffalo hunt in which even Smith and Wesson revolv-

Grand Duke Alexei, later Russian Emperor Alexander III, shoots bison with a Smith and Wesson revolver.

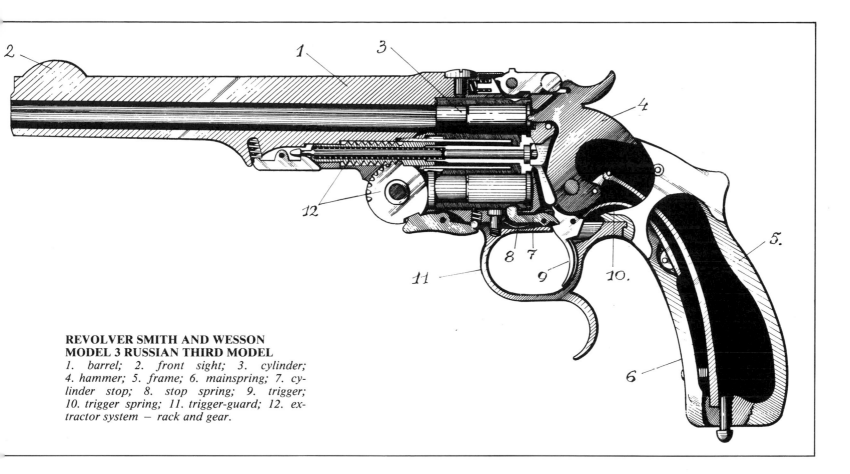

REVOLVER SMITH AND WESSON MODEL 3 RUSSIAN THIRD MODEL
1. barrel; 2. front sight; 3. cylinder; 4. hammer; 5. frame; 6. mainspring; 7. cylinder stop; 8. stop spring; 9. trigger; 10. trigger spring; 11. trigger-guard; 12. extractor system — rack and gear.

ers were used! The hunt was attended by the elite of the then still "wild" West: William Cody, alias Buffalo Bill, Colonel G. A. Custer and the famous Civil War general, Sheridan. It is said that the Prince, impressed by the Smith and Wesson revolver, abandoned his idea of ordering Colt's weapons for Russia and decided on the Smith and Wesson instead!

On January 15, 1873, Gorlov signed a new agreement regarding the delivery of another 20,000 revolvers, this time at the price of US dollars 15.33 each. This was a somewhat modified weapon, with a shorter barrel, and *Smita i Vesona Obrasec 2* inscribed on it in Cyrillic script. The contract was twice extended: in December 1873 and October 1874. In the period between 1873 and 1878, Russia received a total of 70,000 revolvers of the second model.

By patent no. 158,874 of January 19, 1875, the revolver underwent further changes, the barrel being shortened. The earlier models were withdrawn and placed in the Russian military reserves for the possible needs of the infantry and artillery, whilst an order for 41,138 revolvers of the newest type, *Obrazets No. 3* were ordered from the US for the cavalry. In the period between 1871 and 1878,

Russia purchased from the USA a total of 131,152 revolvers of all three models.

When the contract between the US producer and the Russian government expired in 1878, Ludwig Löwe and Co. of Berlin appeared on the scene. The Germans continued to produce these arms under American licence and delivered another 70,000 revolvers of the third type to the Russian Imperial Army. Moreover, the Russian Tula works in the period between 1884 and 1893, produced unknown quantities of weapons based on the Smith and Wesson principle.

Apart from Russia, Spain, Turkey, Argentina, Japan, and Mexico many other states opted for these revolvers. In the period between 1873 and 1883, Turkey bought 3,000 S and W No. 2 revolvers with a 7-inch barrel, and 5,641 No. 3 revolvers with a 6.5-inch barrel. As early as 1880, Russia had given Bulgaria a large number of its Smith and Wesson weapons as part of its "charitable" mission in the Balkans. Moreover, according to a letter from the Ministry of Foreign Affairs, dated April 15, 1904, a Russian imperial gift of 30,000 then very out-of-date Smith and Wesson revolvers, was sent from Odessa by the ship *Junona* to Montenegro!

SMITH AND WESSON MODEL 3 RUSSIAN SECOND MODEL	
- Calibre	11.17 mm ('44)
- Rifling	5
- Capacity	6
- Length	315 mm
- Length of barrel	178 mm
- Weight	1,200 gr

Overleaf:
M.1869/71 Smith and Wesson system revolver with Turkish and Russian inscriptions.

153

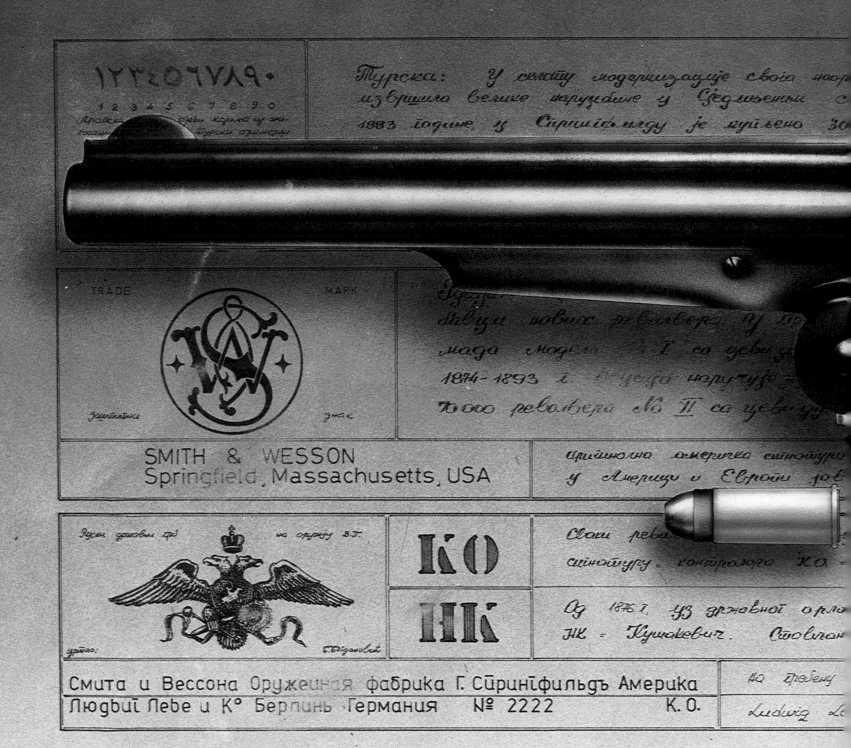

SMITH & WESSON
Springfield, Massachusetts, USA

КО
НК

Смита и Вессона Оружейная фабрика Г. Спрингфильдъ Америка
Людвиг Лебе и К° Берлинъ Германия   № 2222   К. О.

SMITH & WESSON MODEL

RUSSIAN SECOND MODEL

Colt SAA

Colt's company could not remain impassive in the face of the success of the competition, Smith and Wesson. The vice-president and manager of the company, Major-General William B. Franklin, was particularly aware of the fact that the time of percussion weapons had passed. Accordingly, he encouraged the factory constructors to work on inventing new and better-quality solutions. The project offered by one of Colt's staff, Alexander Thuer, was received with great enthusiasm, and patented on September 15, 1868.

At that time, the first generation of S and W revolvers had reached its tenth anniversary. Thuer did not need to be an ingenious innovator, since weapons based on Rollin White's idea could be bought in almost every well-stocked shop. It is understandable, then, that his solution differed little from that of Smith and Wesson's partner. Thuer used special rim-fire ammunition, still loaded into the cylinder from the front, as a basis. The nipples were removed from the cylinder and a special pin was mounted, through which the hammer ignited the explosive mass. This form of adaptation was primarily applied to the famous Colt Army M.1860 revolver. The resulting strange and impractical Factory Conversion revolver was rightly not popular among the military. The army objected to both the manner of loading and the quality of ammunition used. The armed forces insisted on a safe, solid-frame construction, whereas Thuer's solution was based on the out-of-date conception of Colt's revolvers. Only 5,000 revolvers were adapted to Thuer's system in Britain and the United States together.

Three years later (July 25, 1871), C. B. Richards patended a new solution for adapting Colt's percussion weapons. Richard's conversion was a step forward in any case, since it was based on the somewhat more modern rim-fire ammunition. In this project, the chambers of the cylinder were completely drilled to the width of the cartridge, whilst the cylinder itself was given a special plate known as the Richards plate. Furthermore, a loading gate was added to the frame, permitting the loading of ammunition into the chambers from the back of the weapon. Colt's old hammer was given a firing-pin which ingnited the explosive mixture.

The new manner of adaptation was adopted in practice in 1873, and within five years 9,000 Colt revolvers had been altered according to it. As an improvement of this conversion, on July 1, 1872, William Mason patented a method of ejecting the cases consisting of a rod sliding in a sleeve below and to the right of the barrel.

Colt's designers by this time had decided to drop the practice of adapting their earlier products and direct their efforts to some new weapon which would bring back the old glory of the company. In 1871/72, Hartford entered the market with the so-called Open Top revolver, calibre '44 rim-fire. This weapon is today considered the last transitional type in the change from the percussion to the metallic-cartridge revolver, but also the predecessor of the famous Single Action Army (SAA). The Open Top weapon had a design similar to that of the old Colt Army M.1860, from which it had taken over the archaic lower frame.

Colt's factory offered this product to the US Army, but when the *SAA* appeared during the testing period, the USA finally decided on the latest revolver model. Having lost the army as a potential buyer, the Hartford factory produced only 7,000 Open Top revolvers (barrel length 7.5 inches) and sold most of them to South America and Mexico. Of the companies in the home market, only the Union Railroad Pacific and American Express opted for it.

The famous Colt Army (SAA) soon became immensely popular and placed the factory back at the top. This weapon became part of the legend of the Wild West and has stayed a synonym for revolvers to this very day. When it appeared officially in November 1872, the SAA was called the New Model Army Metallic Cartridge Revolving Pistol. The first tests made in the army, parallel with the testing of Open Top weapons, showed that the new revolver met all the military norms. In the first place, it used the modern '45 central-fire ammunition, as well as having the solid frame the armed forces had insisted on. Accordingly, the government signed an agreement with the factory for the delivery of 8,000 cavalry SAA revolvers. After three years of use and troop testing, the Colt Army M.1873 was adopted, in 1875, as the official weapon of the US Army, and retained this status until 1892.

The factory programme included the production of this weapon in three versions: with 7.5, 5.5 and 4.75-inch barrels. In this way the needs of the cavalry and artillery were satisfied, as well as those of the civilian market.

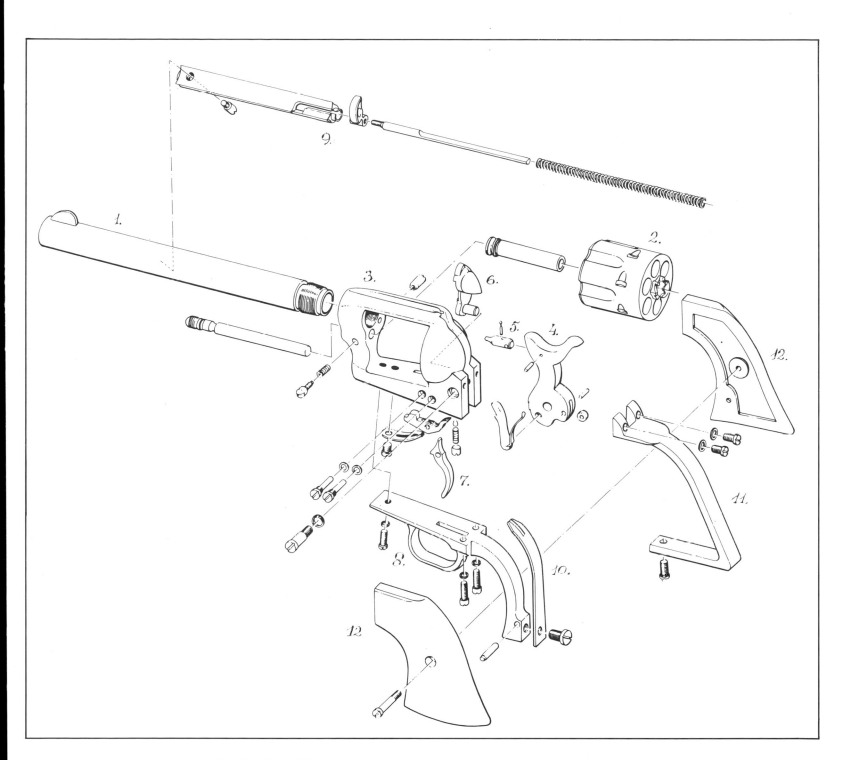

COLT SAA REVOLVER	
- Calibre	11.43 mm ('45)
- Rifling	6
- Capacity	6
- Length	279 mm
- Length of barrel ...	140 mm
- Weight	990 gr

COLT SAA 1873

1. barrel; 2. cylinder; 3. frame; 4. hammer; 5. firing pin; 6. loading gate; 7. trigger; 8. trigger-guard; 9. extractor; 10. main spring; 11. receiver; 12. stock.

Overleaf:
American Colt SAA system revolver.

NEW MODEL ARMY METALIC
PISTOL

COL

Valentian

CARTRIDGE REVOLVING

SAA 1873

Webley

Many other talented constructors worked in Britain apart from Adams. Their revolvers are still well known today, but none reached such a degree of fame as the Webley.

In 1852, Joseph Bentley, a Birmingham gunsmith, patented a revolver which had a spring safety catch on the hammer to hold it clear of the cap. Somewhat later, Bentley transferred this patent right to his fellow citizens, Philip and James Webley.

The capable James Webley improved Bentley's construction and already on March 29, 1853, patented it as his own invention. After James's death, his brother Philip devoted himself to the production of several prototypes of percussion weapons on the basis of this first family patent. His work resulted in single-action, Longspur and double-action revolvers. Most of these weapons were first used in the Crimean War and the Indian Mutiny, and a large number was also sold to the Confederate side during the American Civil War.

In about 1865, Webley produced his last muzzle-loading revolver. However, this weapon already used rim-fire ammunitation, in which it was similar to the Colt-Thuer conversion. It was on the basis of the 1865 project that Webley started to develop his own breech-loading revolvers. After the appearance of the first prototype using rim-fire ammunition, the constructor switched to the centre-fire system. Philip also adopted a solid-frame construction, Boxer ammunition calibre '450 and an exceptionally short 4.5-inch barrel. The firm Philip Webley and Sons made similar revolvers for the commercial market in 1867. Already in the next year, they became a success as police weapons, since they were promptly adopted by the Royal Irish Constabulary (hence their popular name: the RIC).

What is important is that Philip Webley had a talent for recognizing and adopting all the technical innovations that would promote the sale of his weapons. Accordingly, only a year after the appearance of Charles Pryse's locking patent for break-downarms, he adopted it and, combining it with the star-shaped extractor and double-action system, in 1878 produced the Webley-Pryse revolver.

WEBLEY-FOSBERY AUTOMATIC REVOLVER 1901
1. front sight; 2. grooves; 3. barrel; 4. chamber and cartridge; 5. hammer; 6. frame; 7. walnut stock; 8. rebound lever; 9. ejector spring; 10. ejector and rotchet; 11. crane; 12. trigger-guard; 13. trigger.

WEBLEY AND SCOTT MK VI REVOLVER	
- Calibre	11.5 mm ('455)
- Rifling	7
- Capacity	6
- Length	279 mm
- Length of barrel	152 mm
- Weight	1,050 gr

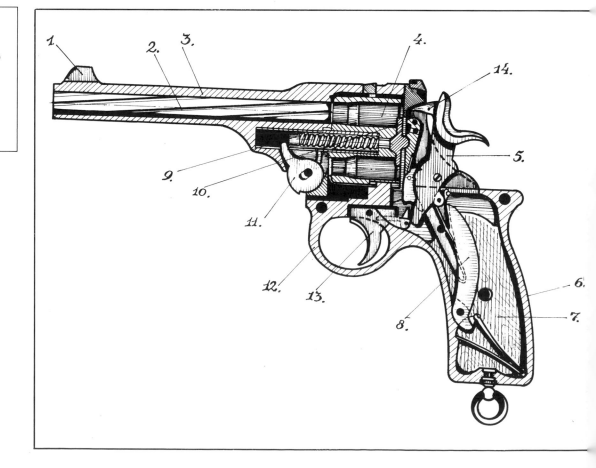

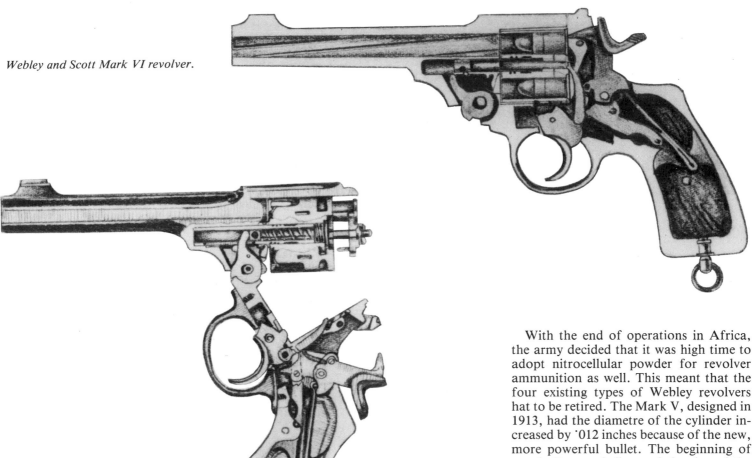

Webley and Scott Mark VI revolver.

Only two years later, Webley changed the locking arms and, together with the talented British inventor, Michael Kaufmann, produced a new double-action revolver calibre ·45. Both projects made jointly with other designers, helped the Webley company to lay the foundations of its own revolver construction in 1892. After many years of improvements, the British government was offered the Webley Mark I, the first of the famous dynasty of British-made revolvers, in 1886. By a decree of the Board of Ordnance, the following year the army ordered 10,000 Mark I revolvers, of which the first contingent of 2 to 3,000 was supposed to be delivered by March 3, 1888.

In the period between 1882 and 1891, Webley perfected two new projects: by changing the shape of the butt and incorporating a larger hammer, he created and sold to the army the Mark II. At the same time, in a joint venture with Green, he also produced a target version of his revolver, the Webley-Green. The latter was never adopted in Britain as an official weapon, but this did not prevent officers and NCOs from ordering the excellent 1892 version of the same revolver, pretentiously named Army, at their own expense and carrying it into battle. For reasons of mutual commercial interest, the firm of Webley and the Wilkinson Sword Company developed a joint project of a military revolver in 1889. Wilkinson had probably reckoned that it would be easy to sell officers guns as well as his swords. It would seem, though, that this idea was not brilliantly successful but that did not stop the astute Webley from developing the Mark III from the coproduction revolver, a weapon accepted by the British Army in 1897.

Just before the Boer War, in 1899, British soldiers were issued the Mark IV, which was to save the lives of many of them in South Africa.

With the end of operations in Africa, the army decided that it was high time to adopt nitrocellular powder for revolver ammunition as well. This meant that the four existing types of Webley revolvers hat to be retired. The Mark V, designed in 1913, had the diametre of the cylinder increased by ·012 inches because of the new, more powerful bullet. The beginning of war in Europe influenced the size of the orders: the contract provided for the delivery of a total of 20,000 Mark V revolvers by 1915. Finally, at the height of the First World War, Webley produced the last of this famed generation. It was the Mark VI, made by the Webley and Scott Revolver and Arms Co. Ltd, created by the fusion of the Tipping and Lawden, W. and C. Scott and Son, Richard Ellis and Son and Webley companies. The new company was contracted by the original agreement to deliver 250 revolvers per week to the troops, so that a total of 300,000 were produced!

The Mark VI was a powerful and reliable weapon of ·455 calibre. Its muzzle velocity was tremendous and its robust construction enabled it to maintain its reliability even in the mud of the trenches in Flanders.

Overleaf:
British Webley and Scott Mark IV revolver.

161

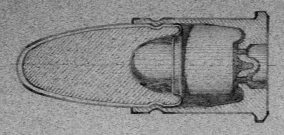

Die Patrone .455 Webley

Abb. 7b

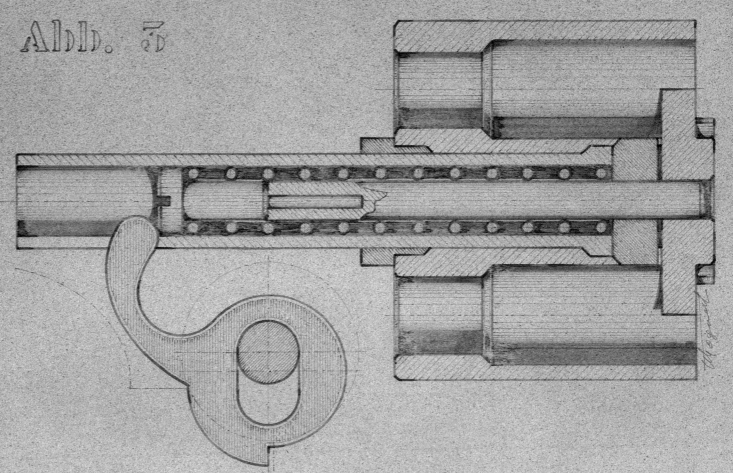

Auswerfer Webley Mark I Br. Pat. 5143/1881

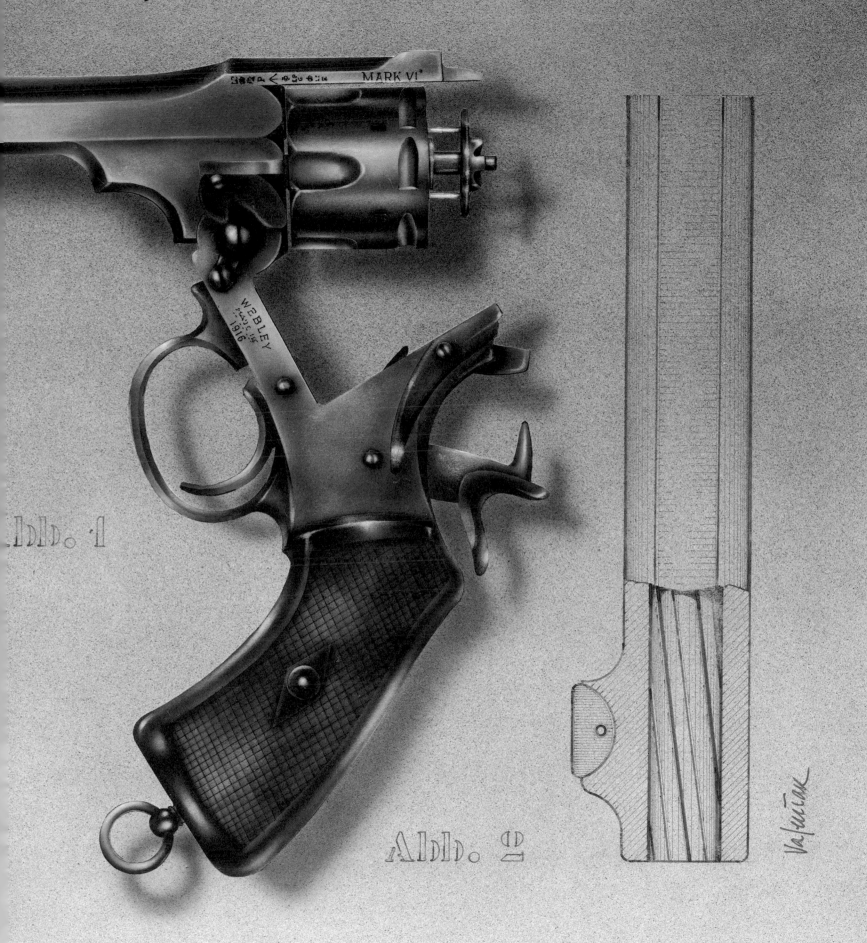

OLVER, .455 No 1 Mark 6

MARK VI

WEBLEY
PATENTS
1916

Abb. 1

Abb. 2

Gasser

Gasser, Leopold, born March 31, 1836, at Spittal am Drau (Austria), died January 9, 1871, in Vienna-Ottakring. Learned the gunsmith trade in Ferlach, Carinthia, then went to Vienna and worked for the gunsmith Scheiningg. Became a master gunsmith in 1862, and after Scheiningg's death took over the workshop. In 1869, patented a military revolver adopted by the Austro-Hungarian Army in 1870, and later also by the Montenegrin Army.

After Leopold's premature death, his brother **Johann** (1847 – 1896) took over the business, which by now had developed into a factory. At the turn of the century the L. Gasser Company merged with Rast and Gasser and continued producing revolvers until the end of World War I.

The first revolver to be adopted by the military forces of the Austrio-Hangarian monarchy was the Colt Navy M.1849, produced under licence by the Peterlongo company of Innsbruck. But only the extravagant Navy accepted this percussion weapon, while the army remained faithful to the single-shot Lorenz M.1859 pistol, awaiting the appearance of some better-quality and safer revolver. In 1869, Leopold Gasser entered the scene with a robust and safe revolver, adopted for the whole Austrian military forces on August 14 (September 5), 1870 (Decree : A. 7. N. 3520). This weapon was intended for all NCOs and soldiers who did not have a carbine, and also for artillerymen, sanitary and transport units and auxiliary troops.

Together with four of his collaborators, Leopold Gasser founded his own revolver workshop in 1862 in Ottakring (earlier a suburb of Vienna, today the XVI arrondissement). The expansion of this company started with the signature of the contract for the delivery of revolvers to the army. At that time, to be precise, on January 9, 1871, Leopold died, and his younger brother, Johann, assumed the firm's management, not less successfully than Leopold. In 1873 he opened a commercial department in Vienna, and took over the St. Pölten factory.

The first weapon, Leopold's revolver construction, had a barrel and cylinder of cast steel, whilst the frame was of cast iron. The firing system was double-action and the barrel all of 9 Austrian zoll (235 mm) long! For practical reasons, the revolver used Werndl carbine ammunition of 11 mm calibre.

After troop testing, it turned out that the iron frame soon became worn and deformed, which led to a deviation of the axis of the barrel from that of the chamber, and thus to instability of the cylinder axis. For this reason, in 1874 Johann Gasser introduced a reinforced frame, cast out of steel, and shortened the barrel to 7 zoll (184.3 mm). Apart from this, the weapon retained its lower-frame construction and Lefaucheux's simple sliding rod. The last version of Gasser's revolver, which appeared on the market in 1877, had a barrel only 5 zoll long — 135 mm.

Montenegro, too, was in possession of Gasser weapons. In modern writings it is often suggested that Prince Nikola of Montenegro had a vested interest in the acquisition of these pistols, and even that he owned shares in the factory. This story has no historical basis, however.

During his trip to Vienna in 1873, Prince Nikola was demonstrated the qualities of the new weapon and, in view of the political climate and the favourable terms of purchase, signed a contract with the Gasser company for the delivery of 7,000 M.1870 revolvers.

M. 1870/74 GASSER SYSTEM REVOLVER

- Calibre	11 mm
- Rifling	6
- Capacity	6
- Length	320 mm
- Length of barrel	184.3 mm
- Weight	1,370 gr

Advertisement of the Leopold Gasser firm for the Balkan area, 1881.

The Principality of Montenegro endeavoured to acquire the revolvers at the lowest possible price. Thus, when the terms of the first contract were fulfilled, it entered into negotiations with the Thomas Sederl Company, wishing to investigate its delivery conditions for the same weapons. Johann Gasser, aware of the potential of the Balkan market, reacted fast and energetically to this. Firstly, he agreed to deliver only the improved M.70/74 version of the revolver. Although these guns cost 20.27 florins in contracts with the Austrian Army, Montenegro was offered a 33% discount, and so paid only 14 florins. For this reason in 1882 the Montenegrin Ministry of War decided on the original Gasser product. The arms were purchased through authorised representatives in Trieste, whence it was shipped to the country. The right of purchase and sale of revolvers was the exclusive prerogative of

the state, through the Ministry of War (and not the Prince). It acquired the Gasser weapons at 13.5 – 14 florins, and sold it to Montenegrins at a price of 15.3 – 18.

It should also be mentioned that it was strictly forbidden by law to buy foreign copies of the Gasser revolver. This primarily meant the commercial Belgian copies which, who knows why, carried the fine-sounding name "Montenegrin". In Gasser's factory, every original revolver intended for Montenegro was given, apart from the usual inscriptions and stamps, another with the initials of Nikola I (N.I) and a crown, on the upper side of the barrel.

Towards the end of 1903, the Gasser factory stopped producing the heavy and already obsolete M.1870/74 revolvers. The third Gasser brother, Michael, did not enter the family plant. In 1877 he founded an independant factory together with August Rast, known as Rast and

Gasser. After Johann's death on July 16, 1896, he set about merging the two companies Gasser and Rast and Gasser. As the Austrian Army at this time already opted for the new, excellent eight-shot Rast and Gasser M.1898 (cal. 8 mm), the new company did not continue production of the M.1870/74. By this time Montenegro had acquired a total of about 20,000 Gasser revolvers, which every soldier was obliged by law to carry.

M.1870/74 Gasser System revolver.

Overleaf:
Exploded view of the M.1870 Gasser system revolver.

165

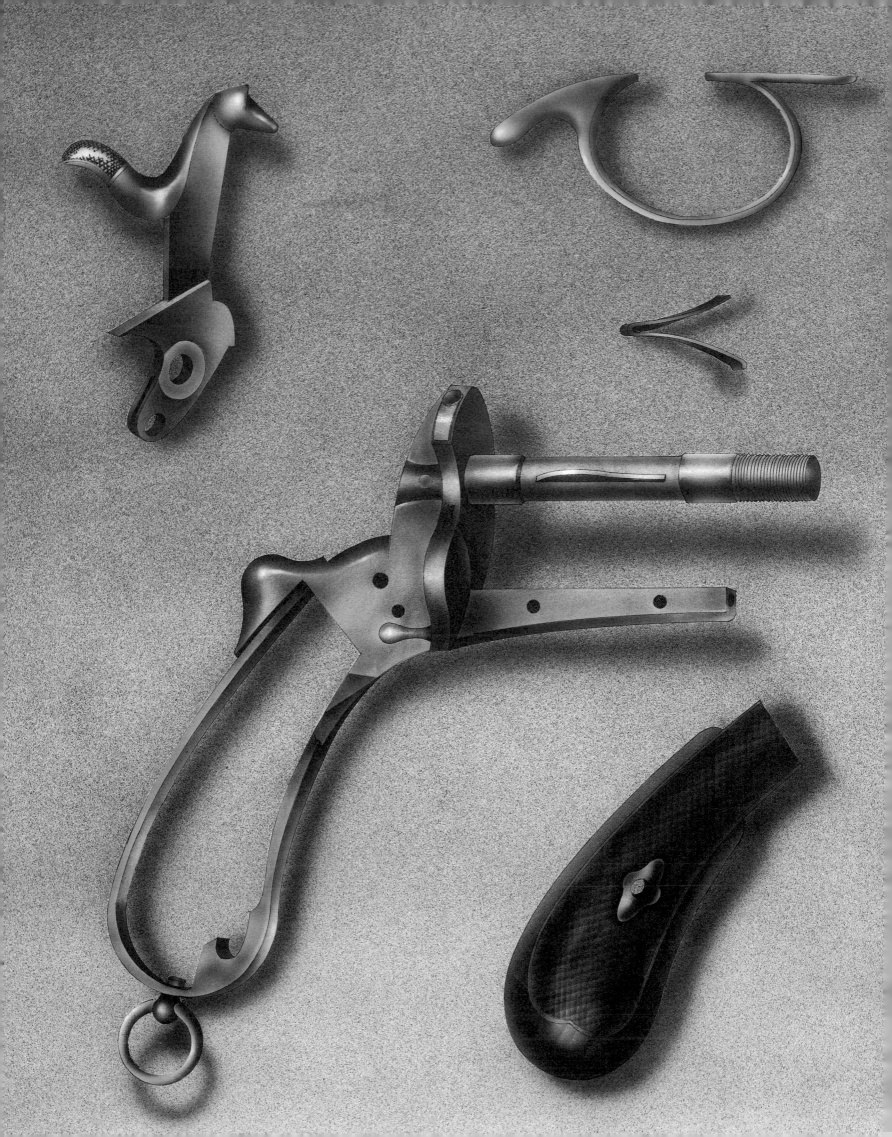

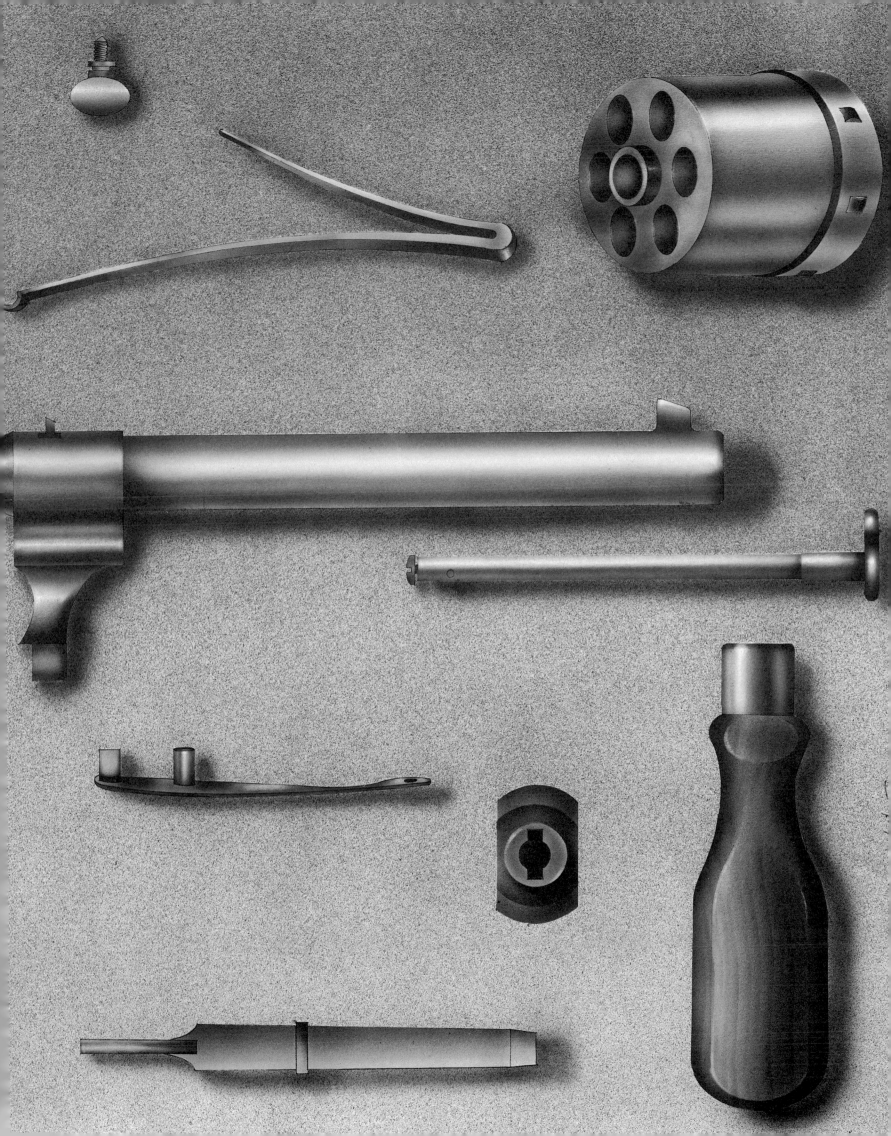

Nagant

Nagant, Emile and **Nagant, Léon**, sibling constructors and arms producers in Liège towards the end of the 19th century. Their revolvers were introduced into the armament of Belgium, Luxemburg, Norway, Sweden, Serbia and some South American countries. Their best known construction: the gas-seal Russian revolver M.1895, produced in the USSR until 1944. In Poland, the gas-seal Nagant was produced in the inter-war period for the needs of the postal services, on original Nagant machines.

In the second half of the 19th century, most European countries decided in favour of several high-quality revolver solutions. As an example, the most numerous were systems based on Nagant and Chamelot-Delvigne.

The Belgian constructor J. Chamelot and the famous French officer H. J. Delvigne made a top-quality revolver with solid frame and a double-action system. Their project served as a basis for the Italian M.1872 revolver of the Glisenti factory, the French officers' and infantry M.1873/74 revolver, the Swiss M.1872 and M.1878 Schmidt, and the Portuguese M.1878/86 revolver.

On the other hand, the Belgian company, Nagant of Liège, produced its own weapon which was adopted by several European countries. In 1878 Belgium decided on the officers' version of Nagant's 9 mm revolver and five years later introduced another Nagant for the *Artillerie de campagne et régiment du Train.* That same year, 1883, Luxemburg ordered from Liège, for the needs of its *gendarmerie,* an attractive version of the Nagant which had a bayonet affixed to its muzzle!

In 1884 the Swedish Navy started testing Nagant's so-called *Föröksmodell* revolver. By royal decree of February 15, 1887, this weapon (cal. 7.5 mm) was adopted for the whole Swedish Army. According to the first contract, the revolver was produced by the original Belgian maker. In 1898, however, the Swedish Husqvarna took over the licence and within seven years delivered to the army 13,732 Nagant M.1887 weapons. Moreover, Sweden greatly improved this gun using *Pionieroberleutnant* T. F. Törnell's project.

All the mentioned types of Nagant revolver had a solid frame, single or double-action system and a sliding rod placed in the hollow of the cylinder axis. At the turn of the century Nagant also made use of an 1882 Abadie patent. This construction allowed the hammer to be cocked when the loading gate was open and the cylinder to turn freely by pulling the trigger. Serbia was the first and only state to adopt this much safer Nagant-Abadie weapon. By royal decree of July 8, 1891, Serbia proclaimed the M.1891 Nagant its official weapon and, accordingly, ordered 12,000 of them from Liège.

At about this time, the Nagant brothers started work on a weapon which would make the best use of the pressure created by powder gasses. This idea was not, in fact, all that new. Back in 1878 Daniel B. Wesson had constructed a revolver in which the cartridge was pushed forward before firing, so that the edge of the case entered the barrel itself. A similar system was applied by the talented Henry Piper, a Belgian gunsmith with a shop in Bayards Street in Liège. But the greatest commercial success with gas-seal weapons was achieved by Nagant. He constructed a revolver whose cylinder, at the same time as rotating, moved forward on its axis. To overcome gas escaping from the gap, a special round was designed with the bullet flush with the end of the cartridge. To further seal the cylinder-barrel gap, the cylinder was pushed forward as the hammer cocked to reduce the gap to a minimum.

The Nagant company first offered weapons on the gas-seal principle, in calibres 6.5 and 7.5 mm, to Norway in 1892. But this solution was only accepted without reserve in 1895 by Imperial Russia. Moreover, St Petersburg also purchased from Liège the licence rights to produce its own M.1895 and M.1905 revolvers. In Russia, the weapon was given the official name *3 linien revolver Nagant obrazets 1895. g.* (cal. 7.62 mm), and was produced in an infantry, single-action, and an officers', double-action version. Until the Tula works were fitted out to produce the new weapons, the Imperial Army received the M.1895 revolvers from Liège. Finally, in 1905, manufacture of Nagant weapons started in Russia. By 1914, the Tula works had delivered the imposing quantity of 460,088 M.1895 revolvers!

The Nagant was considered a very effective and good-qualitiy weapon, and its complexity and the complicated production process were completely overlooked. Russia, or rather, the USSR, was so satisfied with this revolver, that it kept it in its armament until the 1950s. In the inter-war period even Poland bought the licence from the USSR and started its own production of this weapon at the *Fabryka Broni – Radom.*

M. 1891 NAGANT SYSTEM REVOLVER	
- Calibre	7.5 mm
- Rifling	4
- Capacity	6
- Length	238.6 mm
- Length of barrel	124 mm
- Weight	785 gr

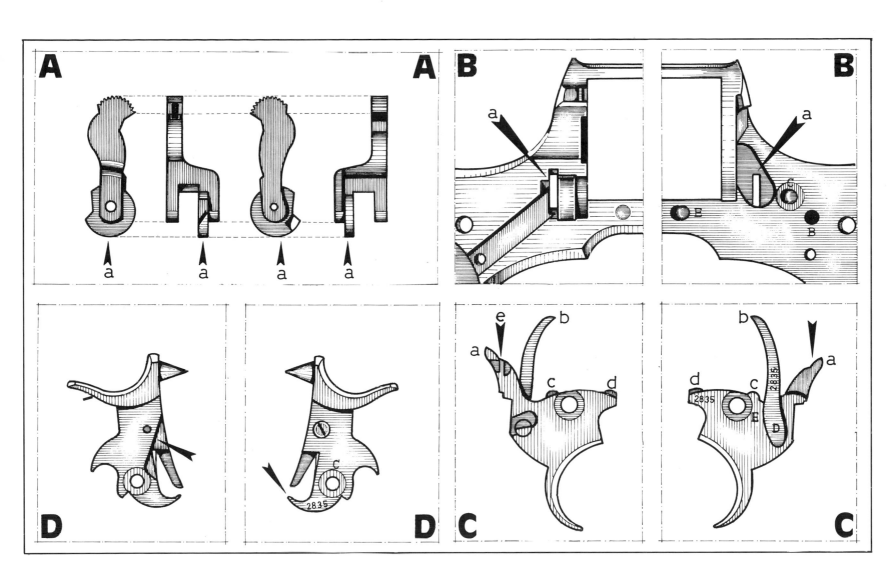

REVOLVER NAGANT M.1891

A. loading gate system Abadie; A.a. lug; B. frame; B.a. notch; C. trigger; C.a. vertical lifter; C.b. lever (bar); C.c. rear cylinder stop rise; C.d. front cylinder stop rise; C.e. notch; D. hammer.

M.1895 Nagant System revolver.

Overleaf:
M.1891 Nagant-Abadie system revolver with cartridge and detail of barrel of the M.1895 revolver of the same system with Russian cartridge.

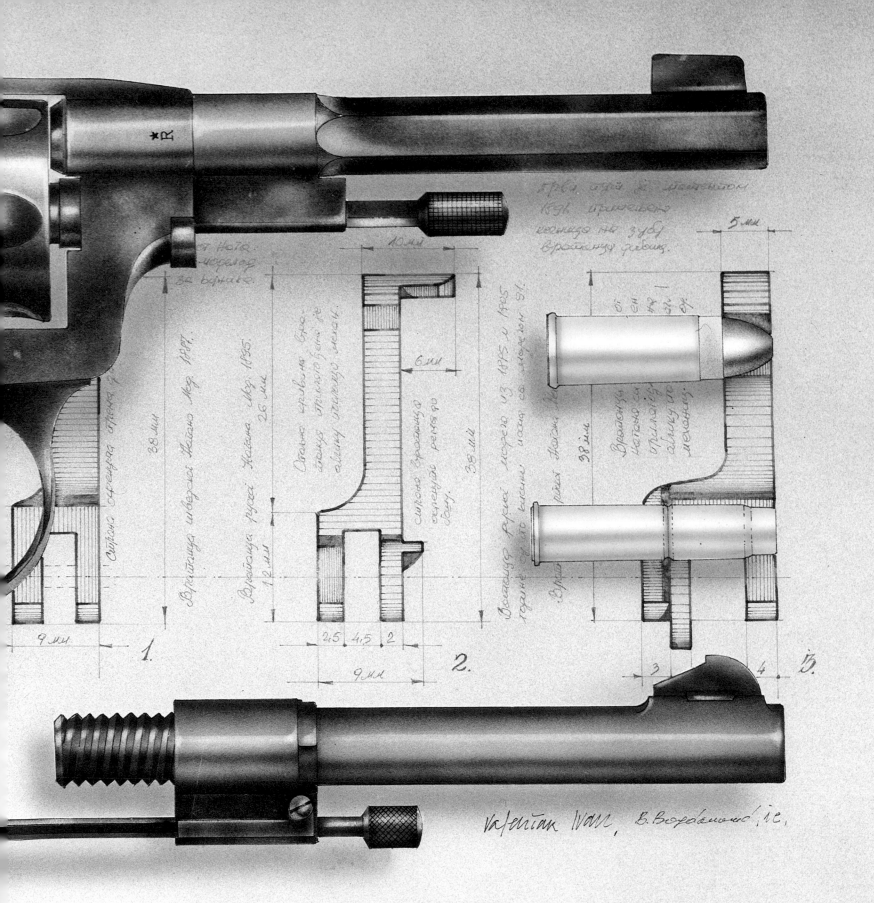

прва, при 1 шпеншок
взд примкьет
конада на зубь
враценуд ребис.

от нота
порелод
за вínako.

5 мм

Служонс офицерна отпри

38 мм

Враценца шверсей Навана мод. 1887.

10 мм

Враценца русси Навана мод. 1895.
26 мм

6 мм

Свобо чробым бро-
ленур тилала бен је
алику отличую ален.

Село враценца
оселило релеро
бесу.

12 мм

38 мм

38 мм

Враценца русси мореро из 1895 и 1905
годин Пло висин пош со моделон 91.

Враценуд,
неолно со
прилодiу
алику со
механ.

9 мм

1.

2.5 4.5 2

9 мм

2.

3   4   5.

Valentian Ivan, B. Boydanovid, ic.

German Revolvers

Unlike the other countries of Europe and America, Germany was rather late in introducing revolvers into the armed forces. There were several reasons for this. The division into a number of small states until the unification did not permit uniformity of armament. Moreover, the revolver had never been a popular weapon in these territories, so that the appearance of self-loading pistols was warmly welcomed in Germany.

German constructors did, however, produce several projects of revolvers which are worthy of mention, if only for their originality.

In 1853 Franz von Dreyse, son of Nikolaus, started serial production of needle-fire revolvers. Two decades later, another German rifle constructor tried his hand in the revolver field. This was the famous Peter Paul Mauser, who in 1878 patented his zig-zag revolver. This strange but high-quality weapon possessed a constructional innovation which was to be used, much later, by the self-loading Webley-Fossbery. The cylinder of the revolver was turned by means of a rod which slid along the barrel catch! Because of its complexity and the high production cost, this weapon was never officially acclaimed by military circles.

REICHSREVOLVER M. 1883
- Calibre .... 10.6 mm
- Rifling 3
- Capacity 6
- Length .... 255 mm
- Length of barrel .... 121 mm
- Weight .... 950 gr

Map of the German Empire, second half of 19th century.

"Schutztruppe" fighting rebel natives. German South-West Africa, 1905.

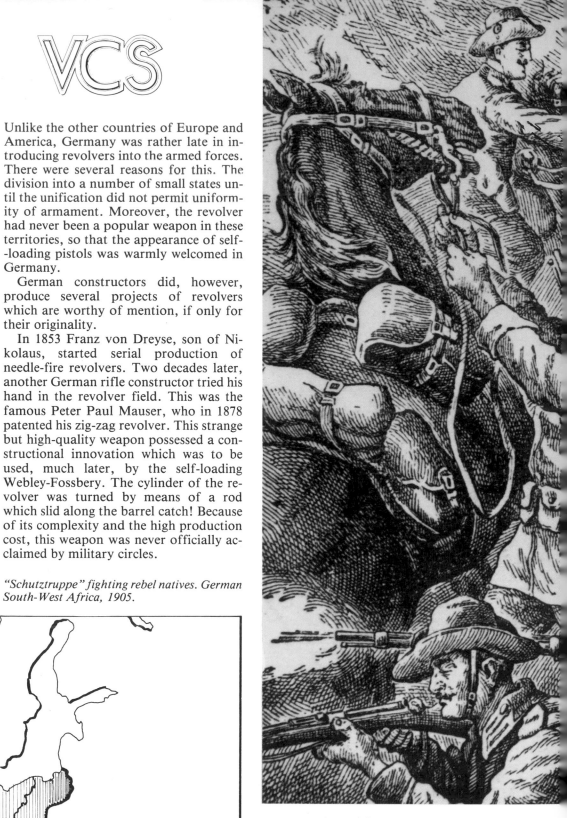

The victory in its war with France in 1871, as well as talk of the successful use of the Colt SAA by the American dragoon cavalry, finally prompted Germany to make its choice of a revolver. After a certain time, the government was offered a weapon produced by – the Commission for the Choice of Weapons itself! This collective project was adopted for use by the whole German Army by a decision of the A.K.O. (Imperial Cabinet Decree) of March 21, 1879.

It should be said that the Commission did not do too good a job. The so-called Reichsrevolver M.1879 was a bulky six--shooter of 10.6 mm calibre which used central-fire ammunition filled with black powder. The Commission cleverly placed a lever safety catch on the left-hand side of the frame, but completely overlooked the need to provide any means of ejecting the cases!

The Germans soon came to the conclusion that a revolver weighing 1,350 gr and 340 mm long was not particularly practical for carrying and use. Four years later, in accordance with these objections, local designers shortened the weapon by 85 mm and made it 400 gr lighter. This created the "new" Reichsrevolver M.1883,

which retained the same calibre, ammunition and faults, but was certainly easier to carry and use than its predecessor.

The muzzle velocity of the lead bullet of both revolvers was approximately Vo = 205 m/s, the energy Eo = 35.4 kpm. Although the Germans wanted this ammunition to be the equivalent of the Russian ˙44 cartridge, it is obvious that they managed to achieve only about 85% of the desired effect.

Overleaf:
German Reichsrevolver M.1883 with holster.

173

Valentak

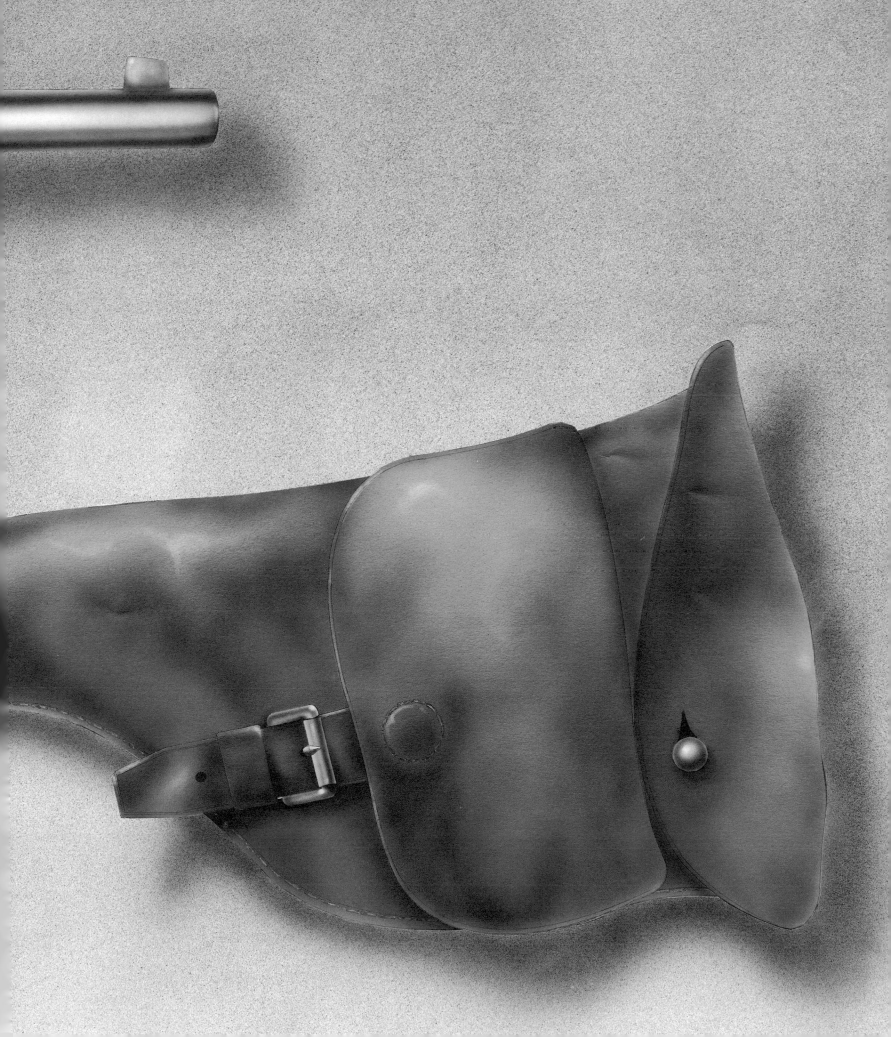

Japanese Type 26 Revolver

It is a well-known fact that the penetration of the western world into the Land of the Rising Sun started in 1853 with US Commodore Perry's mission. The contact with the industrially-developed countries of the West had a direct impact on the modernization of the Japanese Army. This was speeded up after the overthrow of the last Shogun, Yoshinoby. In accordance with this policy, Japan ordered 17 modern warships in 1871 and two years later introduced compulsory military service. The rapid growth of the Army and the Navy confronted the country with a new problem: how to provide adequate quantities of modern weapons. Japan's industry was then still in its infancy,

priority being given to heavy industry (shipbuilding and railroads), while the light metal industry, necessary for the production of infantry weapons, lagged behind. All these reasons forced Japan to turn to import and the simple reproduction of foreign revolvers and rifles as a solution.

At this time the Smith & Wesson Company in the USA, influenced by the commercial success of the "Russian" revolver, turned out a domestic version of the same weapon. The new revolver, which retained the good qualities of its "Russian" predecessor, was produced in the single--action version in '44, '38 and '32 calibres. Impressed by the qualities of this

MEIJI 26 NEN KENJU REVOLVER	
- Calibre	9 mm
- Rifling	4
- Capacity	6
- Length	235 mm
- Length of barrel	119 mm
- Weight	910 gr

Promotion of the Smith & Weeson revolver in Japan.

gun, the Japanese bought up almost a third of the total output of Smith & Wesson New Model No. 3 revolvers through the Takata Trading Company, mostly for the needs of the Imperial Navy.

This weapon also served as the basis for the development of the first home-made Japanese revolver, known as the *Meiji 26 Nen Kenju.*

The Japanese revolver, created in 1893 in the Arsenal at Tokyo, was a strange synthesis of existing European and American firearms, in which technical elements taken from the S & W, Nagant and Galand could be recognized.

The revolver was loaded by breaking the barrel downwards and the star-shaped extractor ejected all the cases automatically. The firing principle was single-action, and was achieved by self-cocking. The hammer was so constructed that it could not be thumb-cocked. The revolver had a technical characteristic which, two years later, would be found on the

Austrian M.98 weapons: access to the mechanism was trough a large side plate, similar to the one found on the Rast & Gasser.

The name of the weapon derived from the Japanese tradition of counting years according to the reign of a certain dynasty. Thus 1893 was the 26th year of Emperor Mitsuhito's reign, called the era of Meiji (enlightenment).

This extremely poor weapon was intended primarily for the unfortunate cavalry. The only good side was that Japanese officers and cavalrymen traditionally paid little attention to firearms, and never depended on the quality and reliability of their revolvers. Moreover, with the Type 26, Japan virtually finished its work on revolvers.

During this period, Europe and America entered the final phase of perfecting the same weapon. The only technical innovation on revolvers, if one ignores the abortive attempt to make them

Fighting around the Port Arthur fort. Russo--Japanese war, 1905.

automatic, was Colt's loading system from 1889, in which access to the cylinder was obtained by pulling back a thumb--catch on the left side of the frame, allowing the cylinder to be swung out sideways, to the left, on its separate yoke.

This system was improved over the next few years and is mostly used today in contemporary revolvers.

It should be added that with the appearance of self-loading pistols the revolver lost none of its importance. Its popularity was particularly sacrosanct in Anglo-Saxon countries. However, compared with revolving pistols, rifles with revolving magazines had neither as long nor as brilliant a career.

Overleaf:
Japanese Meiji 26 cavalry revolver.

明治 弐六 9mm

二十六年式
46195

Valentar

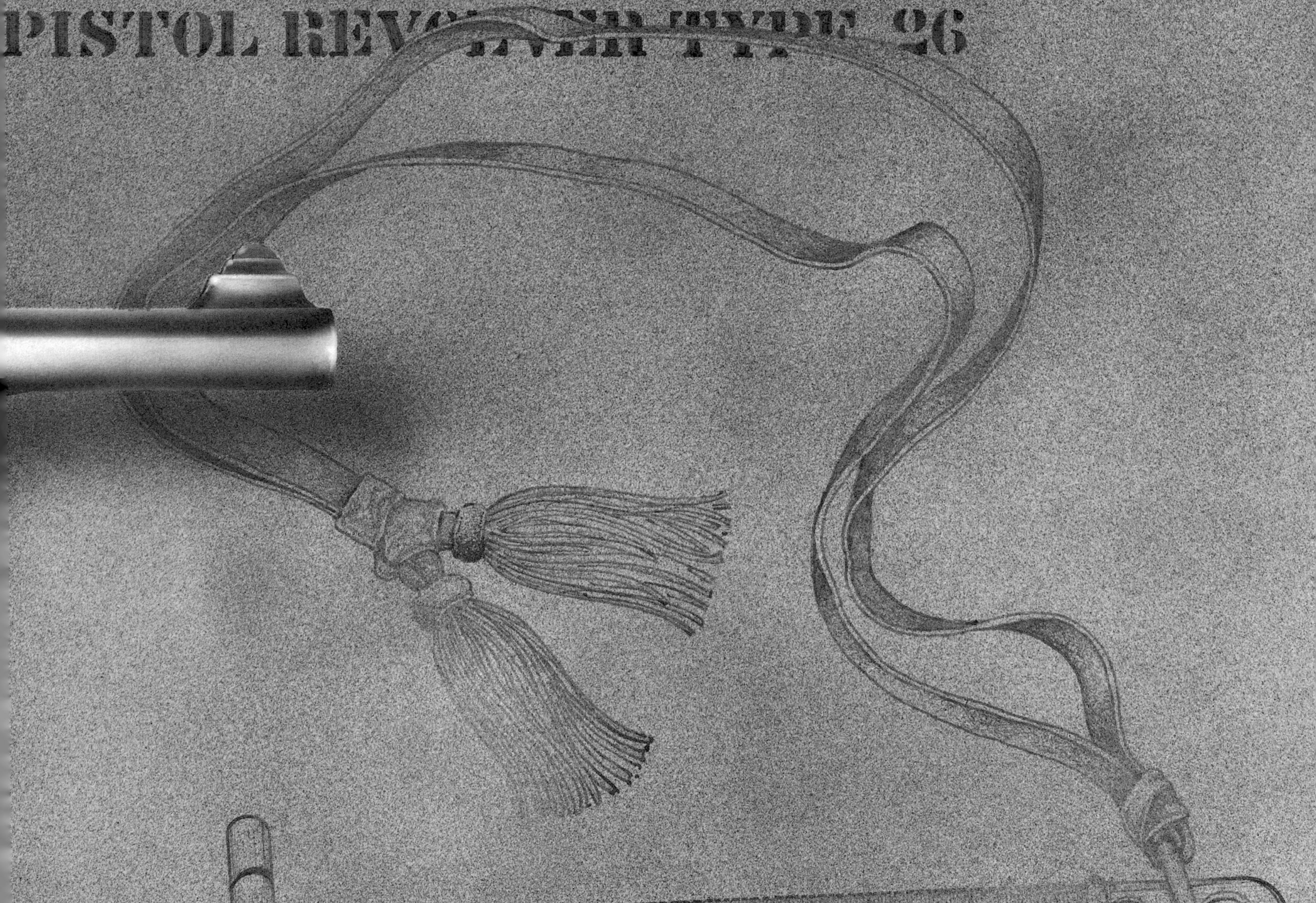
PISTOL REVOLVER TYPE 26

REVOLVING RIFLES

Colt Percussion Repeating Rifles

In March 1837 Colt offered the Army Ordnance Board at West Point the patent of a rifle and carbine based on the principle of his revolver, produced two years earlier. However, the Board rejected Colt's multi-shot arms, using arguments identical to those that conservative European experts were to employ somewhat later.

As we all know, this rejection did not particularly dishearten the constructor. Packing up his goods, like all good salesmen, he left Paterson, New Jersey, and set off on the long and uncertain road to Florida. Colt was well aware that the so--called "small war" was still raging, after two whole years, against the Seminole Indians, led by their fierce chief, Oseola. The young inventor concluded that his weapons would show their true worth best on the difficult and marshy terrain of Florida. However, Colt underestimated the stubbornness and shortsightedness of the upper echelons of the military: although the field officers, with their fighting experience, warmly welcomed multi-fire arms for their own protection, the official administration bought a total of only 50 Colt carbines! The 2nd Dragoon Regiment was partially equipped with these during battle. The extent to which the antagonistic attitude of the experts contrasted with its practical value is best illustrated by the experience of one of these Dragoons. This tough cavalryman personally informed Colt that he felt safer with this carbine than with an all-round guard of 10 to 15 soldiers armed with standard single-shot muskets!

On March 2 and on July 23, 1841, two orders for a total of 160 rifles and carbines M.1839, which arrived from the Dragoon School, Carlisle Barracks, Pennsylvania, brought a ray of hope for the constructor, financially almost ruined by now. But when, after a number of tests, the revolving percussion arms were rejected here too, the Paterson factory was closed, the machines sold off and the patents returned to the inventor.

However, Colt had lost the battle, but not the war. Following the failure of US negotiations with Mexico for the purchase of New Mexico in April 1846, President Polk sent troops into the disputed area and the army remembered revolving arms. The orders that started flowing in permitted Colt to open a new factory, in Hartford, Connecticut, and finally start exploiting his ideas financially.

Basing its production on the rifle and carbine models of 1836, 1837 and 1839, and

M. 1839 COLT SYSTEM CARBINE	
- Calibre	13.3 mm ('525)
- Rifling	5
- Capacity	6
- Length	1,100 mm
- Length of barrel	610 mm
- Weight	3,630 gr

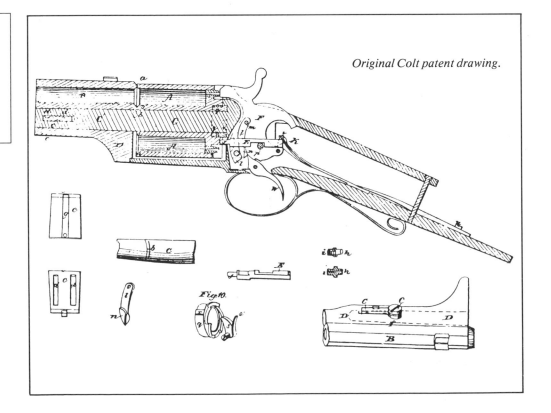

Original Colt patent drawing.

on the revolver technology of Superintendent Elisha K. Root (US Patent 13,999 of Dec. 25, 1855) Colt's Patent Arms Manufacturing Company started serial production of M.1855 long arms in 1857. The same year brought an order for 401 revolving rifles for the needs of the Army and Navy, the price per rifle ranging from US $ 42.50 to 50. Over the next two years the government bought Colt's rifles and carbines, equipped with sword bayonets at the price of US $ 32.50 to 42.50.

It was inevitable that the Civil War should lead to a sharp rise in the demand for these weapons. Contracts with the Navy and the Militia of a number of northern states followed, and the 1st and

2nd Sharpshooters' Regiments even replaced their excellent Spencer rifles with Colt's arms. The factory in Hartford produced around 7,000 revolving rifles and carbines.

Colt's rifle never attained such popularity with the soldiers as did his revolver. Dangerous powder gasses emanated from all sides of the cylinder of Colt's rifle during use. This was certainly one of the reasons why Colt's long arms, so dearly paid for during the war, were rejected soon after it ended and sold at the very low price of only 42 cents per gun.

Regardless of all its shortcomings, and the appearance of a number of more practical solutions, Colt was by no means alone in pursuing the use of cylinders in rifles. Although this construction was not recognized and accepted by any contemporary army, it nevertheless had a certain value on the free market, meeting civilian needs.

Many Belgian manufacturers started copying this system, usually completely ignoring the concept of licences. On the other hand, a number of similar technical solutions developed in Europe and the USA independently of Colt. The makes popularly named Buggy rifles, produced by C. B. Allen, B. Bigelow, N. S. North, Needham, Smith and Wesson, the Roper Repeating Rifle Co. and many other constructors and companies, are also worthy of mention.

Overleaf:
American M.1839 Colt system carbine with powder-flash.

181

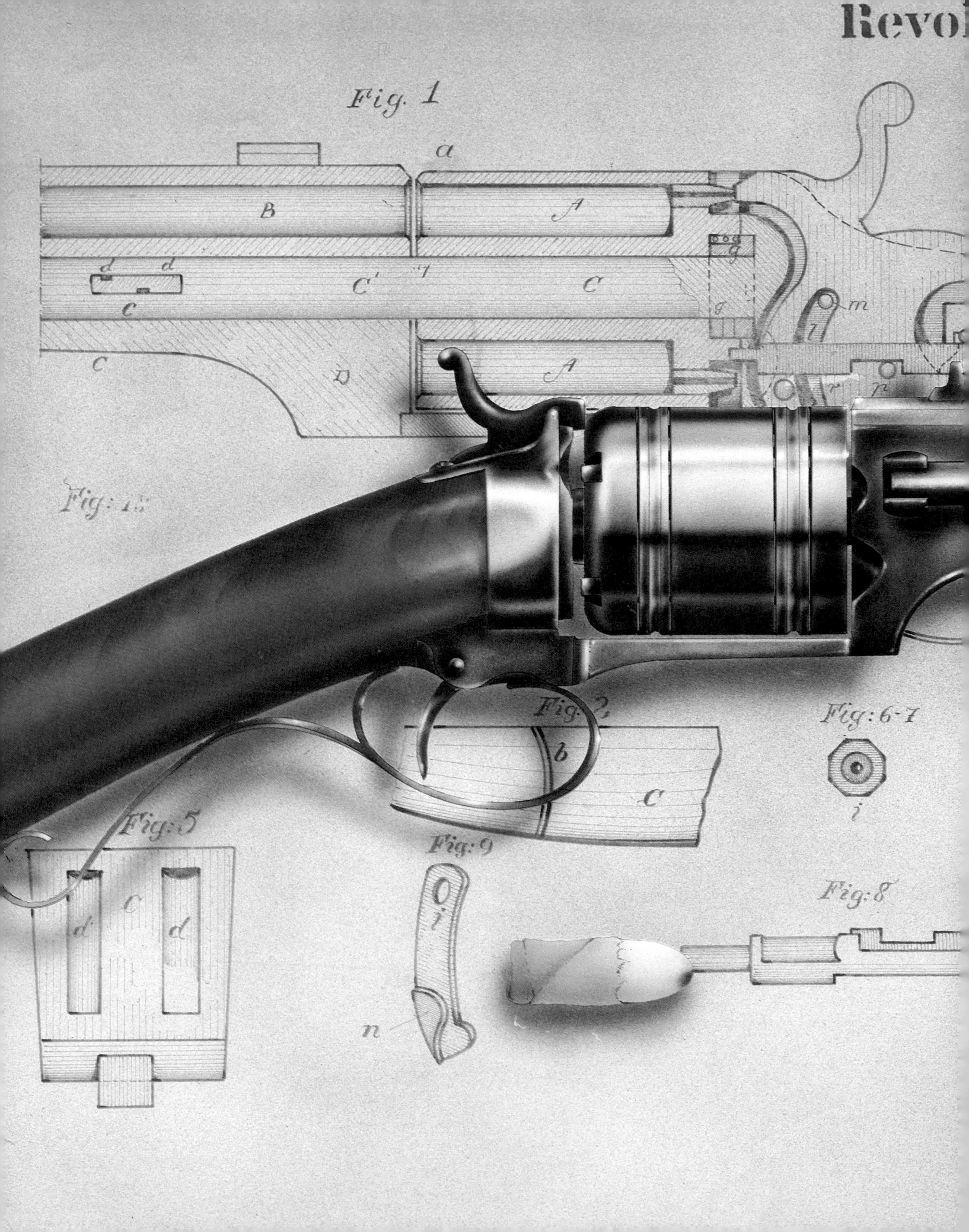

Fig. 1

a

B

A

d   *d*

C'

C

g

g

c

m

c

A

r

r'

C

D

Fig: 13

Fig: 2

b

c

Fig: 6-7

i

Fig: 5

Fig: 9

Fig: 8

d   *c*   *d*

i

n

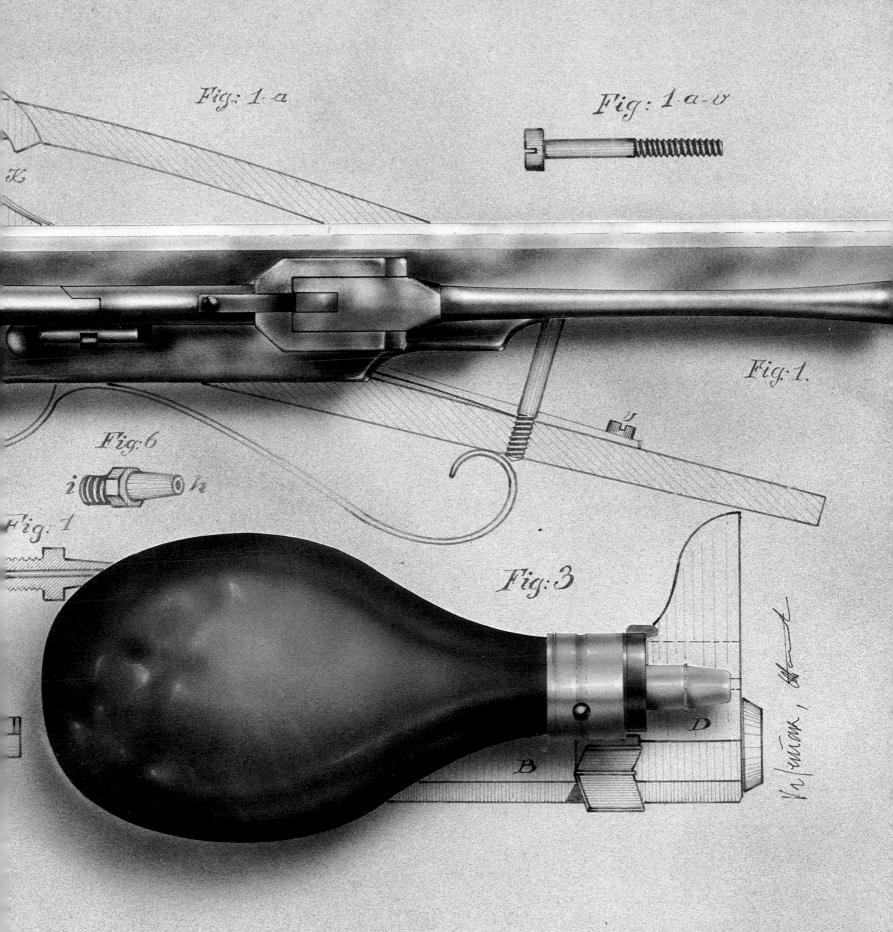

er

Patented   Aug: 29.   1839

Fig: 1·a

Fig: 1·a·v

Fig: 1.

Fig: 6

Fig: 1

Fig: 3

MAGAZINES IN THE BUTT

Spencer

Spencer, Christopher M., born 1833 in Manchester, Conn., died January 14, 1922, in Hartford, Conn. Mechanic and innovator in various fields. Spencer's most famous weapon is his repeating gun, patented in 1860, and successfully used during the Civil War (1861–1865). Worked for a time in Colt's factory, and in 1883 organized his own Spencer Arms Co. in Windsor, to manufacture rifles of his own new construction, but the whole project soon fell through.

AMERICAN SPENCER SYSTEM RIFLE	
- Calibre	13.2 mm ('52)
- Rifling	3
- Capacity	7
- Length	1,195 mm
- Length of barrel	762 mm
- Weight	4,540 gr

Gunsmiths of the late 17th and early 18th centuries sometimes placed the cartridges in the butt of their guns. Since, at that time, paper cartridges were used, such a construction only complicated the handling of the weapon. It was the appearance of the cartridge with metal case that permitted the more rational use of all magazine types.

It would seem that the American constructor, Christopher M. Spencer, from South Manchester, Connecticut, was the first to return to the idea of placing the ammunition in the butt of the gun. Like most innovators, he was very versatile, and has gone down in history also as the inventor of the first automatic lathe. Spencer built a tubular magazine, capacity 9 cartridges, 0.56 inch calibre, into the butt of a breech-block rifle. This invention was patented on March 6, 1860, under No. 27,393. But after the first tests, it became obvious that Spencer's original solution was probably more dangerous for the user than his target: due to the vibrations and recoiling of the joints in the rifle, explosions of the ammunition in the butt were not infrequent! In order to increase the space in the magazine, the

constructor was forced to reduce the calibre of the ammunition to 0.50, and the number of cartridges to 7. Thus every marksman was given special carrier with 7–10 reserve magazines, which greatly speeded up the process of loading the rifle. A new patent, No. 36,062 of July 29, 1862, was submitted to the military board. After it was tested, only the Navy ordered 10,000 Spencer rifles. Although the Civil War was an ideal opportunity for this weapon to be tried out by the Army as well, the latter took up a very wary attitude towards it. Eventually, Spencer decided to personally persuade the troops on the battlefield to buy his rifles. He made contact with the commander of the 1st Brigade Mounted Infantry, Col. John Wild, who took over and guarranteed payment for 4,000 Spencer rifles. The new repeaters proved excellent in combat, particularly in the battle of Chickamauga. This finally shook higher military circles out of their lethargy, and, by the end of the war, contracts for some 200,000 Spencer rifles and carbines had been signed. After the victory of the North, the US army continued using these carbines in the Indian wars. But their popularity did not end in the USA: France, too, urgently bought and used a certain number of Spencer's carbines in the critical stages of its war with Prussia, in 1870/71.

Technical drawing from 1879, Spencer system rifle: breech-bolt, extractor, hammer, chamber, trigger, trigger-guard lever, tubular magazine in the butt; magazine spring and follower.

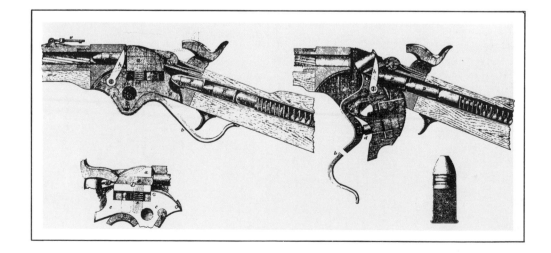

Evans
and Hotchkiss

A few years after Spencer, Warren R. Evans of Thomaston, Maine, started working on similar constructions of rifles. On December 8, 1869, and then on September 19, 1871, he patented his construction of a breech-block rifle with a four-part tubular butt-magazine which could take 24, 26 and even 34 cartridges (US Patent 199,020). However, as the ammunition was placed in the magazine in the form of an Archimedean spiral, the magazine had to be rotated at the same time as the cartridges were loaded, which called

carbines. These were tested during the Pacific crossing, and long remained the personal weapons of the sailors on the ships.

Several dozen rifles based on principles similar to those of Spencer and Evans had been patented in the USA by the end of the 19th century. The constructions of Mogerty, Meigs, Elliot, Watson and Chaffee-Reece are certainly worthy of mention. A greater commercial success than all these was enjoyed by the American, B. B. Hotchkiss with his guns

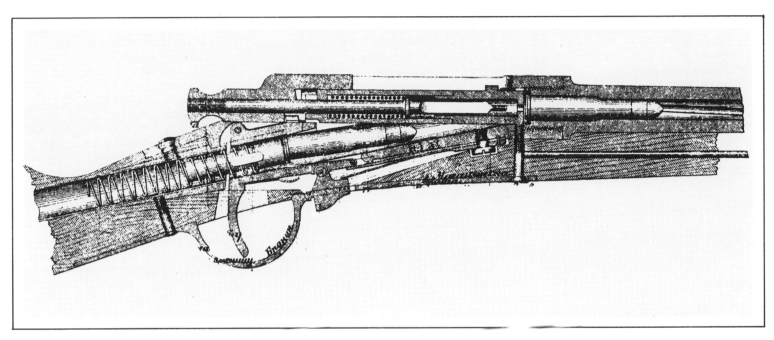

Technical drawing from 1879, Hotchkiss system rifle: barrel, chamber, cartridge, receiver, bolt, firing pin and firing pin spring, cocking piece, tubular magazine in the butt, magazine spring, follower, trigger and trigger-guard.

HOTCHKISS MAGAZINE CARBINE	
- Calibre	'450
- Rifling	?
- Capacity	5
- Length	1,120 mm
- Length of barrel	610 mm
- Weight	3,632 gr

for the use of both hands. This was probably one of the reasons that Spain, after testing Evans' weapons in 1881, abandoned the idea of introducing it in its army.

Unlike Spain, Imperial Russia had adopted a different attitude to this weapon three years earlier. The Russians probably purchased Evans' arms after their devastating experience of the Turkish Winchesters, during the Russo-Turkish War. When taking over two cruisers commissioned from the USA a few years earlier, the Russian Navy insisted that they be equipped with 2,000 Evans

invented in 1860 and 1879. In 1881, the year China had to pay an indemnity to Russia for the return of the Ili valley, the Chinese army bought 16,000 Hotchkiss rifles with a cylindrical bolt-action mechanism and five-shot butt magazine.

In the 1880s, a number of European constructors also experimented with butt magazines. As a point of interest it may be mentioned that the famous Austrian inventor, Ferdinand Ritter von Mannlicher, started his career in 1880 with the construction of a three-part tubular butt magazine.

But time would show that these solutions had no future. The placing of ammunition in the butt greatly weakened the weapon, the most endangered part being the small of the stock. Moreover, such constructions were complicated, slowing the loading of the magazine, and caused the rifle's centre of gravity to vary, depending on the number of cartridges in the magazine. The attention of the military experts thus turned increasingly to weapons with tubular magazines in the forestock.

MAGAZINE IN THE FORESTOCK

Henry

Henry, Benjamin Tyler, born March 22, 1821, in Claremont, New Hampshire, died June 8, 1898, in New Haven, Conn. Learned the gunsmith's trade with J. B. Ripley and Company in his home town, then worked for several gunsmiths and in the Springfield Armory. When O. F. Winchester organized the New Haven Arms Company, Henry was appointed works manager. Here he improved the Volcanic repeating rifle and ammunition with rim-fire as well as their production. Even today, ammunition with rim-fire produced by Winchester carries the mark "H" (Henry).

AMERICAN M. 1860 HENRY SYSTEM RIFLE

- Calibre	11.17 mm (`44)
- Rifling	6
- Capacity	15
- Length	1,105 mm
- Length of barrel	610 mm
- Weight	4,200 gr

The first contemporary tubular magazine was patented on August 21, 1849, by New Yorker Walter Hunt (US Patent 5663). However, Hunt's construction remained unnoticed because it was so complicated. The inventor would probably have had more success had he paid his weapon as much attention as he did his main invention – the sewing machine – which finally brought him world fame.

The same year, 1849, the year that saw the invention of the expanding-base bullet, his fellow townsman and factory owner, A. Arrowsmith, acquired Hunt's patent rights. It would seem that this man, a model maker by profession, was not particularly impressed by the weapon. He placed all the documents relating to it at the disposal of his employee, Lewis Jennings, who simplified Hunt's construction and patented it under his own name. Courtland C. Palmer was the first to realise the value of these constructions, as he immediately bought all rights to both Hunt's and Jennings' patents. The astute merchant naturally wished to turn his investment into profits as soon as possible. Accordingly, in 1850 he authorised the Robbins and Lawrence company to start production of 5,000 rifles of Jennings' improved construction. This is the moment when the unknown but ingenious gunsmith, Benjamin Tyler Henry,

then employed at Robbins and Lawrence's entered the story. On his own initiative he considerably improved the construction of the rifle with the tubular magazine, but with his modest means, he was not able to patent his innovation. This is why Henry was forced, on August 26, 1851, to accept the more or less profitable offer of Horace Smith, an arms-factory owner from Worcester, to sell all his rights to his innovation. Smith, now the owner of Henry's construction (US Patent 8317), invited his long-standing collaborator, Daniel B. Wesson, also an employee of Robbins and Lawrence's, to work with him on the further development of this gun. The two constructors made some more improvements on Hunt's, Jennings' and Henry's repeating rifle and registered it under the new patent No. 10,535. Certain of its commercial success, Smith and Wesson asked Palmer and Henry to join in the project. Thus, with Palmer's money and Smith and Wesson's machines and patents, a new company was founded in Norwich, with Henry as superintendent. Soon after the complete factory was moved from Norwich to New Haven and renamed the Volcanic Repeating Arms Company.

Smith and Wesson were not as successful in marketing their new arms as they had hoped to be and soon lost their enthu-

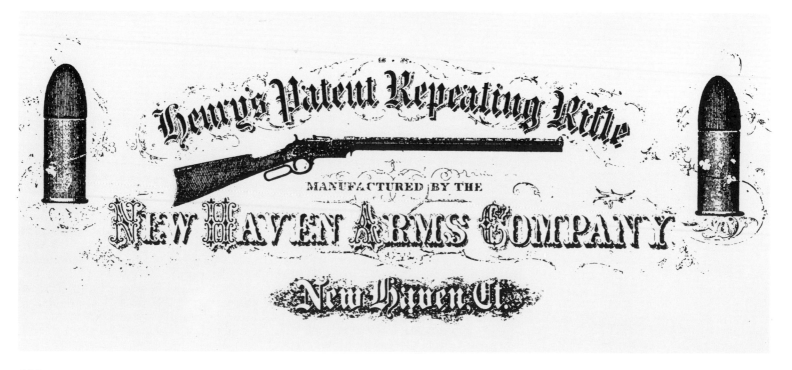

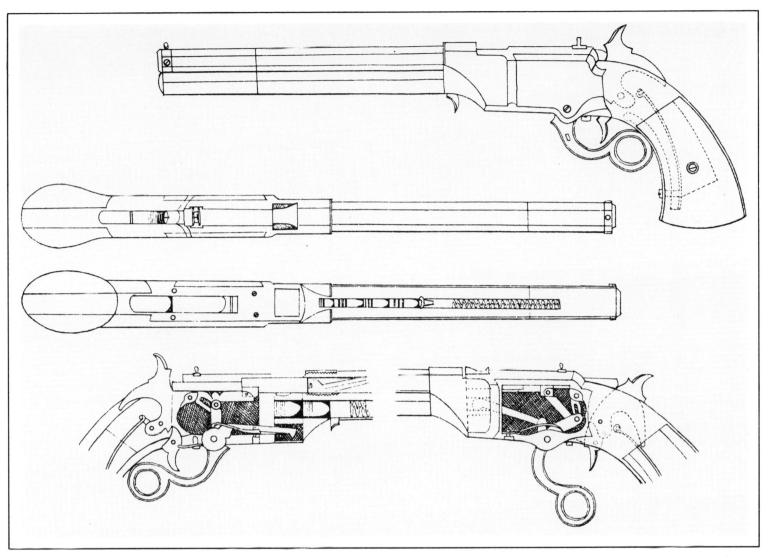

siasm for lever-action weapons with a tubular magazine. They increasingly turned their attention to revolvers and soon, leaving the Volcanic Company all rights to rifles and pistols, started independently producing cylinder weapons. Although Volcanic pistols and rifles soon won a certain reputation, they never achieved any significant degree of commercial success. For this reason the company became insolvent already in 1857 and was only saved from bankruptcy by the reorganizing of the New Haven Army Company.

From 1848 to 1855 the legendary Oliver F. Winchester famous in the firearms world, ran a shirt factory, Winchester and Davies, at 59 Court Street in New Haven. In 1855 he bought up Volcanic shares, and when it was renamed the New Haven Arms Company, he placed Benjamin Henry as its manager. The combination of the money earned from shirts, Winchester's business talent and Henry's genius was bound to give results. The first suc-

cessful step was Henry's 1858 improved rim fire cartridge. Then, on October 16, 1860, when Abraham Lincoln was running for President, the same constructor made the final version of this repeater rifle, which was finally patented under his name. Henry's rifle was a curious amalgam of a fast and safe magazine and a very fragile construction, which caused a difference of opinion among military experts. Captain J. A. Dahlgren of the Naval Board for Weapons-Testing was impressed by its speed in 1862. On the other hand, in its report of April 15, 1864, the Army board stressed its shortcomings, such as the high manufacturing costs and the complexity and fragility of a machine which was to be used by the infantry.

The Northern government bought 1731 Henry rifles between 1863 and 1865. Two regiments of Sherman's army, which took part in the Georgia campaign under General Dodge's command, were equipped with these weapons. The Confederates,

Technical drawing from 1879 of the Volcanic system pistols. The mechanism applied in the Volcanic pistols was also used for the Henry system rifle.

impressed by the firing speed of their adversaries, made up the now famous saying: "That damned Yankee rifle that can be loaded on Sunday and fired all week".

By the end of the war, the New Haven factory had turned out and sold about 10,000 Henry rifles. Apart from the Militia of the northern and southern states, the guards of the famous Wells-Fargo Company mail coaches were also armed with these guns.

Winchester

Winchester, Oliver Fisher, born November 10, 1810, in Boston, Mass., died December 10, 1880, in New Haven, Conn. Worked in carpentry and construction, then became a successful shirt-factory owner in New Haven. In 1855 ventured into the production of repeating rifles. After a less than brilliant success with the Volcanic and Henry repeating rifles, founded, in 1866, the Winchester Repeating Arms Company, turning out arms of the same name, which was to become one of the greatest and most famous gun producers in the world.

The American constructor, Nelson King, patented a new idea for loading arms (US Patent 55,012) on May 22, 1866 — the same year that Alfred Nobel invented dynamite. In the old Henry tubular magazine, located under the barrel, ammunition had to be loaded from the front side of the weapon. King introduced a closed type of magazine which was loaded from the back, through a gate in the bronze frame.

The New Haven Army Company (renamed the Winchester Repeating Arms Company in 1867), started mass-producing this improved weapon, although still with the old lever-action breech, in the musket and carbine version. The carbines had a magazine of 12 cartridge capacity, while the musket was loaded with 17 cartridges of 0.44 inch calibre. US military circles adopted as unfavourable an attitude towards the new Winchester rifle as they had previously done to the Henry. On the other hand, Europe, and even South America, proved a lot more flexible.

The first successful breakthrough of this weapon onto a foreign market was made by the famous Winchester agent, "Colonel" Thomas Emmet Addis, alias O'Connor (Brownsville, Texas). The resourceful "Colonel" closely followed the development of the situation in Mexico, where war had been raging since 1861 between Benito Juarez's troops and the Imperial regiments aided by foreign interventionists. O'Connor realized that the right moment had arrived in 1867, when the Europeans withdrew under the open threat of the USA, and Emperor Maximilian Ferdinand Joseph (brother of the Austrian Emperor Franz Joseph) continued to resist Juarez with only the loyalist troops. "Colonel" Addis contacted the Mexicans and offered President Juarez repeater arms which could greatly speed up the overthrow of the royalists. Benito Juarez wisely accepted the offer and bought 1,000 Winchester rifles with 500,000 cartridges. It is an irrefutable fact that this modern weapon speeded up the fall of the artificial empire and brought the unfortunate Habsburg emperor before the firing squad.

The French Emperor, Napoleon III, was well aware of the role played by the Winchester in the Mexican adventure, in which he himself had been embroiled since 1862. It was probably on the basis of this experience that he ordered a large quantity of these American repeater arms in the critical phase of his disastrous war with Prussia. But to no avail — this weapon was not a magic wand which could change the situation and turn the tide of events. The Winchester rifles ended up, after the French defeat, as weapons of the gendarmerie of Corsica, birthplace of Napoleon I Bonaparte.

This same rifle played a far more important role in the Russo-Turkish War in 1877/78. Turkey, which already had well developed trade relations with the American industry, bought 15,000 muskets and 5,000 carbines on November 9, 1870, and another 30,000 muskets — Winchester's M.1866, on November 19, 1871. These modern weapons turned out to be the downfall of the Russians, especially during the siege of Plevna. The Turkish infantry in fortified positions around the fortress were equipped with single-shot Henry-Martini M.1871 rifles for firing a long distances and Winchester M.1866 repeater muskets for short-range shooting. The barage of fire from the Turkish Winchesters in the battles between July 30 and September 11 killed or wounded over 30,000 Russians!

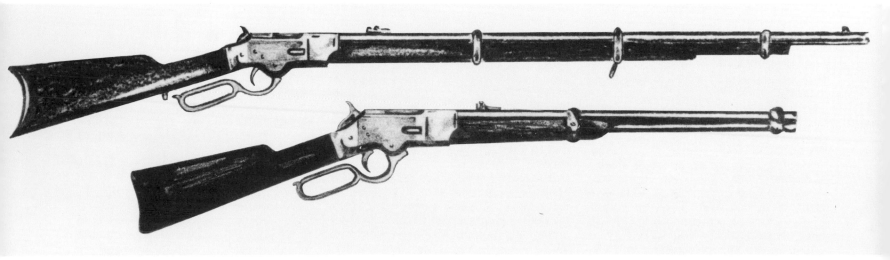

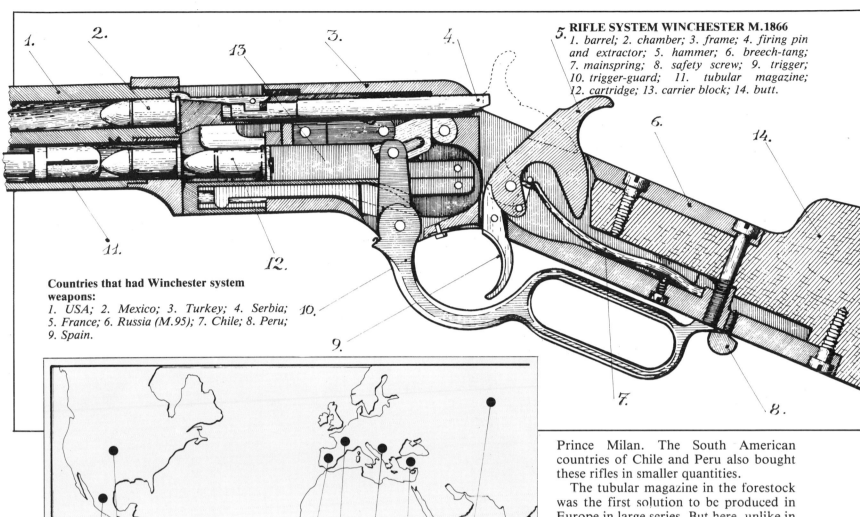

5. **RIFLE SYSTEM WINCHESTER M.1866**
1. barrel; 2. chamber; 3. frame; 4. firing pin and extractor; 5. hammer; 6. breech-tang; 7. mainspring; 8. safety screw; 9. trigger; 10. trigger-guard; 11. tubular magazine; 12. cartridge; 13. carrier block; 14. butt.

Countries that had Winchester system weapons:
1. USA; 2. Mexico; 3. Turkey; 4. Serbia; 5. France; 6. Russia (M.95); 7. Chile; 8. Peru; 9. Spain.

Prince Milan. The South American countries of Chile and Peru also bought these rifles in smaller quantities.

The tubular magazine in the forestock was the first solution to be produced in Europe in large series. But here, unlike in the USA, this magazine was mostly combined with breech-bolt action. Of the larger states, only Spain decided on the improved Winchester rifle with lever action (M.1873).

TURKISH M. 1866 WINCHESTER SYSTEM RIFLE	
- Calibre	11.17 mm ('44)
- Rifling	4
- Capacity	12
- Length	1,117 mm
- Length of barrel	685 mm
- Weight	3,870 gr

Another episode in this war demonstrates the superiority of this carbine over classical single-shot rifles. The Turkish Pasha, Reouf, was one day reconnoitring the countryside around Yeni Zara, accompanied only by his personal guard of 30 Circassians, when this small group was spotted by a Cossack regiment of 600 men, who immediately proceeded to surround them. The Circassians coolly dismounted and opened fire with their Winchesters. Within a few minutes, most of the Cossacks had been put out of action and the rest were forced to flee in a hurry!

The little Balkan state of Serbia, which during this period was still fighting the Turks, acquired 88 Winchester repeater rifles which were immediately introduced as the arms of the mounted guard of

Overleaf:
Turkish M.1866 Winchester system infantry rifle.

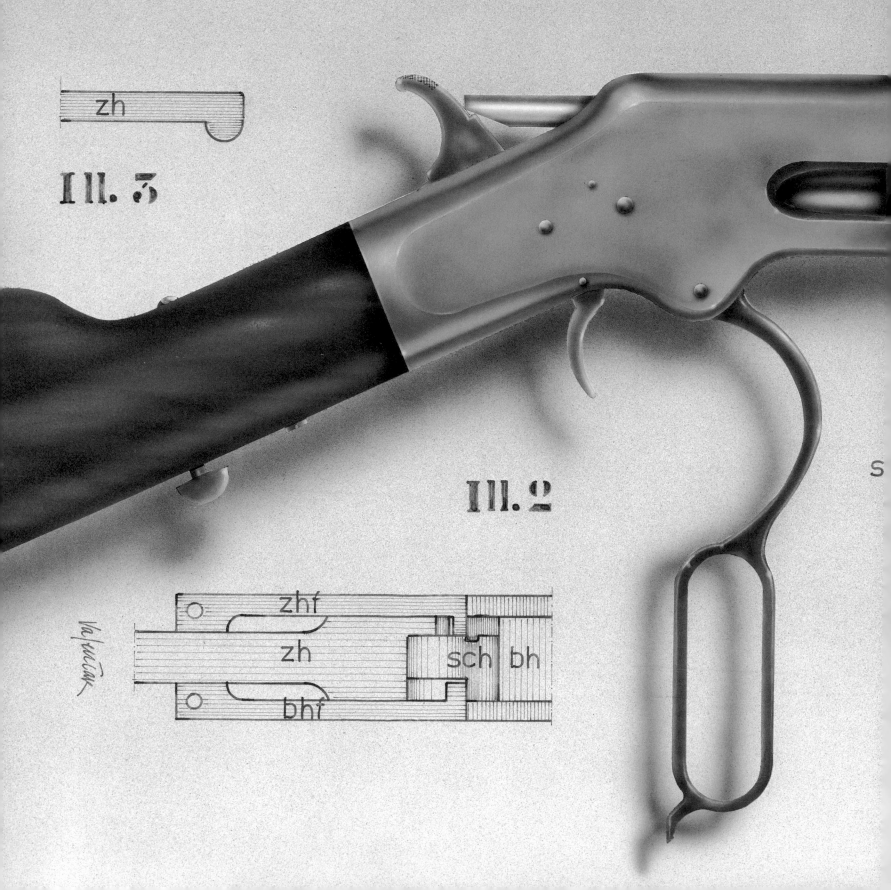

zh

Ill. 3

Ill. 2

zhf

zh

sch bh

bhf

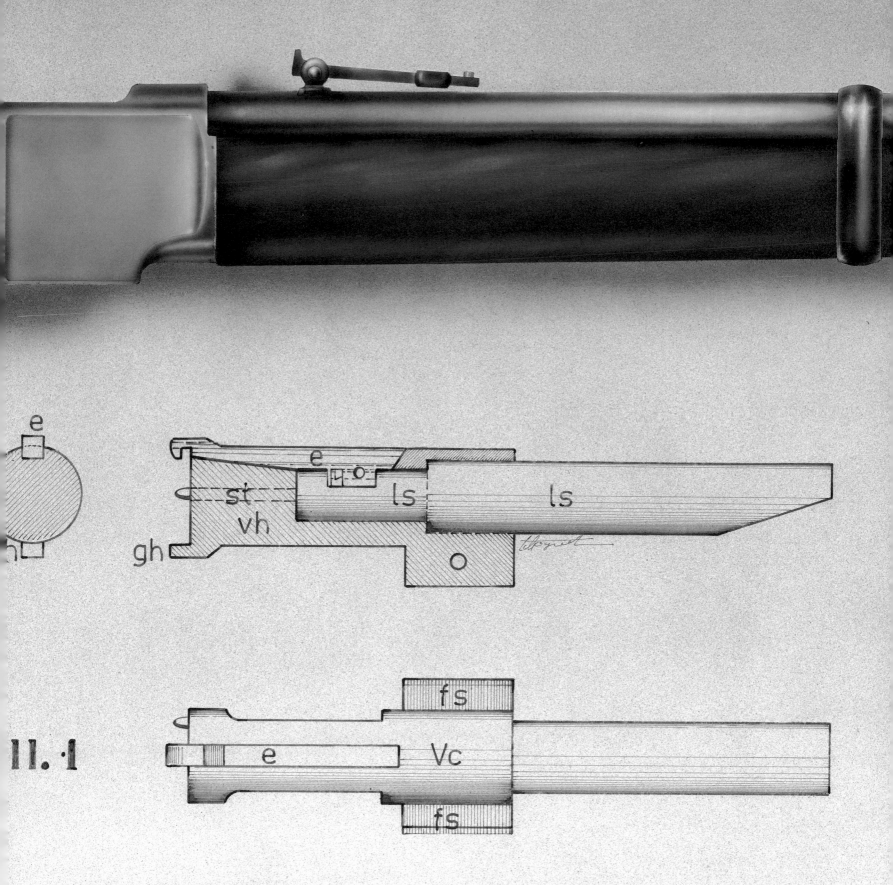

II.1

Fruhwirth

One of the first constructions in Europe of repeater arms with breech-bolt action and a tubular magazine was patented by the director of a Swiss arms factory in Neuhausen, Fridrich Vetterli. These rifles, calibre 10.4 mm (rim fire) and 13-cartridge capacity, were introduced into the Swiss infantry in 1868.

Relying on central-fire cartridges, Vetterli improved his weapons several times over the next decade. This is how the Italian Mousqueton M.1872 and Swiss rifles M.75, M.79 and M.81 originated.

The famous Austrian gunsmith, Fruhwirth, started working on a similar solution for the carbine in 1871. Bearing in mind the conservative circles, but also the financial and technical possibilities of the domestic arms industry, Fruhwirth retained the barrel and ammunition of the single-shot Werndl system carbine (M.1867, cal. 11 mm), which he combined with a tubular magazine in the forestock and a bolt-action mechanism. By imperial decree of May 23, 1872, the new weapon, of 6-cartridge capacity, was adopted for the needs of the Cisleithania gendarmerie (the gendarmerie in the Austrian part of the Empire) and the *berittene Tiroler Landesschützen* (Tyrole mounted Sharpshooters).

ČE WG

Austrian Emperor Franz Joseph reviews troops from Bosnia-Herzegovina.

Austrian M.1871 Fruhwirth system gendarmerie carbine.

AUSTRIAN M. 1872 FRUHWIRTH SYSTEM RIFLE

- Calibre .... 11 mm
- Rifling 6
- Capacity 6
- Length .... 1,037 mm
- Length of barrel .... 568 mm
- Weight .... 4,060 gr

CARBINE SYSTEM FRUHWIRTH

1. barrel; 2. chamber; 3. breech-bolt; 4. firing pin; 5. tubular magazine; 6. zubringer; 7. zubringerplate; 8. zubringer feder; 9. trigger; 10. trigger-spring; 11. trigger spring screw; 12. breech-tang; 13. screw hole.

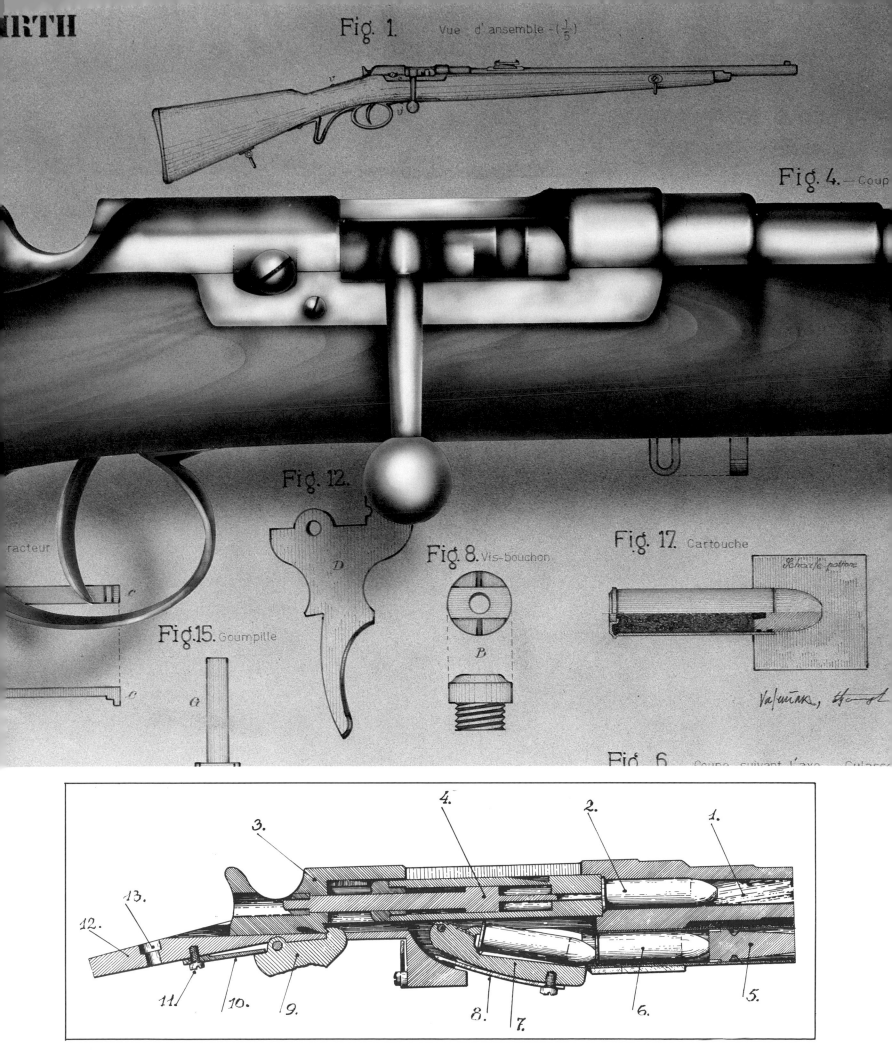

Fig. 1. Vue d'ansemble -(⅕)

Fig. 4.— Coup

Fig. 12.

racteur

Fig. 15. Goumpille

Fig. 8. Vis-bouchon

Fig. 17. Cartouche

Fig. 6. Coupe suivant l'axe Culasse

Kroppaczek and Spitalsky

Kroppaczek, Alfred, born January 30, 1839, in Blielitz, Silesia, died 1911 in Lovrana. Started his military career as a 16-year-old artillery cadet in Pest, and rose to general inspector of the Austro-Hungarian artillery in 1895. Started work on firearms as a member of the Commission for the choice of a new model for the Austro-Hungarian Army. Organized research and testing of the Gasser M.1870 revolver and together with Johann Gasser, constructed the officers' revolver. Constructed a box-magazine rifle adopted by the gendarmerie of Hungaria and Bosnia-Herzegovina, and later by the French Navy and Portuguese Army. In 1899, introduced the fast-firing cannon into the Austro-Hungarian artillery. Author of many scientific works in this field.

Two years after accepting Fruhwirth's construction, on September 24, 1874, Captain Alfred Kroppaczek registered his own construction with the Military Administrative-technical Committee of the Austrian Ministry of War.

Kroppaczek's rifle was considered to be among the best weapons with a tubular magazine in the butt, and it was certainly of a better quality than Fruhwirth's. However, the Austrian administration seemed to think that this construction belonged to the realm of fantasy and spent a full 12 years studying Kroppaczek's papers and prototypes, only to decide on taking the Mannlicher magazine rifle instead! Furthermore, in 1876/77, when the army stated its need for 150,000 new rifles, priority was again given to the Werndl single-shot rifle, although the offer of a cheap and high-quality magazine rifle lay about in the drawers of the people who made the decisions!

Only a year later, the French Navy decided on introducing rifles with Kroppaczek's magazine solution (7-cartridge capacity) and a Gras M.71 system breech. The French navy weapon, designated M.1878, was improved over the next four

Experimental M.1879 Spitalsky system rifle.

Technical drawings from 1879, Spitalsky system rifle.

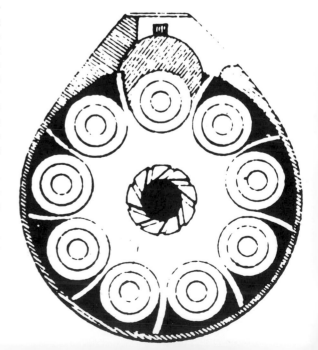

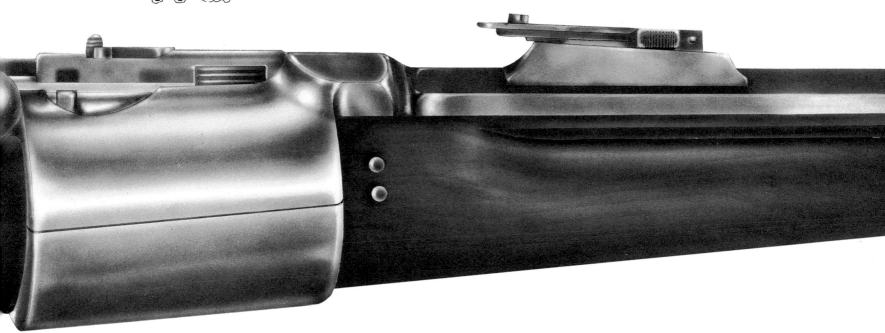

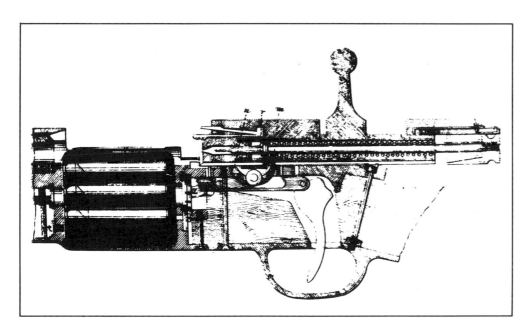

AUSTRIAN M. 1881 KROPPACZEK SYSTEM RIFLE	
- Calibre	11 mm
- Rifling	6
- Capacity	10
- Length	1,044 mm
- Length of barrel	560 mm
- Weight	3,350 gr

24 French Chasseur Batallions had been given 100 M.74/82 rifles.

As for the Austro-Hungarian Empire, it would seem that Budapest was a good deal more imaginative than Vienna. On March 17, 1882, the Hungarian Ministry of Internal Affairs, acting on the opinion of the Department of National Defence (of June 19, 1881), decided to arm the Hungarian and Bosnian-Herzegovinian gendarmeries with Kroppaczek carbines. It was not until a decade later, on October 28, 1893, that the Austrian Imperial Navy introduced the same weapon for sailors on torpedo-boats.

Nevertheless, Austria was aware of the faults of the tubular magazine, and such weapons were therefore given exclusively to auxiliary troops. Before the construction of the box magazine, Vienna had tried to find some better replacement for the tubular mechanism. In the third quarter of the 19th century, experiments were started with the combination of a bolt-action mechanism and revolving magazine. Such a construction, with the ballistic characteristics of the Werndl rifle, was offered the Austrian army by Spitalsky, the manager of the famous factory at Steyr. The subsequent constructions of Kroppaczek, Kromar and Schulhof were based on a similar principle.

years, after which it gave excellent results. By the end of 1884, the factories at Chatellerault and Saint Etienne had produced 6,000 of these improved Kroppaczek rifles, subsequently designates M.74/82. Of this number, 3,000 rifles were immediately dispatched to the 1st, 2nd and 3rd Zouave Regiments in Tonkin (China), and the rest was sent to the Artillery Depot of the Tonkin Expeditionary Corps. By the end of the same year, each of the

Mauser

In Germany, famed for its exceptional weapon construction, conservative resistance to repeater rifles was greater than in both Austria and France. It was precisely the rivalry with neighbouring France that finally forced Berlin circles to modify their unfavourable attitude. Peter Paul Mauser, from Obrndorf am Neckar, was among the first to make use of the changing climate. Mauser based his work on repeaters on the excellent Serbian Mauser-Koka M.1880 single-shot rifle. This weapon incorporated a classical Mauser breech M.71, was of smaller calibre (10.5 mm) and had wedge-shaped grooves, designed by the Serbian Major Koka Milovanović. Peter Paul built a tubular magazine into the forestock of the Serbian version of this rifle and patented this construction on March 16, 1881 (DRP 15,202). But since the first version

In its final version, the Mauser M.1871/84 rifle was of 11 mm calibre, and took 10 cartridges.

The M.1887, calibre 9.5 mm, which Mauser made specially for Turkey, was based on the same principle. The breech of this weapon, with two additional teeth, was somewhat superior to the German prototype.

Peter Paul Mauser made his first contract with the Porte already in 1886. Negotiations conducted in Constantinople were successfully concluded on February 10, 1887, and five days later Mauser headed back to Germany. He carried with him a very favourable contract relating to the Turkish order of 500,000 rifles and 50,000 M.1887 carbines. The agreed price was 362 piasters per rifle (c. 68.8 RM). Turkey accepted the complete consignment of infantry arms, but took three

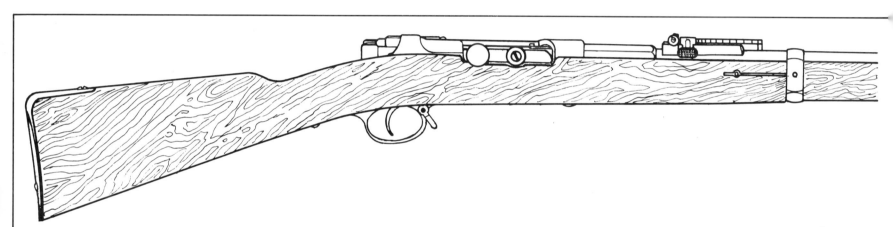

did not prove particularly successful, Mauser produced another, of far better quality, the following year. At about this time Emperor Wilhelm II became personally interested in the work going on to improve magazine weapons, and this served to speed things up. Already in 1882, 2,000 experimental C.82 rifles, distributed among the soldiers of four garrison batallions, were in the process of being tested. In practice, it turned out that the ammunition used, M.71, showed most defects. The pressure of the ogival nose of the old cartridge on the powder charge, which resulted from the sequence-loading of ammunition, frequently caused explosions in the magazine itself. But after the introduction of the new M.71/84 cartridge, with a flattened bullet and certain alteration to the weapon itself, the new rifle was adopted by the German Army in January 1884, the same year that Hiram Maxim invented the recoil-operated gun.

M.1871/84 Mauser system rifle.

years over the receipt of the cavalry weapons. By 1890, two years after Turkey granted Germany the concession to build a railroad to Ankara, only 4,000 carbines had reached Instanbul, the remaining 46,000 being refused by the Porte on the grounds that it had opted for a more modern system in the meantime!

During 1884 Serbia ordered from Mauser 4,000 cavalry and 4,000 M.1884 artillery carbines of 10.15 mm calibre. The capacity of the cavalry carbine was 5 + 2, that of the artillery 6 + 2 cartridges. These weapons cost 78 – 87 dinars at the time (1 dinar = 1 French franc).

Lebel

The last significant weapon with a tubular magazine, produced in 1886, caused considerable confusion in Europe, particularly in Germany. The French chemist, M. Vieille, perfected the so-called smokeless "B" gunpowder in the same year, though, in fact, this type of powder had been known in Europe since the 1850s. Moreover, Germany had started producing the "RCP" powder (Rottweiler Chemisches Pulver) two years before Vieille's "invention". In France, however, the "B" powder was viewed primarily from the political aspect — it was a ray of hope for irredentist circles that a weapon might soon be produced with which to regain the territories lost in the war with Germany 1870/71. The French Minister of War, Boulanger, author of the slogan "Smokeless gunpowder — revenge for Alsace-Lorraine", demanded, in the general enthusiasm, that a new weapon suited to this type of powder be produced in as short time as possible. Thus the Lebel M.1886 rifle was constructed in only two months, without any previous studies.

It is true that the new weapon, calibre 8 mm, had a flatter trajectory path of the bullet and a great initial speed, but it also had a number of weakness which would only come to light during actual use.

This was, at the same time, the swan song of tubular magazines. The placing of ammunition in the forestock moved the weapon's centre of gravity forward and thus tired the shooter. The loading of such a gun was rather slow, and the ammunition was frequently deformed by the pressure of one bullet on the cartridge of the next and even occasionally exploded. Finally, some considerably superior systems appeared on the scene.

Lebel, Nicolas, born August 18, 1838, died June 6, 1891, in Vitré. French army officer. Appointed (1876) commander of the Sharpshooters' School in du Kuchard, where he started constructing infantry arms, particularly cartridges. Later was appointed commanding officer of the Sharpshooters' School at Chalons, where he tested the new "small-bore" M.1886 rifle bearing his name.

French seamen exercising, end of 19th century.

FRENCH M. 1886 LEBEL SYSTEM RIFLE	
- Calibre	8 mm
- Rifling	4
- Capacity	8
- Length	1,303 mm
- Length of barrel	798 mm
- Weight	4,245 gr

French M. 1886 Lebel system rifle.

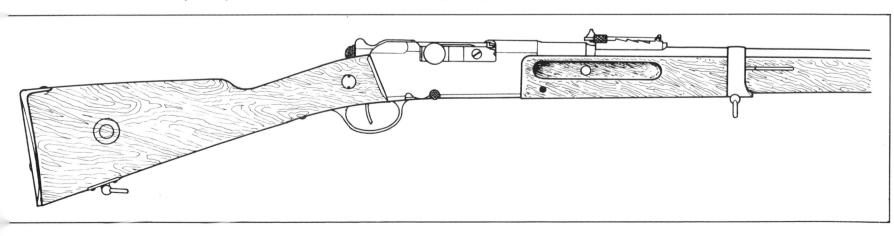

ARMS WITH BOX MAGAZINES

Mannlicher

Mannlicher, Ferdinand, born January 30, 1848, in Nort, Bohemia, died January 30, 1904, in Vienna. After completing engineering studies in Vienna, worked as a designer for the Austrian railroad corporation. After visiting the World Exhibition in Philadelphia, turned to the construction of repeating rifles. In 1886, Austria-Hungary introduced the Mannlicher rifle as standard arms, a status it retained (in several variations) until the break-up of the Empire in 1918. His rifles were also used in Bulgaria, Romania, Czechoslovakia, Yugoslavia, etc. Also constructed semi-automatic (self-loading) weapons, and had most success with his 1900 pistol, adopted in Argentina.

Apart from their tactical-technical shortcomings, all the types of magazine mentioned also had the disadvantage that they markedly raised the cost of production. In the large world armies, the replacement of single-shot rifles by repeaters called for a huge expenditure that few countries were able to support.

This prompted the idea of simply adding the existing weapons a new mechanism which would increase the speed of laoding. Thus, a number of disassembling magazines, known as *Schnelladers* (fast loaders) appeared.

These were simple metal, leather or even cardboard boxes, square or horseshoe shaped, and could be easily affixed to the breech area. The ammunition was raised from them by means of a spring, usually "W" shaped.

A number of well-known names tried their hands at the construction of the *Schnelladers*, such as Karel Krnka, Josef Werndl, M. Lindner, Fosbery, Mannlicher, Mauser and Ludwig Löwe. During 1880/81, the Serbian Major Koka Milovanović also came out with two different types of additional magazines. His solutions, constructed for accelerating the loading of the Mauser M.71, Berdan II M.71, Gras M.74 and Mauser-Koka M.80 weapons, were patented in Germany, France, Austria and Italy.

It soon became obvious, however, even to laymen, that this partial solution could not satisfy the needs of modern armies. The only good side of the idea was that it finally turned the experts' attention to the correct positioning of the magazine – the central part of the butt, in the breech area.

The ideal solution for the box magazine placed in the butt, one which with minor adjustments is in use to this very day, was patented by the American gunsmith, James P. Lee of Illion, New York, on November 4, 1879. Three years after his first patent, Lee's magazine was accepted in the USA for application to military weapons.

In Europe, Lee's mechanism brought about a strange turn of events. Namely, a number of constructors set about improving, further developing and also copying it. Thus the clear distinction between original, authentic constructions and outright copies was lost, leading to many patent disputes.

Ferdinand Ritter von Mannlicher, started work on the so-called box magazines as early as 1881. His construction was based on the improved Lee system, of which there will be further mention in the following chapter. After lengthy experimentation with this idea and the introduc-

57. MANNLICHER SYSTEM RIFLE M.1895
1. barrel; 2. chamber; 3. receiver; 4. firing pin spring; 5. firing pin; 6. locking lug; 7. schlagbolzenmutter; 8. abzughebel; 9. grenzstollen; 10. trigger; 11. trigger-guard; 12. magazinhalter; 13. zubringerhebel; 14. forestock; 15. bolt handle.

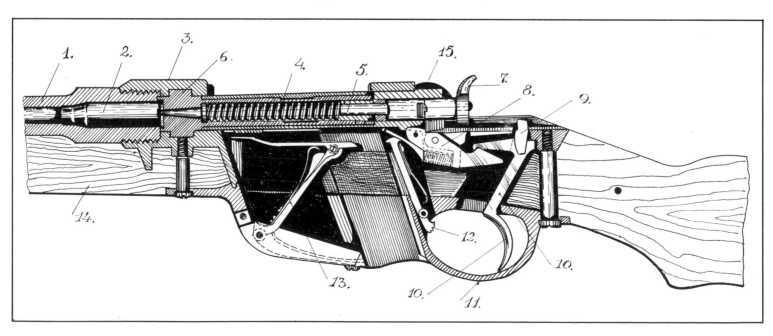

AUSTRIAN M. 1886 MANNLICHER SYSTEM RIFLE

- Calibre .... 11 mm
- Rifling 6
- Capacity 5
- Length .... 1,320 mm
- Length of barrel .... 808 mm
- Weight .... 4,530 gr

tion of the bolt-action breech, Mannlicher offered his new weapon to the Austrian army for inspection. Following the testing of the prototypes in two Czech infantry corps, Mannlicher's rifle was approved by imperial degree on January 27, 1887, for the Austrian Imperial Army. The gun, given the official designation M.1886, was constructed for Werndl 11 mm ammunition. The Austrian M.1886, in fact, inaugurated the new era of weapons with box magazines.

At about the same time, the French Lebel rifle appeared on the European scene, causing confusion with its small 8 mm calibre and use of smokeless gunpowder. Austria was the first to react to the challenge. In 1888, at a time of tension in Franco-Italian relations, Austria ceased production of the M.86 weapons (by which time 96,000 rifles had been made) and introduced a new one, the M.1888, with classic Mannlicher elements, but a more modern, smaller 8 mm calibre. Very soon Vienna was to turn also to the production and use of ammunition with smokeless gunpowder with the M.1890 rifle.

Familiar with the development of the situation in Austria, but most afraid of the French rifle, Germany made desperate efforts not to be left behind in the arms race.

Overleaf:
M.1886 Mannlicher system rifle with detail of barrel and M.1886 bayonet.

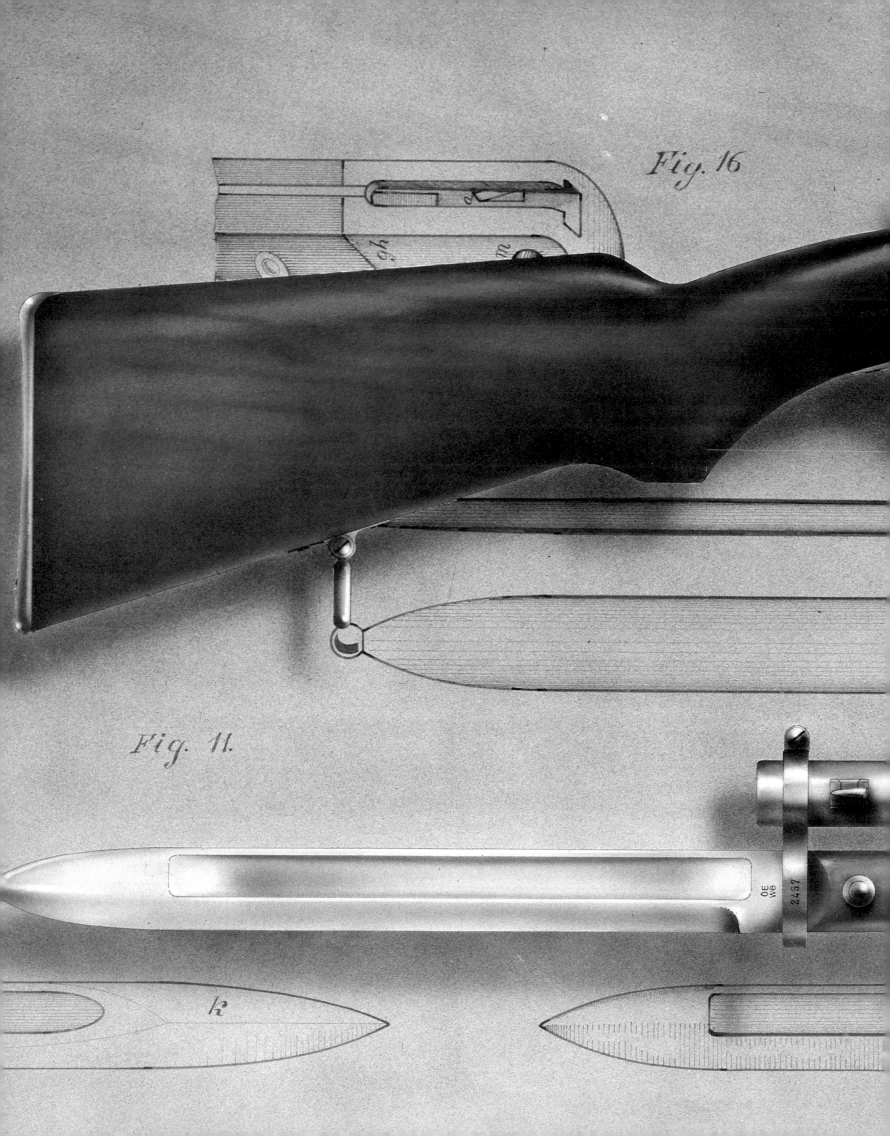

Fig. 16

Fig. 11.

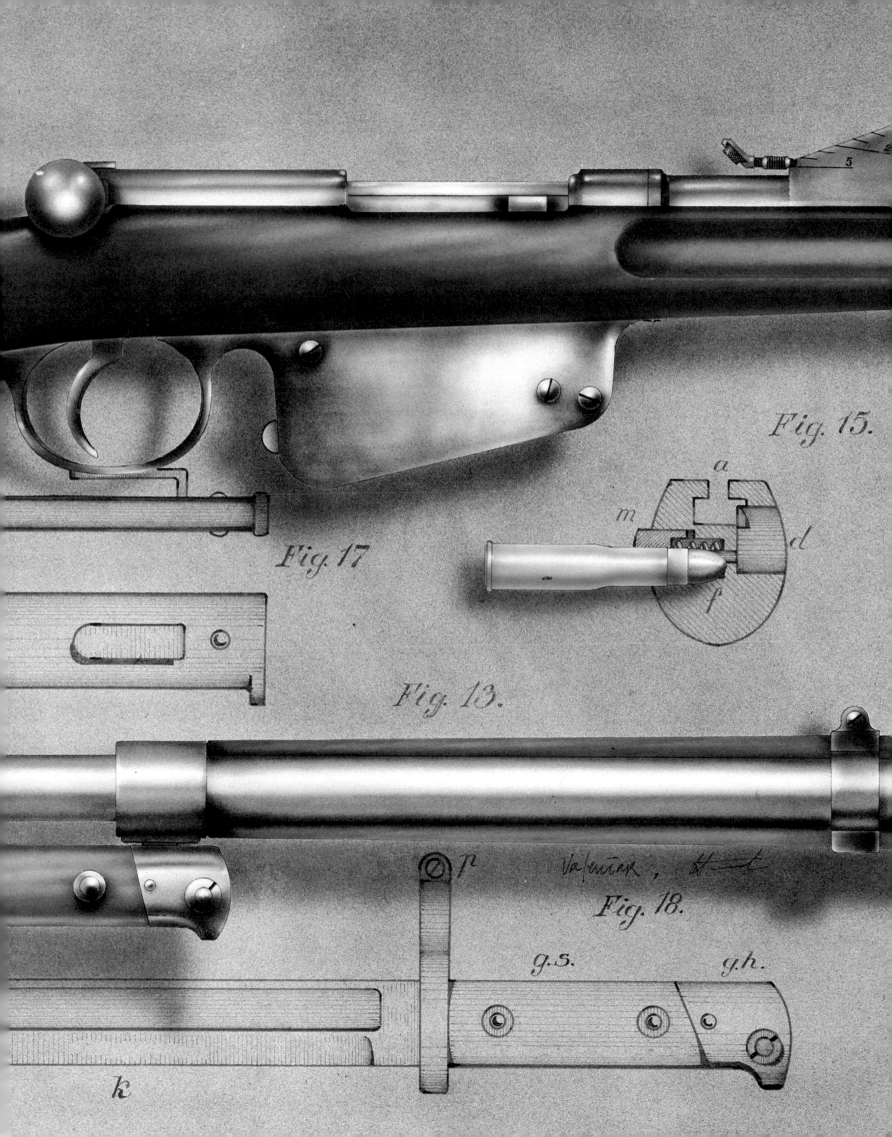

Fig. 15.

a

m

d

f

Fig. 17

Fig. 13.

Valencia,

Fig. 18.

g.s.

g.h.

k

Kommiss rifle, Mauser M.89

The *Gewehr-Prüfungs-Kommission* (weapons testing board) rejected the suggested alternative, that existing M.71/84 weapons should be adapted for use with the new ammunition and decided that work should start immediately on a new rifle which could be a fitting answer to the Lebel. Mauser's bolt-action breech was kept as the basic construction, its development being left to Louis Schlegelmilch, the Spandau Arsenal technician. The relentless political pressure on the board and constructor resulted in the time period granted for work on the new rifle being shortened beyong reason. The result was a strange conglomerate of contemporary European constructions: a hybrid rifle. Besides Mauser's breech, this gun also incorporated a Mannlicher-type magazine, Lebel's construction of the barrel and a barrel jacket of Armand Mieg's construction! The introduction of such weapons into the German Army created a real scandal. In addition to this, German Anti-Semitic circles also added to the rifle's poor reputation by naming it *Juden-flint*. The culmination, however, was the reaction of Mannlicher and Mieg, who demanded protection of their rights. When Prussia ordered 300,000 Kommiss rifles from Steyr in Octobre 1889, the Austrian government halted all work, demanding compensation for the violation of a patent-protected magazine designed by its compatriot, F. Mannlicher. Hearing of this international affair, Mauser commented resignedly, that it was in fact the ÖEWG (Austrian Arms Factory) taking its tribute. At the same time as Mannlicher, Armand Mieg also demanded a compensation of 300,000 RM for the unpermitted exploitation of his patent from 1887. In order to hush up the affair, the Prussian government tried to pacify the constructor with a "bonus" of 50,000 RM. As this sum was nowhere near enough, the dispute dragged on at length.

Regardless of all these problems, the M.88 rifle was retained in some units of the German Army until the very end of World War I. Ludwig Löwe, one of the producers of the Kommiss rifle, even managed to make a deal for the delivery of 350,000 M.1888 rifles to China!

Since Mauser had not been directly involved in the work on the "scandalous" rifle, he was not caused much trouble by this affair. This does not, however, mean that his activities passed without friction. Parallelly, and completcly independently of the GPK (weapons testing board) in Spandau, Mauser worked in his factory in Oberndorf on his own construction of a box magazine rifle. The first prototype of the new weapon, patented on April 18, 1888 (DRP 45,561), left the board in Spandau indifferent, while experts in Belgium and Great Britain voiced a number of criticisms of it. But this did not dishearten or sway the determined German. The development department of Mauser's factory, managed by Fidel Fi-

German colonial troops, beginning of 20th century.

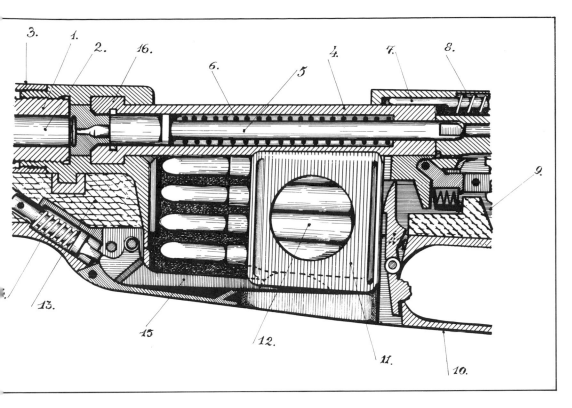

GERMAN RIFLE M.1888
1. barrel; 2. chamber; 3. barrel jacket; 4. breech-bolt; 5. firing pin; 6. firing pin spring; 7. extractor; 8. extractor pin; 9. trigger; 10. trigger-guard; 11. clip; 12. cartridges; 13. forestock; 14. zubringerhebel und zubringerfeder; 15. zubringerplate; 16. locking lug.

GERMAN "KOMMISS" RIFLE M. 1888	
- Calibre	8 mm
- Rifling	4
- Capacity	5
- Length	1,245 mm
- Length of barrel	740 mm
- Weight	3,850 gr

derle, removed all the main defects of this rifle by the autumn of 1889. The improved version appeared on September 11, 1889, the very next year, but too late to compete in Germany. This weapon was, however, immediately adopted by the Belgian Army, under the designation Mle. 1889. It must be said that the success of Mauser's rifle on the foreign market owed much to the dust raised by the Kommiss rifle. Turkish officers staying in Germany in order to collect the M.87 weapons at once informed Instanbul of the orientation of the local army to rifles with box magazines. The Porte showed itself ready to follow this technical innovation as well, and purchase a large consignment of the new German arms. But the distrustful Turkish Sultan, Abdul Hamid II, had followed the whole affair in Europe through his officers and confidants. When news reached him of the technical failings of the M.1888 (ammunition explosions in the chamber and magazine), it was logical for Turkey to choose once again a purely Mauser construction from 1889 (designated by the Porte as M.1890, cal. 7.65 mm).

But it was precisely this gun, which laid the foundations for Mauser's monopoly over half the world, that brought its author his first troubles. James Lee had protected his patent in Germany as early as September 11, 1879 (DRP 9,637). After a public demonstration of the weapon in Bruxelles, Lee came to the conclusion that a magazine of his construction had been used on the rifle. Consequently, he filed a suit against Mauser's factory for the protection of his patent rights with the State Court in Rottweil. The court commission, made up of the engineer Prof. Ernst and Major D. Lehr, after giving their expert opinion, rejected Lee's charge as unfounded. If we presume that the commission was quite impartial, the question still remains of the great similarity between Lee's and Mauser's constructions. To make the whole business even more intriguing, A. Hatch, in his book "Remington Arms in American History", recounts a rather obscure story. According to Hatch, James Lee, then the employee of Remington and Sons, frequently took sketches and drawings with him after working hours to the Osgood Hotel in which he lived. The industrious constructor wished to work on his patents in the quiet of his room. But in the same hotel, in the room above Lee's lived a certain Remington factory mechanic. Hatch calls this man cimply Mauser, but it is obvious that he was speaking of Franz Mauser, brother of the far more famous Wilhelm and Peter Paul. Thus far the actors and locations of events correspond to the historical facts. But the story then begins to contain elements of an improbable crime story. Namely, the diligent Franz was supposed to have drilled a small hole in the floor of his room and, lying down, to have spied on Lee's overtime work!

It is difficult to believe that the fame of the best-known rifle of the world is due to a hole in the ceiling, but the fact of the similarity of the two patents remains unexplained.

Mauser's rifles, either in their original form or made under licence, were adopted in over 30 countries of the world. The only more serious competition to the German dynasty was Ferdinand Ritter von Mannlicher, who also achieved significant success on the market.

Overleaf:
German M.1888 Kommiss rifle with detail of S.1871 bayonet.

203

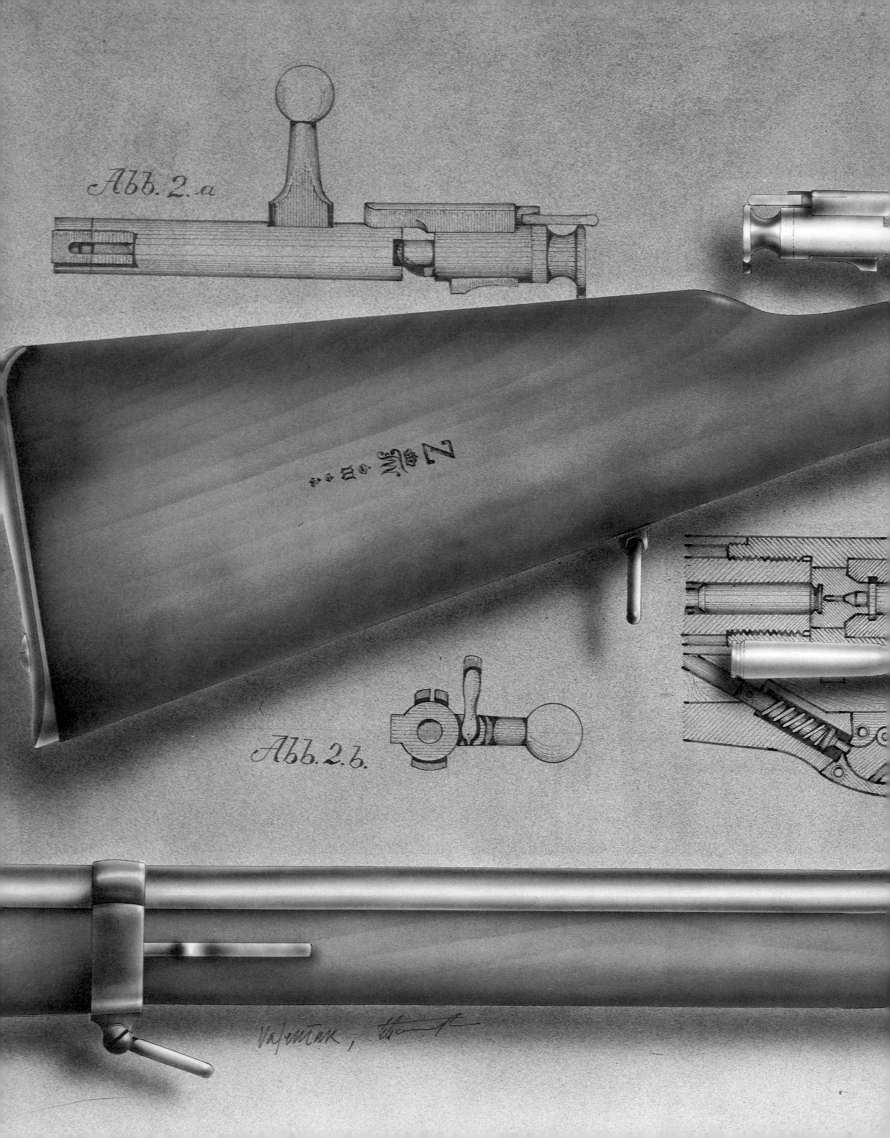

Abb. 2. a

Abb. 2. b

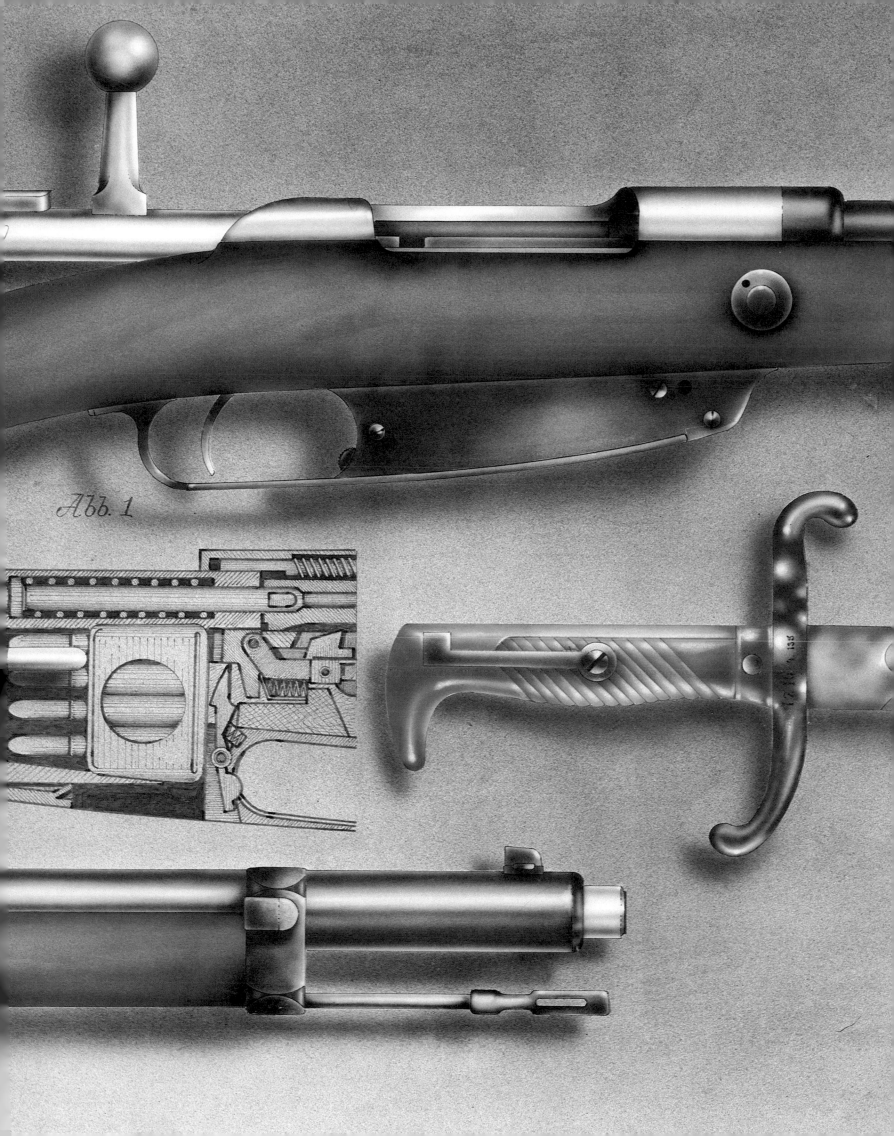

Abb. 1

SELF-LOADING PISTOLS

Introduction

At a time when constructors had brought the repeating rifle practically to perfection, a new field of work opened up in front of them. Technology and industry had reached such a high level by the mid 19th century that the path lay open for automatic weapons. The first real success of this field was attained in 1854 by the famous metallurgist and constructor Henry Bessemer in his work on artillery weapons.

The basic principle of the automation of arms was that the power of the powder gasses could be used for the ejection of the cartridges, opening of the breech, introduction of a new bullet into the barrel and cocking of the firing pin or trigger. At a time when ammunition was filled with black powder and lead shot, these principles were only applicable to massive artillery weapons.

The first and decisive step which laid the foundations of the basic principles of light automatic weapons was taken in 1885 by Hiram Maxim. His machine-gun, based on the short recoil of the barrel, still used the black powder ammunition of the Henry-Martini rifle (cal. 450-577). The gunsmith Plesner had started work on the self-loading pistol as early as in 1872. His American colleague, Lutze, patented his prototype, based on the forward recoil of the barrel, two years later. The first credible model of a pistol with a cylindrical breech dates from 1892. This weapon, based on Maxim's experience, was designed by the Austrian Schönberger, and produced for the civilian market by the factory in Steyr. The following year, 1892, two Frenchmen, the Clair brothers, completed work on their pistol with stiff looking, intended for revolver ammunition M.92 (cal. 8 mm). At the same time, Schwarzlose's pistol, based on the long recoil of the barrel, also appeared on the market.

By this time, Ferdinand Ritter von Mannlicher had become world famous for his repeater rifles. The restless spirit of this man of genius could not resist the new challenge: he decided to try his hand in the field of automatic weapons. Mannlicher's first self-loading pistol models, dating from 1893/94, were a curious synthesis of pistol and revolver elements. Through inertia, the barrel jerked for-

Experimental M.1894 Mannlicher system pistol.

wards, thereby ejecting the cartridge and bringing the next bullet into position. But the marksman still had to pull the trigger for each shot! Developing his ideas further, Mannlicher also experimented with a steady barrel and moving breech, a solution which was certainly much superior to those of 1893. Thus several good pistols were made and offered to European armies for testing. But so strong was the competition on the market that these weapons were not accepted even in their homeland – Austria. Only Argentina decided to buy 5,000 Mannlicher M.1901 pistols for the needs of its army.

1893 was significant as the year that finally secured the pistol's rightful place in the family of light arms. But however much Schwarzlose, the Clair brothers, Mannlicher and many others contributed to the development of the pistol from the purely technical aspect, it acquired its position and wide popularity primarily thanks to Borchardt.

Borchardt, Luger

Luger, Georg, born 1849 in Steinach, Austrian Tyrol, died 1923 in Berlin. Entered the Austrian Army as a cadet. In 1868 promoted to Lieutenant, and in 1872 left the army and married. About 1875, together with Ferdinand Mannlicher, constructed a magazine for Werndl's M.1873 rifle. Continued working on repeating and self-loading rifles until 1895 and travelled twice to the U.S.A. (1886 and 1890). In 1891 moved to Ludwig Loewe and Companie, and in 1897 to the newly formed *Deutsche Waffen- und Munitionsfabriken (DWM)*. Here, amongst other things, he improved Borchardt's self-loading pistol which as the Parabellum (in Europe) or Luger (in the U.S.A.), became one of the most widespread and famous pistols of all times.

Hugo Borchardt, a German by birth, worked for many years in the USA, in the Winchester Repeating Arms Company. Having acquired valuable experience, he returned to Europe, where he first took a job in a Hungarian arms factory in Budapest. But Borchardt was to become famous only with the work he carried out in the famous German DWM factory (German Arms and Ammunition Factory). In 1893, he patented in Germany his first self-loading pistol which used the newly designed ammunition and was based on the short recoil of the barrel and breech. Curious as this may seem to us today, the main innovation with regard to this ammunition was that the cartridge, instead of the previous expanding base, now ended with a rim groove. Such a solution significantly facilitated the automatic ejection of the cartridge and the bringing of the next bullet into position. Borchardt's M.1903 pistol, of 7.65 mm calibre and 8 cartridge capacity, was the first weapon of this kind on general sale. It may be assumed that about 3,000 Borchardt pistols were produced between 1893 and 1899, which was considered an outstanding commercial success! But the same weapon was also the basis on which the famous Pistole 08 was created, for commercial reasons also called the "war pistol" (Parabellum).

During the last decade of the 19th century, a young and talented engineer called Georg Luger also worked in the DWM. Closely following the production of the M.1893 pistol, Luger had the chance of getting to know its faults and advantages. It was on the basis of this experience that Luger decided to create a far more func-

German artillery in action. World War I.

Countries that introduced Luger pistols into their arsenals:
1. Germany, 2. Brasil; 3. Bulgaria; 4. China; 5. Finland; 6. Iran; 7. Luxembourg; 8. Norway; 9. Netherlands; 10. Portugal; 11.Switzerland; 12. Turkey.

DIE LANGE PISTOLE 08 PARABELLUM
- Calibre .... 9 mm
- Rifling 6
- Capacity .... 8 (box) / 32 (drum)
- Length .... 324 mm
- Length of barrel .. 190 mm
- Weight .... 1,050 gr

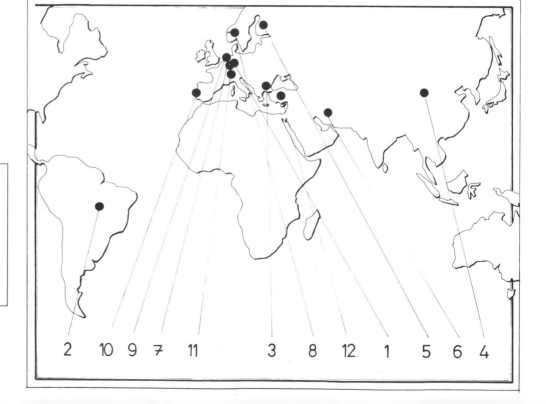

tional and up-to-date pistol by improving this weapon. This resulted in the Borchardt-Luger pistol, which over the next 50 years was to appear in more than 35 versions!

Luger's original solution for the new pistol first entered the scene at the turn of the century. The DWM factory immediately submitted the pistol to the Weapons Testing Board which was deciding at the time on a new hand weapon for the German Army. During testing and comparison with other pistols, the board received the news that Switzerland had already adopted the M.1901 Luger for its forces. Three years later, on April 1, 1904, the German Navy also gave Luger's weapon a favourable assessment and on December 12 signed the first contract with the DWM for the delivery of 8,000 pistols (P.04).

It would seem that the Army was right in delaying its final decision on a pistol. The Parabellum 04, used by the inverventionist forces in South Africa, turned out to have some faults, mostly in the safety system. It was only after these were corrected, and on the imperial recommendation (August 22), that the Ministry of War adopted the Luger P.08 for the whole German Army, on August 31, 1908.

The long Parabellum with a holster that could be used as a butt when necessary (the large 08), was introduced for the field artillery, reserve and auxilliary troops and the staff of mail stations. A special 32--cartridge magazine, the so-called Trommelmagazin (TM.1917) was produced in 1916 for this weapon. The combination of the holster-butt and the new drum magazine turned this deadly weapon into a real automatic.

PISTOL SYSTEM BORCHARDT
1. front sight; 2. barrel; 3. receiver; 4. chamber; 5. firing pin; 6. kniegelenk-verschluss; 7. mainspring; 8. mainspring housing; 9. stock; 10. magazine; 11. trigger; 12. trigger-guard.

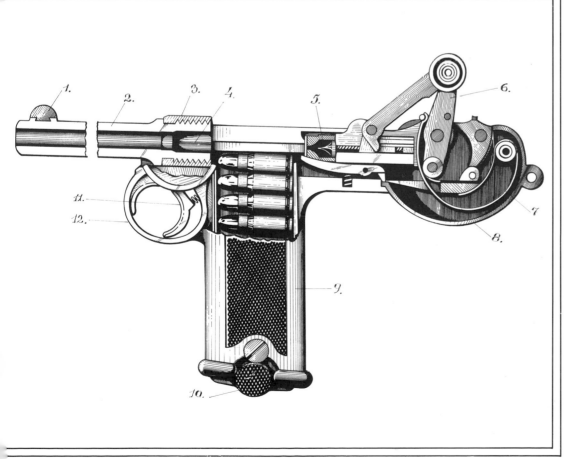

Overleaf:
Borchardt-Luger system Die lange Pistole 08 (Parabellum).

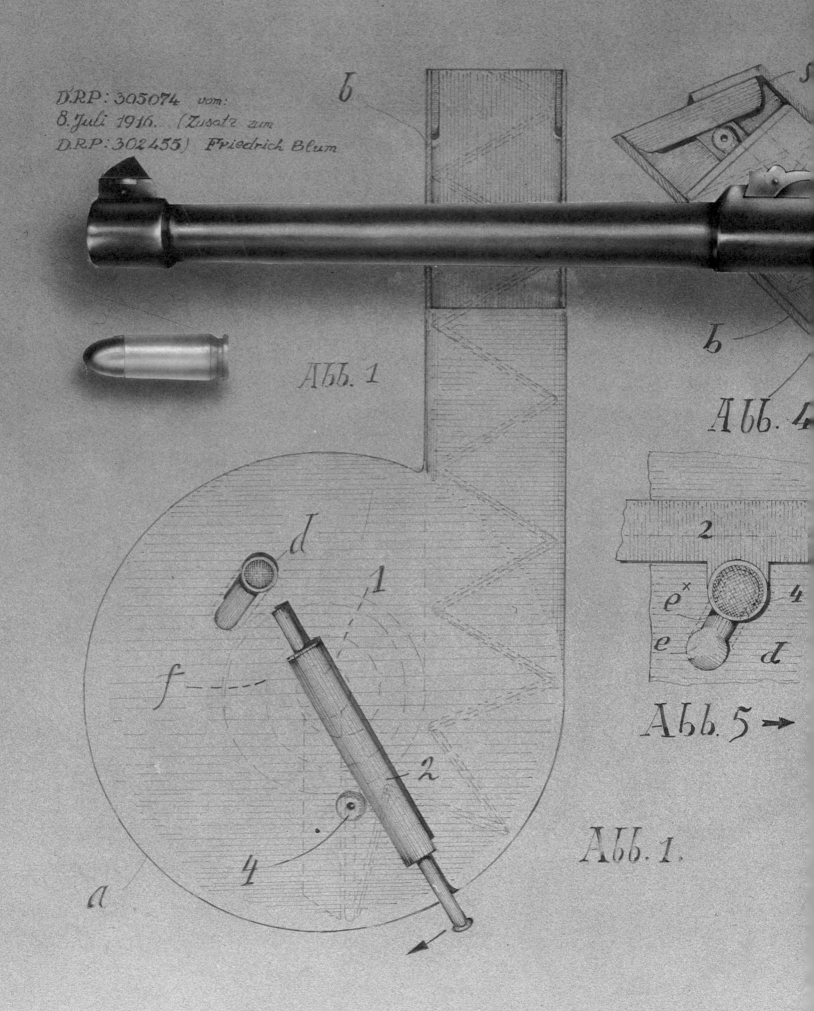

D.R.P: 305074 vom:
8. Juli 1916. (Zusatz zum
D.R.P: 302455) Friedrich Blum

Abb. 1

b

Abb. 4

Abb. 5 →

Abb. 1.

d

f

1

2

4

a

e

e

2

4

d

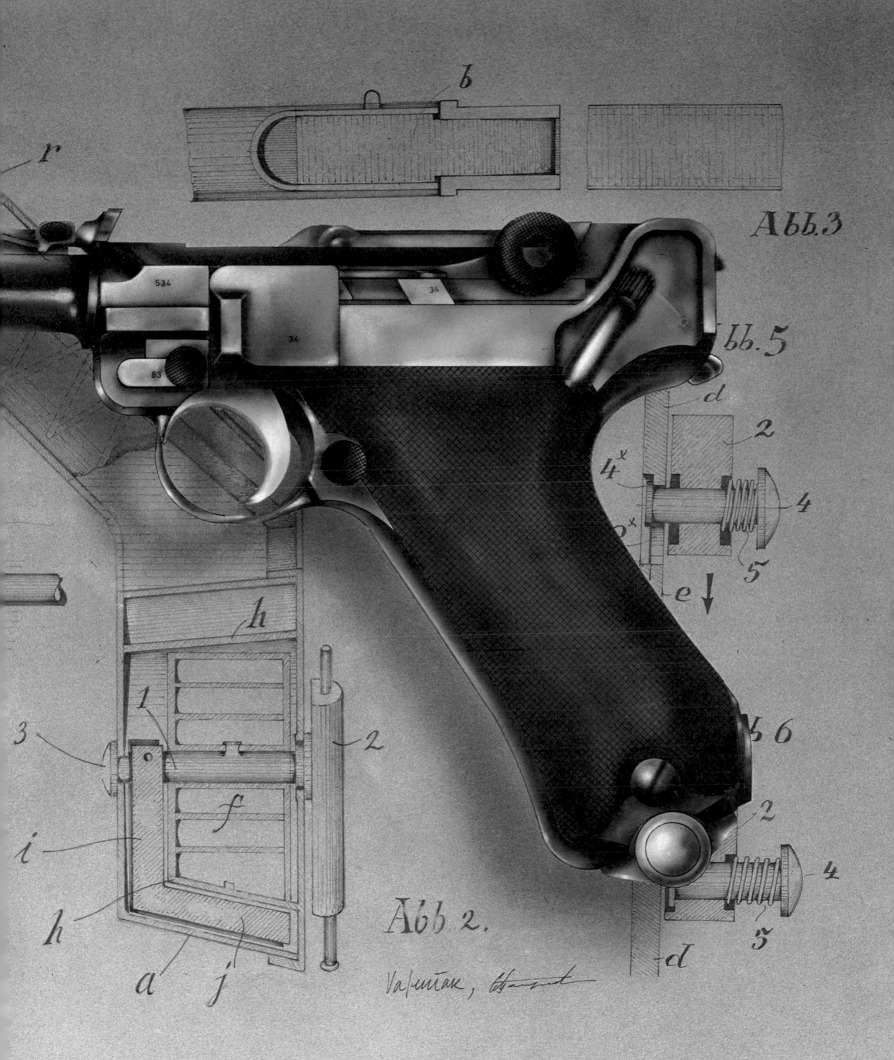

r

b

534

34

34

83

Aьь.3

ьь.5

d

2

4[x]

4

3[x]

5

e ↓

h

1

2

3

j

f

i

h

h

a

j

Abb.2.

Vafentak, Ebaunet

6

2

4

5

d

Mauser C. 96

Mauser, Peter Paul, born June 27, 1838, died May 29, 1914 and his brother **Mauser, Wilhelm,** born May 2, 1834, died January 13, 1892, Oberndorf/Neckar (Germany). Started their careers as gunsmiths of the Royal Württenberger Arms Factory. In the second half of the 1860s, constructed a breech-loading gun mechanism of excellent characteristics, adopted by the German Army as model 1871. In 1872/73, founded an arms factory in Oberndorf which produced a large number of rifles for the German and foreign armies, and revolvers. After 1880, the single-shot Mauser rifles were joined by guns with box-magazines which c. 1900 were considered ideal modern military rifles. The Mauser factory developed and started producing the first successful semi-automatic (self-loading) pistol, the "Construction 1896" (C 96).

Apart from the Luger, another German pistol attained world fame. This was an excellent model of the Mauser company, the famous C.1896. Together with his faithful collaborators, the Fiderle brothers, Mauser patented the prototype of a hand gun (DRP 90,430) on September 11, 1895. In August of the following year, Mauser personally demonstrated this weapon in Potsdam to the Emperor Wilhelm III. Although the Kaiser gave a favourable opinion of the weapon, the German Army decided on the Luger as its pistol. However, two days after the outbreak of the war with France, on August 5, 1914, the Ministry of War ordered a consignment of Mauser C.96 pistols, standard calibre 7.63 mm, for the needs of the field artillery. For the sake of uniformity of ammunition, the same ministry in an order of December 16, 1917, directed Mauser to start constructing the same weapon in the calibre of the 9 mm Parabellum.

By the beginning of World War I, a number of countries had decided to adopt the C.96, many of them basing their decision on experience with the rifle of the same name. But in the first battles, the Mauser pistols demonstrated its undoubted qualities. The C.96 was tested by the Expeditionary Corps in China, and during the Boer War, 1899 – 1903, both sides used it.

This pistol was also the favourite weapon of Sir Winston Churchill. As a young cavalry officer, he bought a C.96 in London as a precaution, before his regiment left for Africa. It should be noted that such a decision was a sort of precedent, as all British cavalry officers carried just a sword and revolvers. In any case, the future prime minister practised using this pistol while the troops moved down the Nile. The tide of events was to prove how far-sighted Churchill had been. At a battle in a dry riverbed near Omdurman, the British uhlan and hussar regiments were charged by the fanatical rebels with swords and lances, in the best manner of the Light Brigade. The result was as catastrophic as in the battle of Balaklava. Of Churchill's regiment alone, which numbered 310, over 70 cavalrymen had been put out of action within a few minutes. Winston himself could only thank the speed and precision of the "automatic Mauser" for his life, and he even had to load it twice!

Churchill and Mauser are also connected by yet another episode, this time set in the Boer War. In this war Churchill took part not as a soldier but as a military correspondent. Even so, he always carried his C.96 with him. On November 15, 1899, the Boers made a surprise attack on the unit to which the famous British "journalist" was attached. By accident, Winston had left his pistol on a locomotive which had gone distance away from the battlefield. When a powerful Boer horseman, equipped with a Mauser rifle, charged him, Churchill had no way of defending himself from the shame of imprisonment or certain death. Today it is well known that Churchill opted for the former. Yet it is less well known that the man who captured the future British prime minister was Louis Botha — the future prime minister of Transvaal!

The Mauser pistol decided the fate of another ruler. In 1934, King Alexander I of Yugoslavia was shot in Marseilles. It is difficult today to judge the efficiency of the French security service at the time, but it is also hard to believe that the assassin, who pushed his way through the crowd and jumped on the running board of the car, succeeded in hiding the massive C.96 from the security and police in a bouquet of flowers ...

By the beginning of World War I, Mauser's pistol was being successfully sold in a number of countries throughout the world. Through its agent in St Petersburg, Farnossolski, the German factory sold 4,568 C.96 pistols to Russia alone between 1879 and 1905. Thanks to the long-standing cooperation of the Mauser company with Turkey, and through its representative in Istanbul, Hubert Preres, the Porte was sent 1,000 ten-shot C.96 pistols on January 11, 1898.

This pistol was also involved in Balkan history of the period in 1897, at a time he was offering Turkey his pistol, Mauser was impressed by the decision of the Serbian government to buy 12,000 revolvers. The factory owner, also a clever salesman, decided to persuade the little country of the qualitiy of his guns. In this, he probably counted on the support of the circles with which he had previously made contact in 1879, during negotiations over the delivery of rifles. Unfortunately, Belgrade remained adamant in its choice of the Nagatan M.91. But the guerilla units formed by the Serbian government for combat on Macedonian territories then still belonging to Turkey, used precisely the C.96 Mauser, often mounted in silver. It is difficult to say whether this weapon was legally acquired on the then rather free European market, or whether there was, in fact, a secret contact signed with Mauser for the delivery of the pistols.

After World War I the Mauser pistol became famous in its automatic version,

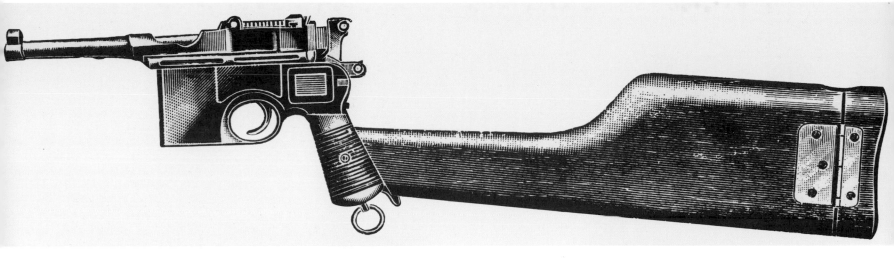

Advertisement of the Mauser firm for the Balkan area.

Charger.

today frequently designated the M.712. However, this number was only the nomenclature for the Mauser M.1930/32 from a commercial catalogue of the GECO company.

Countries that introduced into their arsenals Mauser C.96 system pistols:
1. Germany; 2. Turkey; 3. Russia; 4. Austro-Hungary; 5. China; 6. Spain; 7. Italy.

C-96 MAUSER SYSTEM PISTOL	
- Calibre	7.63 mm or 9 mm
- Rifling	6
- Capacity	10.20 & 40
- Length	298.5 mm
- Length of barrel..	139 mm
- Weight	1,330 gr

Overleaf:
C.1896 Mauser system pistol with holster-butt.

6 1 4 7 2 3 5

WAFFENFABRIK MAUSER
OBERNDORF A. NECKAR

tzbarem Hol

r Pistole

— Anschlagkasten

ALFA 1911

126/129

Pistolen

Mauser.

Valentin, thend.

Patronen auf Laderahmen

Kal. 7,63 mm

Ausfürliche
Beschreibung
kostenlos

Browning

Browning, John Moses, born January 21, 1855, in Ogden, Utah, died November 26, 1926, in Herstal – near Liège. Learned the gunsmith's trade in his father's workshop. Patented his first construction, a single-shot breech-loader, in 1879 and later sold it to the Winchester Repeating Arms Company. Winchester also took over his constructions of repeating "lever action" rifles and small-bore rifles of various systems. In c. 1890, started construction of automatic (self-loading) weapons. Machine-guns and pistols of his construction were produced by Colt's Patent Fire Arms Company, and later also by the Fabrique Nationale d'Armes de Guerre in Herstal. They are sold and used throughout the world.

Original patent drawing by J. M. Browning of April 20, 1897. The patent was registered under the number 580,923. Browning's original signature can be discerned in the lower right-hand corner.

In the last decades of the 19th century work started on yet another pistol, or better to say, on a whole series of pistols, which, with the Mauser and Mannlicher, made a so far unsurpassed triumvirate.

These were the constructions of the famous American, John M. Browning (1855 – 1926). Granted, Browning had attained fame in his homeland by a series of models even before the appearance of his self-loading pistols. This is why it is interesting that he had to start his conquest of the gun market from the Old Continent, from Belgium. But this is perfectly understandable if one takes into account the traditional attachment of America, and even Great Britain, to "good old revolvers". This attitude, at least in the USA, was to be somewhat modified only by Browning's patents produced in the Colt factory.

Since nearly all the famous Browning pistols were produced in the 20th century, a good deal more will be said about them in the chapter on World War I. For this reason, we must mention here the one that lit the fuse of the First World War.

In his work, "Pistols and Revolvers" the noted British author, Major F. Myatt, states that the assassination of the Austrian Archduke Ferdinand, in 1914 in Sarajevo, was committed with a Browning M.1900 pistol. Historical facts only partially confirm this.

It is known that the young assassins acquired their weapons in Belgrade, on May 27, 1914. At the time, the Serbian government had exclusively Nagant M.1891 revolvers in its arsenal. The assassination was carried out in Sarajevo with bombs and guns, and a Browning M.1910 cal. 9 mm at that. The assassins told the investigating judge that these were the precise weapons they had wanted to buy in a Belgrade shop. The two facts already tell us something more: the most diverse weapons, even such modern pistols as the Browning M.1910, were on general sale in the Balkans at that time.

The high price of the Browning (60 dinars per gun) having discouraged the poor students-assassins from buying their own weapons, they were forced to get some from a certain Ciganović, one of the guerillas who had fought in Macedonia. The assassins received four M.1910 pistols, four spare magazines filled with six cartridges each, three boxes with 25 bullets and six hand-grenades of the Vasić system M.1904.

In Sarajevo, on June 28, 1914, the first grenade missed its target. But in the hands of Gavrilo Princip, the Browning M.1910 was infallible. The Austrian Archduke was dead, and the curtain was being raised on World War I.

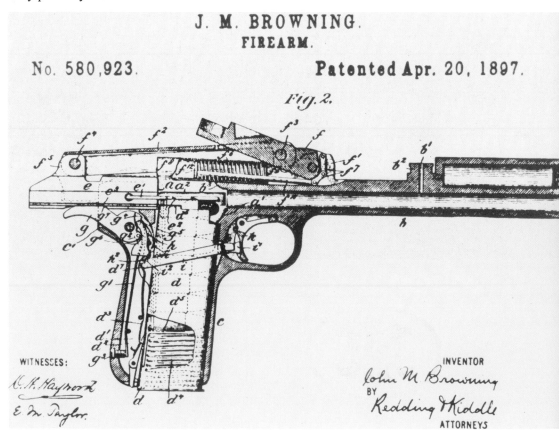

Assassination in Sarajevo, June 28th, 1914.

M. 1910 BROWNING SYSTEM PISTOL
- Calibre .... 9 mm
- Rifling 6
- Capacity 7
- Length .... 154 mm
- Length of barrel .... 88.5 mm
- Weight .... 570 gr

Overleaf:
Weapons of the Sarajevo assassins: M.1910 Browning system pistol and M.1904 Vasić system hand grenade.

K.u.k. Armeeinspektoraf
zu Res. № 450/i

Skizze

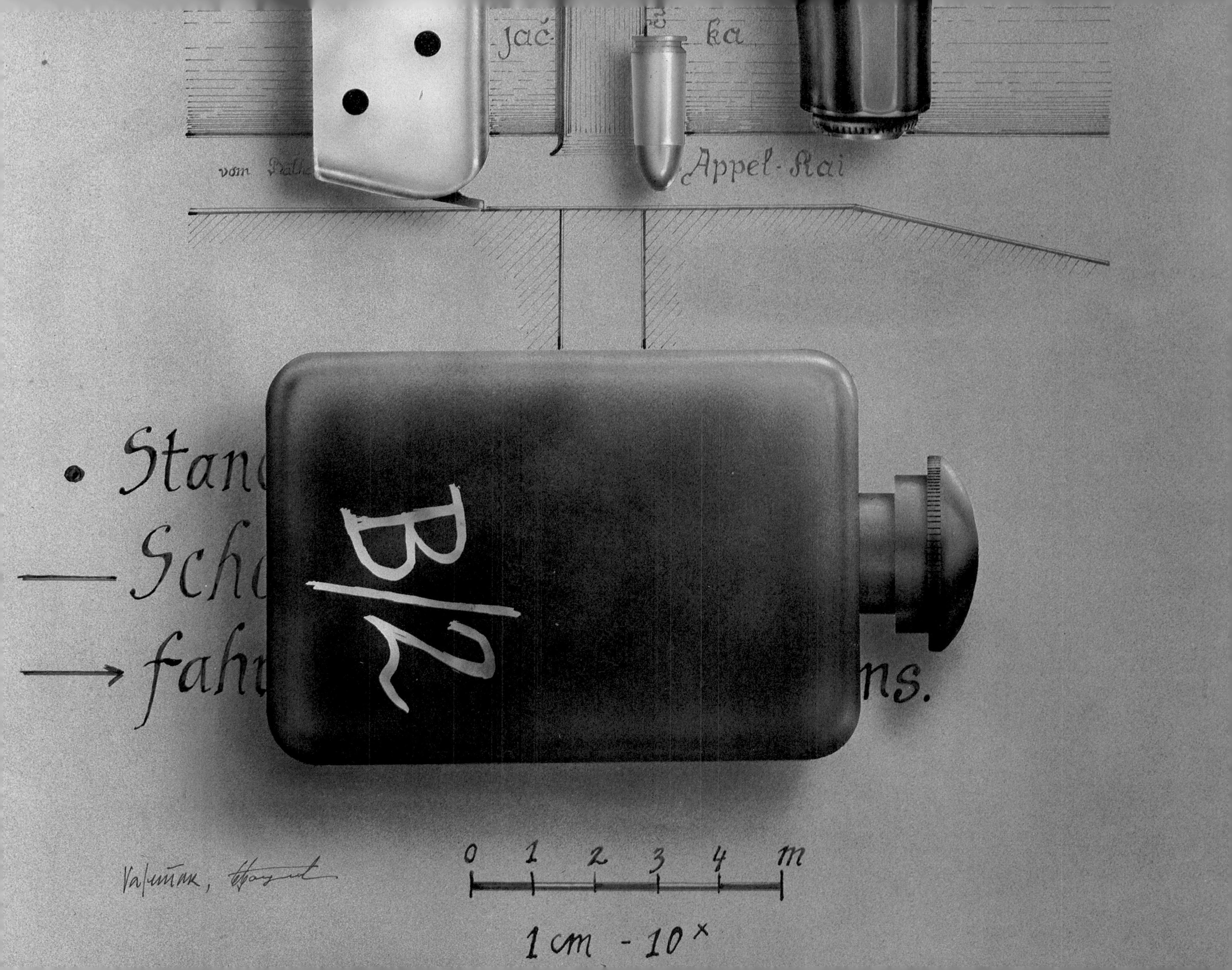
jać
ka
vom
Appel-Kai
• Stan
— Sch
→ fah
ns.
B/2
0 1 2 3 4 m
1 cm - 10×
Valuták,

WORLD WAR I WEAPONS

German hussars, World War I.

Mauser

Most of the countries involved in the First World War went into battle in 1914 with weapons developed during the 19th century. True, work on automatic weapons, which were to stand the harsh test and prove their worth had been intensified just before the war. But this does not mean that World War I was the swan-song of military repeating arms. On the contrary, even the next conflict of worldwide scope was to be fought with the same rifles and pistols or their somewhat modified variants.

The burden of battle in the cruellest war in human history till that time was borne mostly by two rifles: the Mauser and the Mannlicher.

Mauser started to make headway on the world market with the Belgian M.1889 rifle. This weapon, however, still had a number of weak points which had to be eliminated. Finally, when he introduced, on the Spanish model of 1893, an improved breech-bolt, an internal staggered-row box magazine, and loading which could be single-round or with a metal charger, his weapons were adopted by 26 countries throughout the world! It is surprising that Germany was among the last to accept the improved Mauser rifle.

The Prussian Commission for testing arms started work on small-bore ammunition as early as 1892. When word came of the success of the M.1893, the Commission started parallel testing of Mauser's export weapon in December 1893. Work on its construction was intensified from

M. 1898 MAUSER SYSTEM RIFLE	
- Calibre	7.92 mm
- Rifling	4
- Capacity	5
- Length	1,250 mm
- Length of barrel	740 mm
- Weight	4,100 gr

Countries that had Mauser system rifles:
1. Argentina, M.1891; 2. Belgium, M.1889 and M.1898; 3. Bolivia, M.1891; 4. Brasil, M.1894; 5. Costa-Rica; 6. Chile, M.1895; 7. China, M.1871, M.1888, M.1983, M.1895, M.1906; 8. Ecuador, M.1891; 9. Germany, M.1871, M.1871/84, M.1898; 10. Guatemala; 11. Honduras; 12. Iran, M.1895; 13. Serbia, M.1880, M.1884, M.1899, M.1907, M.1908, M.1910, M.1880/07; 14. Columbia, M.1891; 15. Congo, M.1894; 16. Luxembourg, M.1896; 17. Mexico, M.1895, M.1902, M.1912; 18. Nicaragua; 19. Oranje, M.1895; 20. Paraguay, M.1907; 21. Peru, M.1891; 22. Portugal, M.1904; 23. Salvador; 24. Sweden, M.1894, M.1896; 25. Spain, M.1891, M.1893; 26. Transvaal, M.1895; 27. Turkey, M.1887, M.1890, M.1893, M.1903; 28. Uruguay, M.1895.

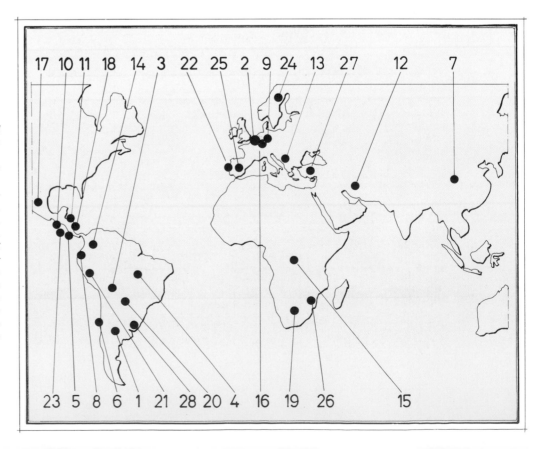

Street fighting in Berlin. Revolution in Germany, 1919.

1895 on, when a series of 2,000 rifles was ordered for further testing, with all the characteristics of the new breech-bolt and magazine, but also with the old Mieg barrel jacket.

After a number of changes on this weapon, including the rejection of the old barrel-jacket, the M.1898 Mauser system rifle, cal. 7.92 mm was adopted, on April 5, 1898, for the German military forces.

This was a very high-quality and safe weapon, though in contrast to other rifles of similar system, Mauser's breech-bolt had a somewhat longer movement, which slowed the operation of the weapon. On the other hand, its robust construction and closed magazine stood up to the dust and mud of the trenches.

It is thought that in the period between 1898 and 1918 about 5,000,000 M.98 rifles were produced in Germany! During the war, the German and Turkish Mausers were opposed by the very same weapon in the hands of Belgian, Portuguese, Serbian and Luxemburg soldiers.

Overleaf:
German M.1898 Mauser system rifle with S.98/02 bayonet.

223

7,92 mm G

G.T.B.2.25. = Feld-Bäckerei-Kolonne Nr.2, Waffen Nr. 25.
G.T.F.3.25. = Train-Abteilung Nr. 3, Waffe Nr. 25.
G.T.L.3.25. = Feld-Lazarett Nr. 3, Waffe Nr. 25.

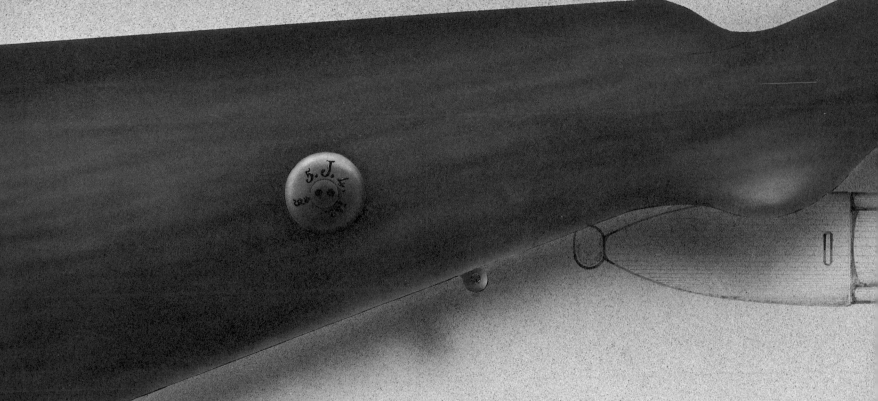

SEITENGEWEHR

ewehr 98

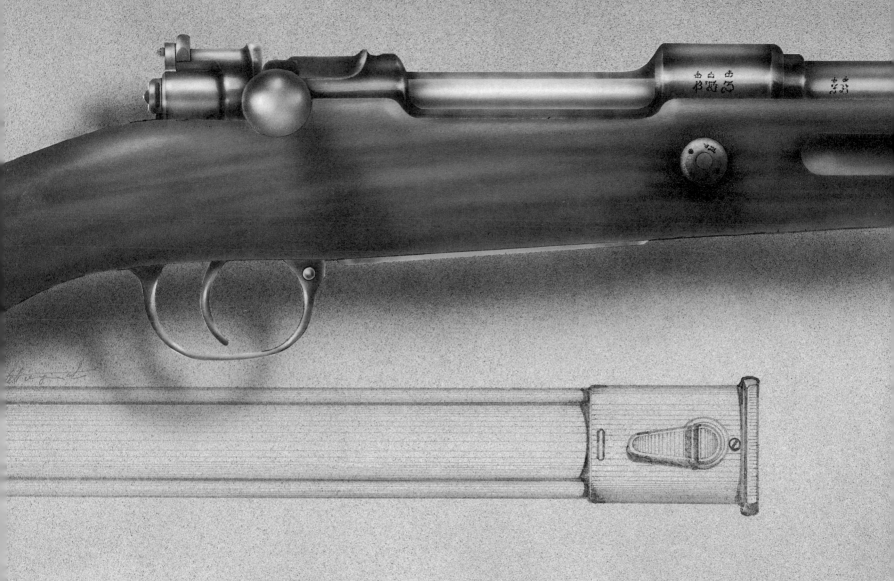

98/05 aA

WAFFENFABRIK
MAUSER-A.G.
OBERNDORF A/N

Mannlicher-Carcano

In contrast to Mauser's turn-bolt action, Mannlicher had decided early in his career to opt for the straight-pull bolt-action. His arms, adapted in 1888 in Austro-Hungary to 8 mm ammunition did not, however, last longer than two years. Taking Germany and France as models, Austro-Hungary changed to nitrocellular smokeless powder in 1890. The change of ammunition turned the production of firearms in Steyr and Budapest into two directions: the construction of new M.1890 weapons and the adaptation of the old, M.1888. The final version of the Austrian rifle, which appeared in 1895, had a somewhat modified bolt-action and wooden hand guard over the barrel.

Mannlicher's breech-bolt had a faster mechanism than Mauser's, but was sensitive to dirt. The second, more serious weakness of the M.95 was its magazine: it could be loaded only by a clip, and the

M. 1891 MANNLICHER-CARCANO SYSTEM RIFLE	
- Calibre	6.5 mm
- Rifling	4
- Capacity	6
- Length	1,285 mm
- Length of barrel	780 mm
- Weight	3,800 gr

ITALIAN M.91 MANNLICHER-CARCANO SYSTEM RIFLE
1. barrel; 2. chamber; 3. receiver; 4. firing pin; 5. breech-bolt; 6. firing pin spring; 7. bolt-handle; 8. cocking piece; 9. trigger-guard; 10. trigger; 11. clip; 12. zubringerplate; 13. magazinhalter; 14. butt.

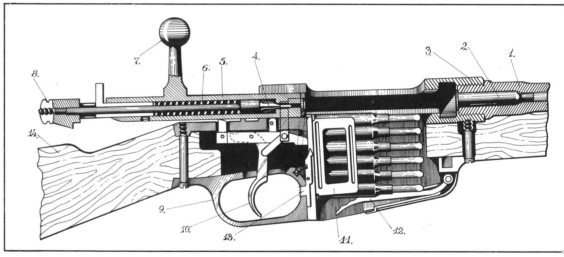

Countries that had rifles based on the Mannlicher system:
1. Austro-Hungary; 2. Greece (Mannlicher-Schonauer); 3. Rumania; 4. Bulgaria; 5. Italy (Mannlicher-Carcano); 6. France (Mannlicher-Berthier); 7. Netherlands.

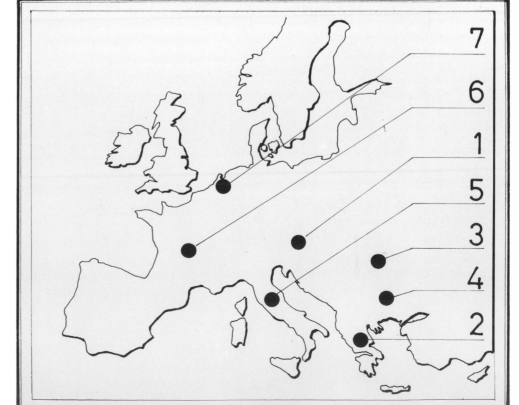

Italian offensive at Carso.

Italian attack on Monte Nero.

opening on the lower side (through which the clip dropped out) allowed mud, dust and snow to penetrate the mechanism, thereby causing frequent jamming.

The Austro-Hungarian Army produced its weapons, in accordance with tradition, in three versions: as an infantry rifle, a *stutzer* and a carbine.

In the 1870s F v. Mannlicher worked on other types of magazines as well. Possibly under the influence of the already mentioned constructions of Schullhof and Spitalsky, in 1875 Mannlicher patented a type of revolving magazine. This solution, combined with a cylinder bolt-action, was applied to his M.1887 rifle.

Two years before the appearance of Mannlicher's experimental weapon, the Austrian designer Otto Schönauer patented, jointly with J. Werndl, a similar rotary magazine. In 1890 Mannlicher and Schönauer joined forces, and by combining their magazines and turn bolt-action, produced a new and rather good--quality rifle. But this weapon was given the cold shoulder by the Austrian Army in 1900. Three years later the Kingdom of Greece accepted the same weapon without hesitation and adopted it for use by its army under the name of Mannlicher--Schönauer M.1903 (cal. 6.5 mm)!

Mannlicher also combined his classical box magazine with a turn-bolt action, producing a weapon adopted (in 6.5 mm calibre) by Romania (M.1893) and the Netherlands (M.1895).

The Austrian magazine solution was also accepted by two other major countries: Italy and France.

Italy started parallel work on the adoption of small-bore weapons and smokeless-powder ammunition rather late — in 1888. The decision regarding the calibre and cartridge was made relatively fast: Italy decided on 6.5 mm ammunition. In 1890, the State Commission, headed by General Parravicino, turned to the far more delicate task of choosing an appropriate firearms system. The Commission worked on the principle of having all state arms factories offer their constructions as well as considering foreign solutions (Mauser, Mannlicher, Lee, etc.).

Finally, on December 31, 1891, the best marks were obtained by the solution of the famous *Fabbrica d'Armi di Torino* (SAFAT, today FIAT). The basic construction of the so-called *Fucile modello 91* was provided by the technical director of the factory, Artillery Lieutenant-Colonel Salvatore Carcano.

Carcano used Mauser's bolt-action from 1889 as his starting point, and changed its bolt-sleeve safety mechanism. Combining his modification of the breech-bolt with Mannlicher's clip-loading magazine, Carcano only succeeded in producing a poor hybrid weapon. Regardless of this, General Parravicino was delighted with the rifle which, probably for this precise reason, is occasionally referred to under his name.

During 1892 the new weapon was sold to the Italian infantry. After this, cavalry carbines began to be produced, and in 1897, a *moschetto per le truppe speciali* (short rifle for special troops) − PTS − 91.

Italian designers were forced to eliminate numerous faults of the Mannlicher-Carcano system weapons. In the period up to World War I, adaptations and improvements were made in 1895, 1897, 1907 and 1912!

Regardless of its obvious inferiority, the *Moschetto 91* survived both the First and the Second World Wars. Moreover (if one is to believe the Warren Report), John F. Kennedy was killed, in 1963, from the Texas School Book Depository in Dallas, by a Mannlicher-Carcano!

Overleaf:
Italian M.1891 Mannlicher-Carcano system rifle; plan of the Dallas assassination according to the Warren Report.

6,5mm FUCILE

PLAN VIEW OF FREEWA
WEST OF TRIPLE
DALLAS,

STEMMONS ST

0   10   20   30   40
SCAL

F

COMMERCE ST. EAST

FBI
FEDERAL
BUREAU

F

MODELLO 91

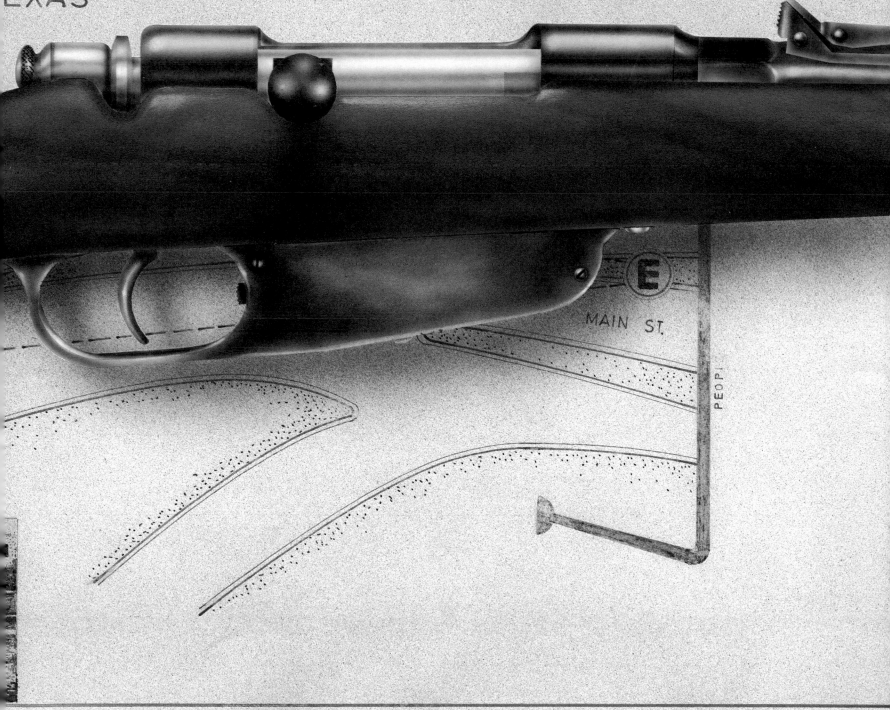

CONVERGENCE
UNDERPASS
EXAS

MAIN ST.

PEOPI

E

Mannlicher-Berthier

M. 1907 MANNLICHER-BERTHIER SYSTEM RIFLE
- Calibre .... 8 mm
- Rifling 4
- Capacity 3
- Length .... 1,321 mm
- Length of barrel .... 797 mm
- Weight .... 3,900 gr

In 1914, France was in possession of a new rifle, the Mannlicher-Berthier. But before we move on to this weapons it is necessary to say something about the old Lebel as well. It is "touching" to see just how devoted the French were to this long obsolete rifle, which took part in all the colonial conflicts, and survived World War I. The French even tried to stop the Germans in 1940 with this antique, after which the Vichy government used it in Syria against the British, and it was even fired in Indochina against the Japanese!

In 1893, the Lebel M.86 underwent its first and last alteration, consisting of a modification of the sights, receiver and furniture. Its tubular magazine and slow bolt action could certainly not parry the modern German firearms. Aware of this, in 1890 the French founded a Commission, headed by André Berthier, which was to modify French rifles and adapt them to the conditions of modern warfare. Already that same year the com-

Charge of the Allied cavalry, 1917.

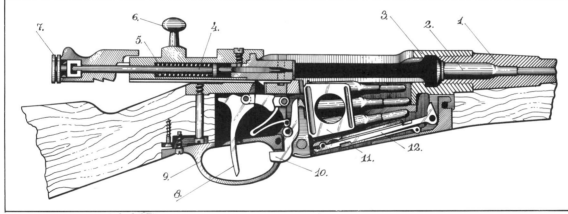

FRENCH MANNLICHER-BERTHIER SYSTEM RIFLE
1. barrel; 2. chamber; 3. receiver; 4. firing pin; 5. firing pin spring; 6. bolt-handle; 7. cocking piece; 8. trigger; 9. trigger-guard; 10. magazinhalter; 11. clip; 12. zubringerplate.

mission "designed" as many as three types of carbines: the cavalry (total length 945 mm), gendarmerie (945 mm) and cuirassiers' carbine (950 mm).

The complete irresponsibility with which the French approached the project is surprising. The Commission made insignificant changes to Lebel's bolt-action and, combining it with Mannlicher's clip-loading magazine, pronounced this unfortunate hybrid to be the solution to all their problems. What is more, the magazine was planned for three cartridges only!

During 1892, artillery and gendarmerie *musketoons* were made on the same principle, four years later also a rifle for the Indo-Chinese troops and, finally, in 1907, a rifle intended for all colonial troops.

The *Fusil modele 1907 dit Colonial* was intended, after slight changes in the bolt-mechanism and sights, for the whole

230

French infantry in 1915. Because of the inadequate capacities of the home industry, a number of M.1907/15 rifles were ordered from the American Remington factory.

Despite all its faults, the M.1907/15 should be given credit for bringing France victory. The old Lebel also finally justified the role assigned it as far back as in 1886: Alsace and Lorraine were joined to France.

Berthier rifles (named after the head of the Commission) were sent as military aid to Imperial Russia during the war, and in October 1916, the whole of the Serbian Army was issued weapons of the same make (106,000 M.07/15 rifles, 1,900 M.1892 musketoons and 1,000 M.1890 carbines).

French soldiers had a great deal of trouble with the impractical Lebel-Berthier bolt-action. And even if they eventually got used to it, three cartridges in a magazine were definitely not acceptable for any soldier. It was not until 1916 that Paris took serious account of

Infantry in position.

this problem and redesigned the Mle 07/15 to accommodate five rounds. The result was the Fusil Mle 1916, which could be recognized by the protruding magazine below the handguard.

Overleaf:
French M. 1907/15 Mannlicher-Berthier system rifle with M. 1886-93 bayonet.

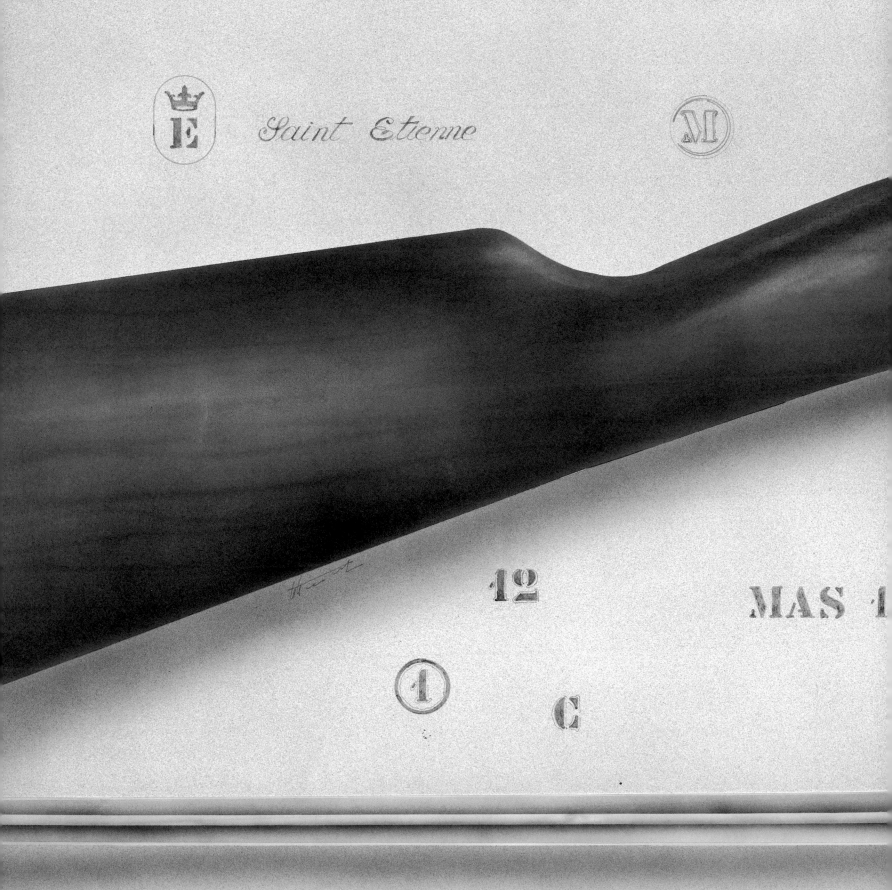

Fusil d' Infantrie 1907

Saint Etienne

12

MAS

C

Epée baïonnette Mle 1886 (Lebe

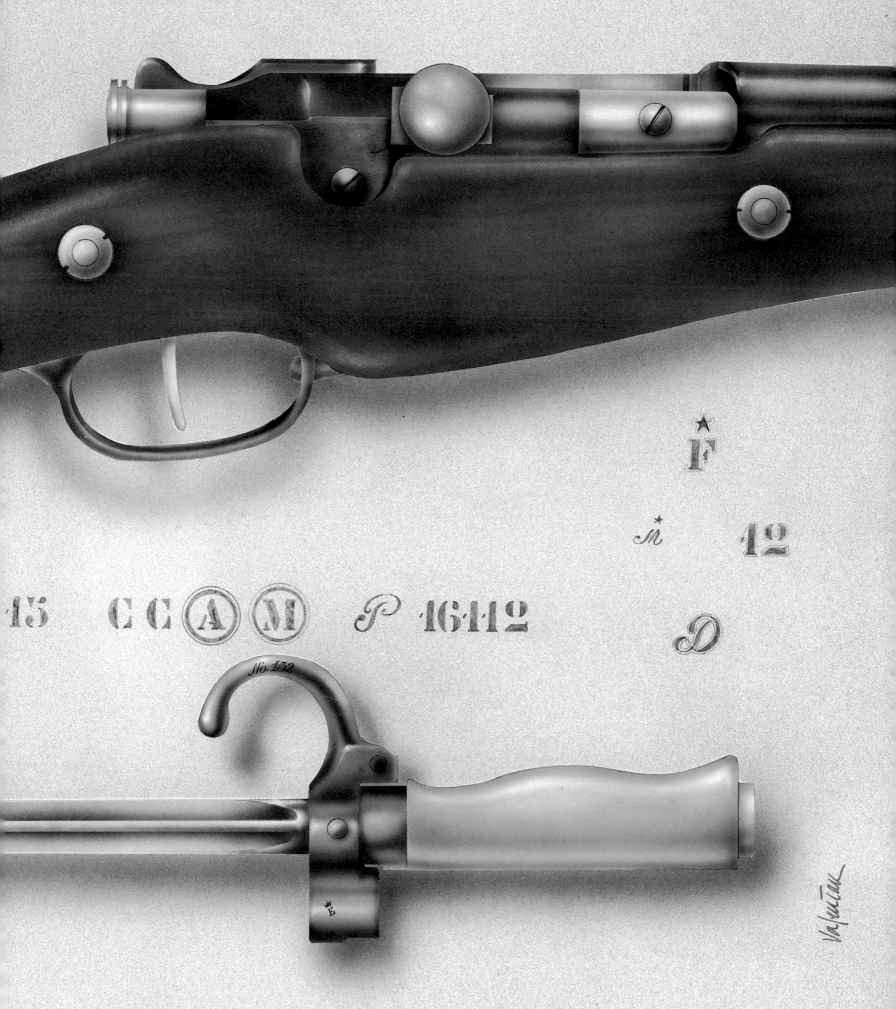

Lee-Metford, SMLE

Metford, William Ellis, born October 4, 1824, in Taunton, Somerset, died October 14, 1899, in Bristol. A railway engineer by profession. Constructed rockets, cartridges and firearms barrels. Explosive bullets of his construction were used by the British Army from 1863 – 1868. Precise barrels of his construction were used for sporting guns as well as for the new British Lee-Metford magazine rifle.

(SMLE) NO. 1 MARK III RIFLE	
- Calibre	7.7 mm ('303)
- Rifling	5
- Capacity	10
- Length	1,133 mm (44.6 in.)
- Length of barrel	640 mm (25.19 in.)
- Weight	3,930 gr (8.656 lb)

Engineer William Ellis Metford and Scotsman James Paris Lee had a decisive influence on the development of British repeating and magazine arms. Strangely enough, neither of these two constructors was a gunsmith by profession; Metford worked for Isambard Kingdom Brunel on the construction of the Great Western Railway and railways in general (in which he resembles Mannlicher), whilst J. P. Lee was a clockmaker! This did not, however, prevent these two talented men from producing a reliable weapon for the British Army.

Metford started privately researching the effect of grooves on the ballistics of weapons back in the 1850s. He was among the first to reject the theory that the lead bullet must be as soft as possible in order to run through the deep grooves smoothly. In accordance with this view, in 1865 Metford constructed a barrel with seven grooves of a depth of four thousandths of an inch and applied it to a match shooting gun which used a lead alloy bullet.

LEE-METFORD SYSTEM RIFLE M.1889
1. barrel; 2. chamber; 3. receiver; 4. breech-bolt; 5. bolt-handle; 6. cocking piece; 7. trigger-guard; 8. trigger; 9. magazinhalter; 10. zubringerfeder; 11. zubringerplatte; 12. cleaning rod.

so that compressed black powder was first used as a replacement. Fortunately, Nobel's cordite soon appeared and was adopted, in 1892, as the final solution for all British service smallarms ammunition.

The combination of Metford's barrel, the new ammunition and Lee's bolt-action and box magazine created, in 1888, the first British magazine rifle.

Lee's bolt-action differed from Dreyse's and Chassepot's constructions only in its basic working principle. But it also contained some innovations which were unfairly criticised by British military circles. The Lee bolt was held in position when closed by lugs at the rear of the bolt, and also had a separate bolt-head which could be exchanged at wish. This resulted in maximum economy of material in the production of arms and, more important, shortened the path of the bolt-action, making its operation much faster than with both the Mauser and Mannlicher.

At first, when black powder ammunition was still being used (1888 – 1892), Lee's magazine was loaded by means of a clip with 8 cartridges. With the appearance of cordite, the weapon's capacity was increased to 10 cartridges.

As early as 1895 the Metford barrel was modernized in Enfield by reducing the number of grooves from 7 to 5, and the weapon was renamed the Lee-Enfield. In length, both types of rifle, the Lee-Metford and the Lee-Enfield, were suitable only for the infantry, whilst the cavalry did not start receiving modern carbines until after 1897. This neglect of the cavalry cost the British Army dearly in the fighting in South Africa. The Boer cavalry, armed with five-round Mausers, performed miracles in so-called shock-actions by the power of its fire. The British troopers, still equipped with the old Martini carbines, were in no way able to counter these fast and deadly attacks. The mounted infantry, however, was far better off with its magazine rifles and fought on equal terms with the South African "rebels". Impressed by the Mauser rifles of their enemy (Orange and the Transvaal officially adopted the Mauser in 1895), the British took some steps to improve their own armament. In 1892 Lee had invested a charger by means of which five rounds could be loaded simultaneously. When it became obvious that this did not significantly increase firing speed, all Lee-Metford and Lee-Enfield rifles adapted to the charger were issued to the Territorial Force in 1907.

The second and far more important step was towards uniformity of infantry and cavalry weapons.

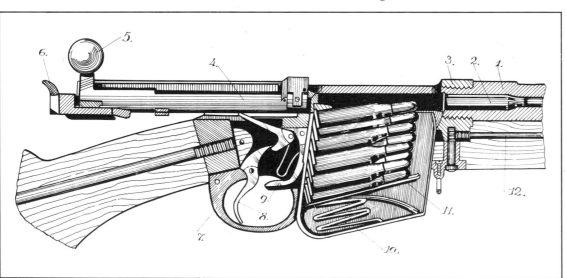

Later, with the appearance of smaller calibres and smokeless powder, it turned out that even this kind of bullet was too soft for the great muzzle velocity. Consequently, in 1888 the British adopted the Swiss Rubin '303 calibre lead bullet encased in a covering of harder metal.

The British were particularly bothered by the question of powder. The French smokeless powder was not suited to the climatic conditions of the British colonies,

British machine gun company, beginning of 20th century.

Attack of British troops on Ahi Baba, World War I.

In 1902 a rifle was produced with all the characteristics of an improved Lee-Enfield, but 130 mm shorter than the earlier infantry weapon. The new, so-called *Short, Magazine, Lee-Enfield (SMLE)* rifle, was equally suited to the infantry and the mounted forces. Accordingly, the British Army issued its troops with the SMLE guns in the period between 1905 and 1907.

These guns proved worthy opponents of the German weapons and even lived to triumph in World War II as well.

Overleaf:
British M.1903 Lee-Enfield (Rifle No. 1 MK III).

235

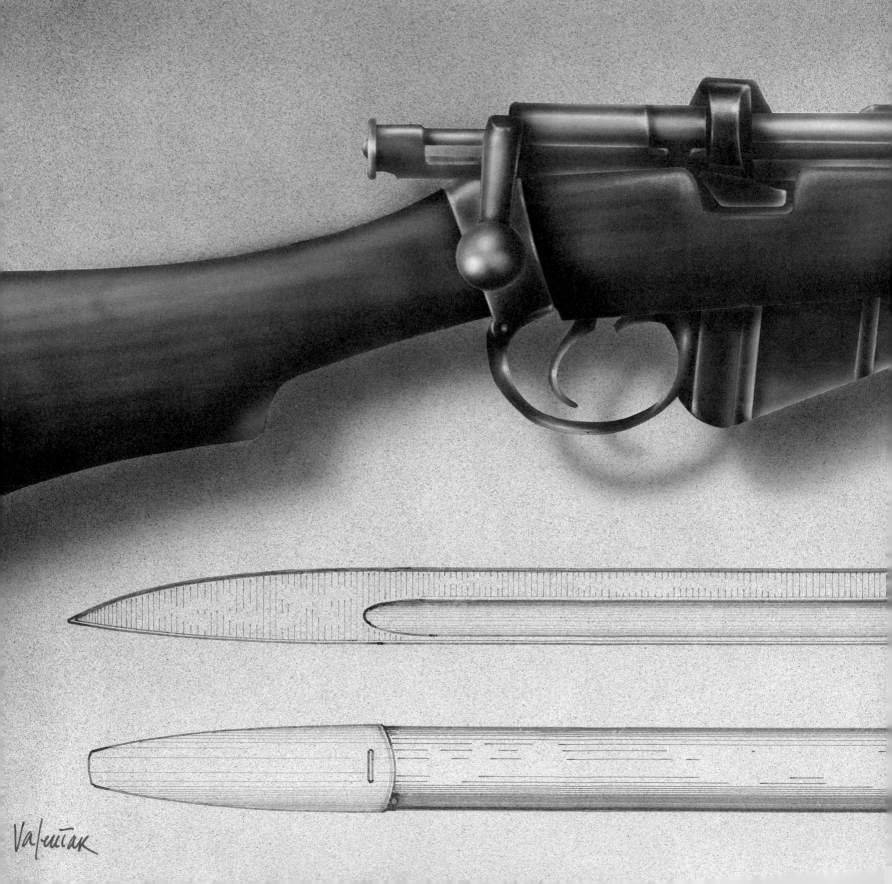

Valentak

FIELD RIFLE (SMLE)

BAYONET 1907 No 1

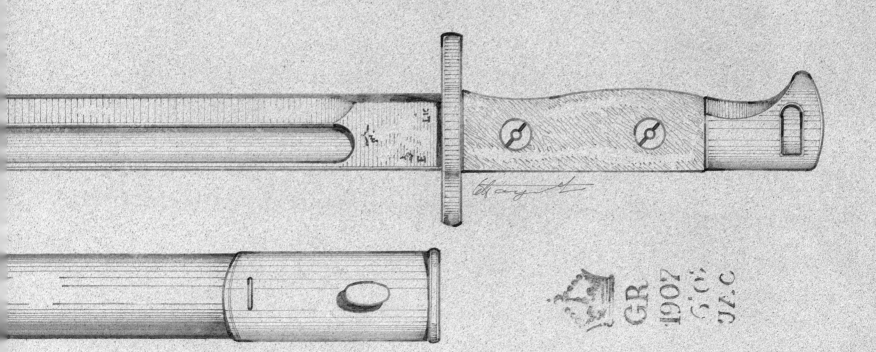

Springfield M.1903, Enfield P-17

SPRINGFIELD M. 1903 RIFLE
- Calibre .... 7.62 mm ('30)
- Rifling 4
- Capacity 5
- Length .... 1,105 mm (43.5 in.)
- Length of barrel .. 609 mm (24 in.)
- Weight .... 4,313 gr

General Pershing disembarks at Boulogne.

It is interesting to note that the Mauser rifle also had a significant influence on the arming of the American forces. In the Spanish-American War of 1898, the U.S. troops first came up against German firearms. It was certainly a shock to them to note the advantages of Mauser's charger which left the U.S. Krag-Jörgensen M.1898 far behind as regards speed.

Taught by this experience, in 1900 the Board of Officers took measures to create a weapon with all the good characteristics of the Mauser. The inventive Americans came up with a solution in record time. First, they purchased the right to use Mauser's bolt-action from him for US $ 200,000; then they made a succesful synthesis of the German and the British Lee magazine; and finally they improved the bolt striker. In 1901 it was already possible to order 5,000 rifles based on the Mauser principle, which were supposed to replace the impractical Krag-Jörgensen.

Before starting serial production of the new weapon, it was decided to shorten the barrel to 24 inches so that the rifle would suit the needs of both the infantry and the cavalry. Finally, the Springfield Arsenal started serial production of the new M.1903 rifle in the same year. The only change on this rifle was made in 1906 when the ammunition was reinforced, thereby increasing the muzzle velocity of

the bullet from 2,300 to 2,805 feet/sec. (855 m/sec)

From 1904 to 1922, the Springfield Arsenal turned out 741,815, and the Rock Island Arsenal (from 1904 – 1918) another 291,685 M.1903 rifles. Unfortunately, the USA entered World War I when in 1917, it turned out that the number of Springfield M.1903 rifles produced was not sufficient for the expeditionary corps. Accordingly, the Americans started adapting Enfield weapons which were being produced at that time in the Remington and Winchester factories for the needs of Great Britain.

The fate of this British weapon is somewhat unusual. During 1912/13, a new rifle was designed in Britain, with small ˙276 calibre and bolt-action with front--locking lugs, which was supposed to replace the SMLE from 1902. The prototype of the new rifle, called No. 3 or Pattern 1913 (P. 13), never went into serial production owing to the sharp criticism it received. When war broke out, the imperial army felt the lack of modern guns. Accordingly, military experts changed the calibre of the P.13 to standard ˙303 ammunition and ordered the rifles from the USA under the designation P.14.

Thus in 1917 the American Army had available a smooth-running production line for high-quality rifles. In order to make full advantage of this, US experts adapted the British P.14 to their own ˙30 calibre ammunition and in this way created an "American" Enfield P.17!

By November 9, 1918, the powerful US industry delivered, 2,193,429 P.17 rifles to its forces.

American troops marching in front of Baker, Minister of War, during his stay in France.

Overleaf:
US M.1903 Springfield infantry rifle with M.1905 bayonet.

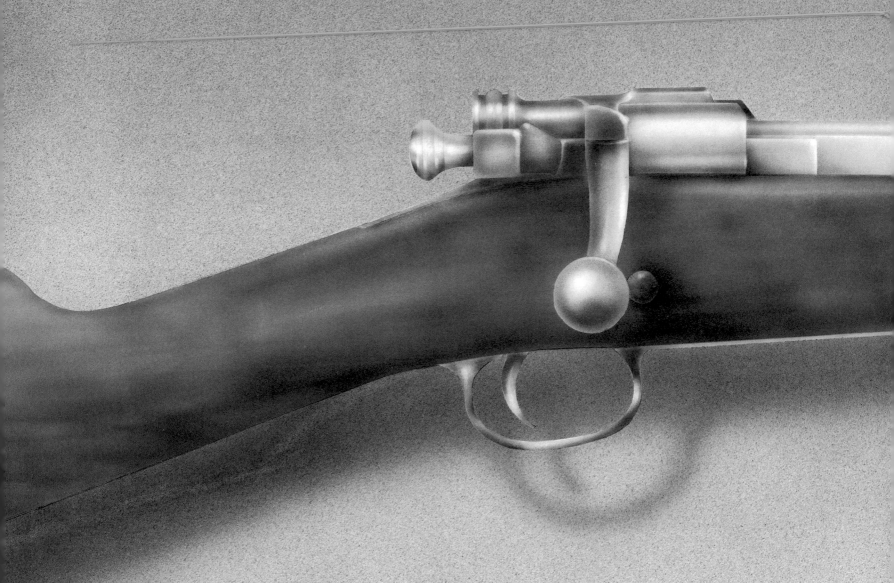

Rifle Cal .30, 1903 with Model 1903 Bay

Valentak

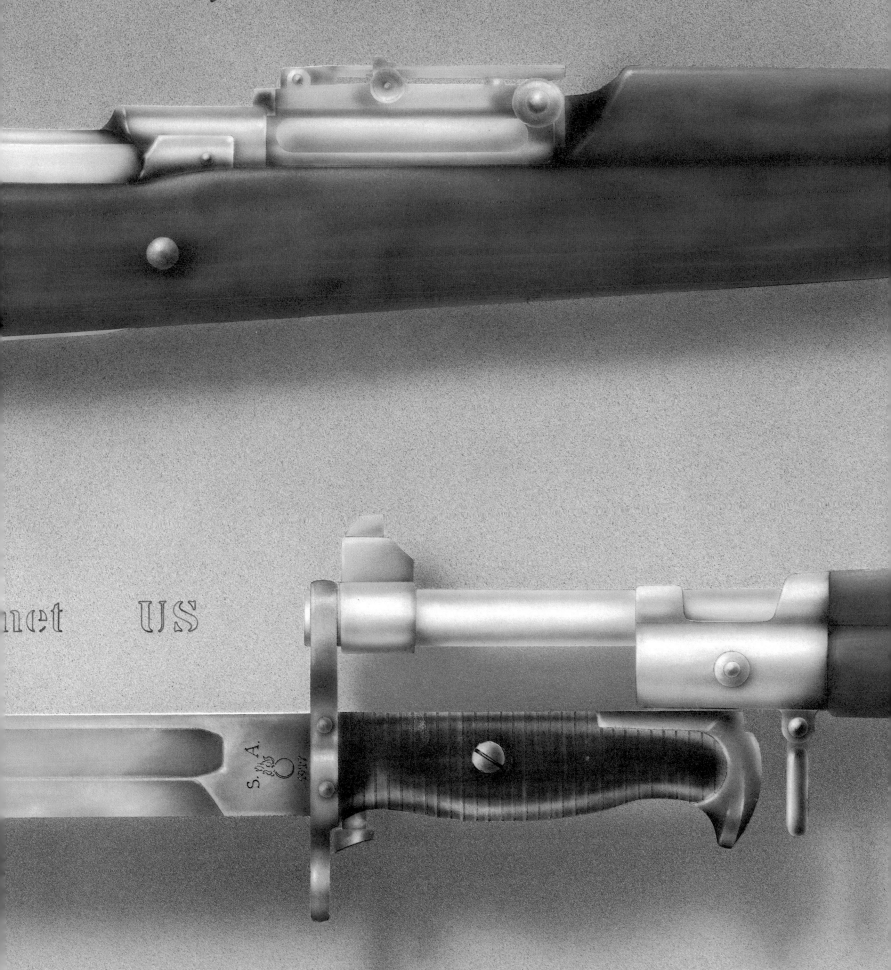

Mosin-Nagant M 1891

Mosin, Sergei Ivanovich, born May 5, 1849, in Ramon near Voronesk, died February 8, 1902 in Sestroreck. Russian artillery officer. After completing the Academy, spent a short time as commanding officer of the Imperial Arms Works in Tula. In 1891 the Russian Army adopted a repeating rifle of his construction which, with minor changes remained the standard Russian and later Soviet rifle until after World War II.

In the 1880s and 1890s Russia passively followed the world arms race. Its military experts were mostly employed in studying new tactics and the influence on them of armaments policies of foreign armies. A commission for assessing magazine weapons existed *pro forma,* but gained a measure of significance only after 1889. At this time, it was renamed the Commission for Work on Small-bore Weapons, and within a short time tested 93 foreign constructions of magazine rifles.

The attention of the Committee members was particularly attracted by the work of Sergei Ivanovich Mosin. This talented constructor had designed a 8 mm calibre rifle with a tubular magazine in 1887, but when the Sestroreck Works produced a prototype of this weapon, it turned out that Mosin had failed to combine successfully the obsolete magazine and advanced ammunition. The constructor then took a step backwards: he designed a single-shot rifle with the same characteristics and offered it to the Commission in 1890. Surprisingly, the Commission took to this already old-fashioned solution, and on July 14 of the same year, issued the order to start serial production of the Mosin M.1890 gun! Fortunately, Sergei Ivanovich had at the time finished work on a five-round magazine rifle, which brought the Commission to its senses and returned it to the investigation of magazine rifles.

Mosin submitted his latest solution, designed for 7.62 mm calibre ammunition, to the Commission in February 1890. But at the same time, L. Nagant appeared in St Petersburg with a very similar five-

Fighting around the fort of Port Arthur, Russo-Japanese war, 1905.

MOSIN-NAGANT SYSTEM RIFLE M.1891
1. barrel; 2. receiver; 3. chamber; 4. clip; 5. locking lug; 6. firing pin; 7. breech-bolt; 8. bolt-handle; 9. firing pin spring; 10. schlagbolzenmutter; 11. trigger-guard; 12. trigger; 13. zubringerplatte; 14. forestock.

M. 1891 MOSIN-NAGANT SYSTEM RIFLE	
- Calibre	7.62 mm (3''')
- Rifling	4
- Capacity	5
- Length	1,305 mm
- Length of barrel	802 mm
- Weight	4,370 gr

Cossacks pursuing the enemy, World War I.

-round magazine rifle which pleased the bureaucratic military circles, always obsessed with the quality of imported weapons.

Simultaneous troop testing of both systems (the Russian Mosin and the Belgian Nagant) began on December 21, 1890. When the first round of tests was completed by the end of February the following year, most of the participants voted for the Belgian weapon. But a professor of the Artillery Academy, Chebishev, energetically opposed the adoption of a foreign solution. Under his influence, the parallel testing of a somewhat improved Mosin rifle and the Nagant continued from March 13 – 18, 1891. Moreover, by April even the members of the Commission (into which Nagant was also coopted) were involved in improving the construction of the Russian favourite. In so doing, some solutions were taken from the Nagant weapon and used on the Mosin.

Finally, on April 16, 1891, the Mosin rifle was finally adopted for use by the Russian Army. Its official name was *trehlinejnaja vintovka obrasca 1891. goda.* It is indicative that the name does not mention the constructor, which was certainly unfair to both Mosin and Nagant.

This same year, 1891, dragoon and Cossack rifles, cal. 7.62 mm, were designed, while the carbine intended for the artillery and machine-gun units, was not to appear until 1907.

Despite a credit of 108.5 million roubles, the Russian industry was incapable of starting production of these new weapons immediately. For this reason, the first contigent of M.91 rifles was ordered from the French Chatellerault works, which delivered 503,539 guns to Russia between 1891 and 1895. Russian ordnance works started production of the Mosin-Nagant in 1893, and only three years delivered to the army 1,470,470 rifles! With this tempo of production, the entire Russian army was equipped with these weapons by 1901, and fought with them in the war against Japan.

It is interesting to note that in the midst of changing its armament in 1898, Russia gave the Principality of Montenegro a gift of 40,000 M.91 rifles. Moreover, when allied Serbia was hardest pressed in 1914, St Petersburg sent a consignment of 120,000 M.91 rifles to Belgrade.

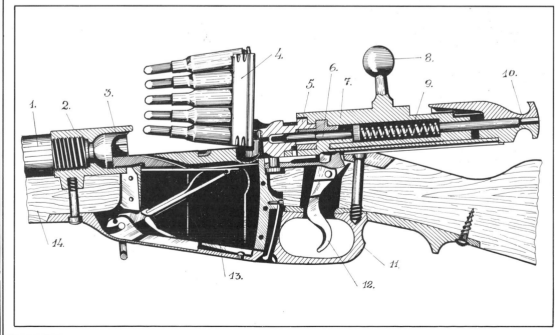

Overleaf:
Russian M.1891 Mosin-Nagant system rifle with M.1891 bayonet.

243

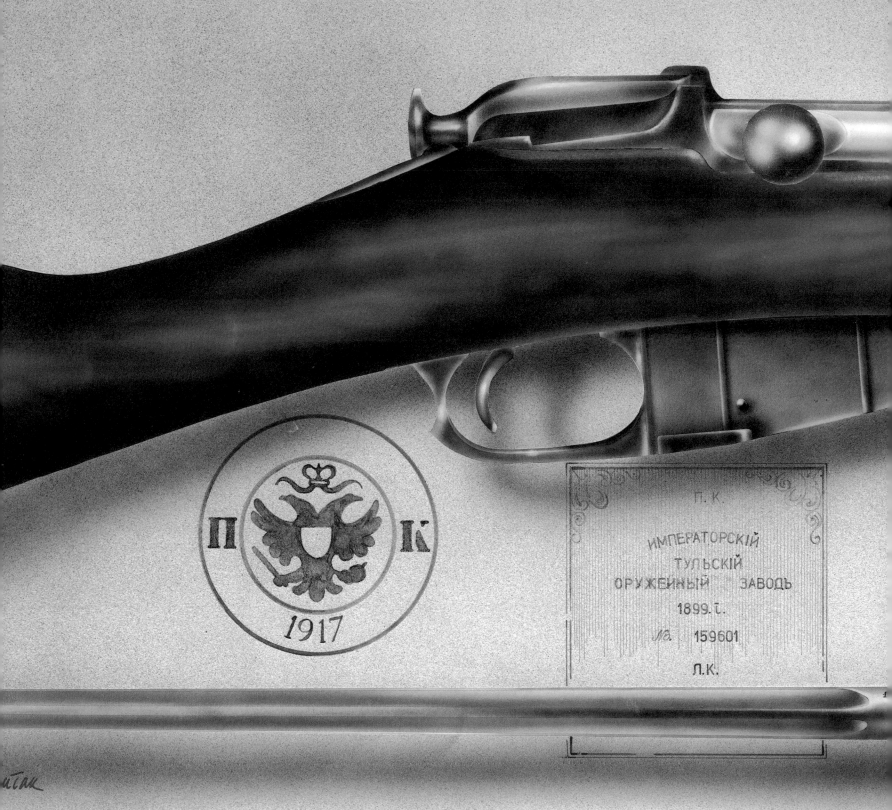

ТРЕХЛИНЕЙНАЯ ВИНТОВКА

П.К. | 1917

	П. К.
ИМПЕРАТОРСКІЙ	
ТУЛЬСКІЙ	
ОРУЖЕЙНЫЙ	ЗАВОДЪ
1899. г.	
№	159601
Л.К.	

7,62 mm Mosin-Nagant Rifle, M 1

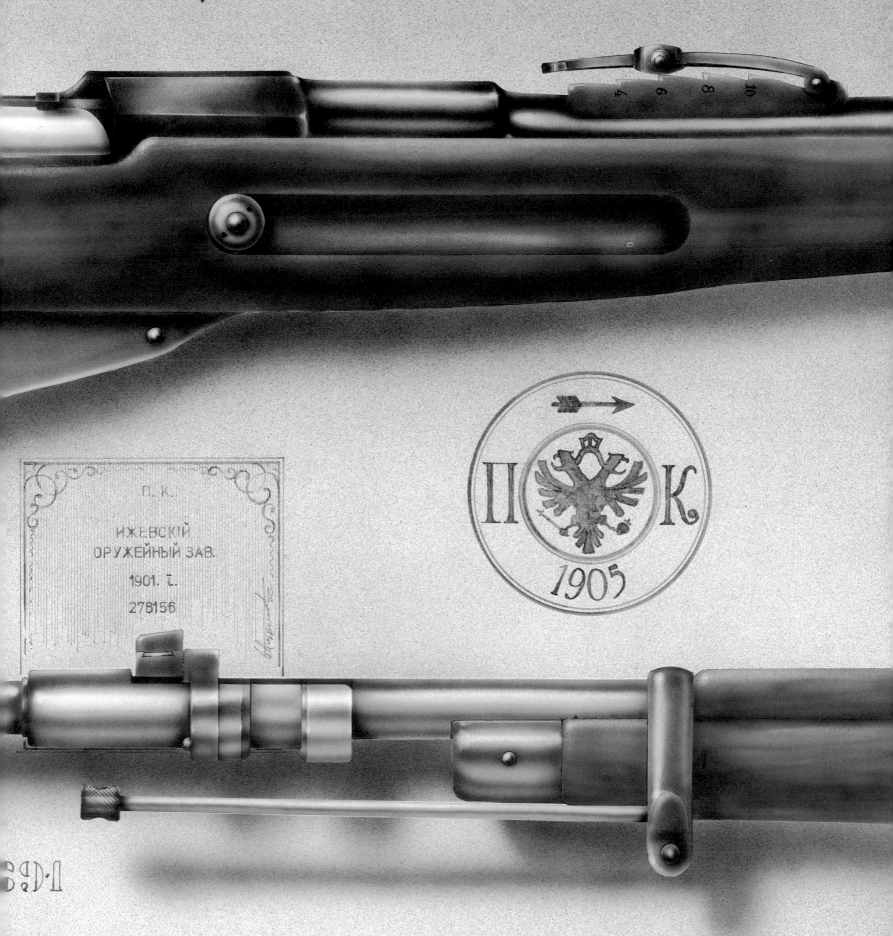

ОБРАЗЦА 1891 ГОДА

П. К.

ИЖЕВСКІЙ
ОРУЖЕЙНЫЙ ЗАВ.

1901. Г.

278156

П·К
1905

Murata, Arisaka

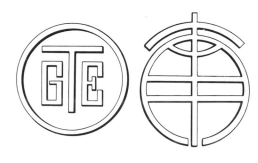

ARISAKA SYSTEM (MEIJI 38) RIFLE
- Calibre . . . . 6.5 mm
- Rifling . . . .
- Capacity 5
- Length . . . . 1,275 mm
- Length of barrel . . . . 797.5 mm
- Weight . . . . 4,200 gr

It is obvious that for the Japanese the problem of arming its military forces with rifles was far more important than the banal question of revolvers. In line with the possibilities of their light industry, the Japanese looked for a solution, in this case as well, in copying existing European models. In the 13th year of the reign of Emperor Mitsuhito, Major Murata used all the characteristics of the French Chassepot and its follower, Gras, and created the first Japanese single-shot turn-bolt rifle. This weapon, named according to Japanese tradition Meiji 13 (1880/81), used a cartridge with paper case in its original version. Realizing in time that this kind of solution was completely outdated, three years later Murata introduced the normal metallic cartridge of 11 mm calibre with all the characteristics of Gras ammunition.

The final version of Murata's weapon was completed in 1887. This rifle resembled the new French Lebel, as it had a tubular magazine for 8 mm calibre ammunition and turn-bolt action without any safety mechanism!

About this time, Colonel Hariakira Arisaka headed the team of experts employed to develop a more modern rifle solution. Without hesitation, Arisaka took Mauser's 1893 weapon as the basis. Today the Japanese are somewhat reproached for this but it should not be forgotten that even the USA took the same step when developing the Springfield M.1903. In any case, the Japanese colonel changed the cocking and safety mechanism of the Mauser and thus "created" the new Meiji 30 rifle. The army made some criticism of this solution, so the final version of Arisaka's five--round 6.5 mm calibre rifle appeared in the 38th year of the Meiji (1905).

It should be mentioned that this solution did not differ in form from the German Mauser: the only noticeable distinguishing feature was the metallic jacket of the bolt-mechanism. The *Meiji 38* rifle (also called *Sampachi Shiki Hoheiju*) used a strange and weak type of Japanese ammunition of 6.5 mm calibre. The only advantage of this cartridge was the slight recoil of the weapon when fired, which made it comfortable to use. On the other hand, the archaic length of 1,275 mm, to which a bayonet with a blade 398 mm long was to be added, caused the Japanese soldiers many problems in battle, especially in wooded areas. For this reason a carbine version, 406 mm shorter, was manufactured in the same year, 1905, and called *Sampachi Shiki Kiju*. Moreover, six years later the Japanese produced another carbine for the needs of their cavalry, the Meiji 44, with a folding bayonet permanently attached to the underside of the barrel. This weapon was namend, after the arm of the forces it was intended for, *Yonyon Shiki Kiju*.

Arisaka's weapons and others produced in the same period did not play a significant role in World War I. It is well known that the Japanese mostly occupied German territories in China (Ching-Tao) and the Marshall, Caroline and Mariana Islands in the Pacific. Arisaka rifles were to come to the fore in World War II.

Opposite:
Battle of Tsushima, May 27 and 28, 1905.
Russo-Japanese war.

Overleaf:
Japanese Meiji 30 rifle with 99 bayonet.

Japanese field-gun system Arisaka M.1898, caliber 75 mm.

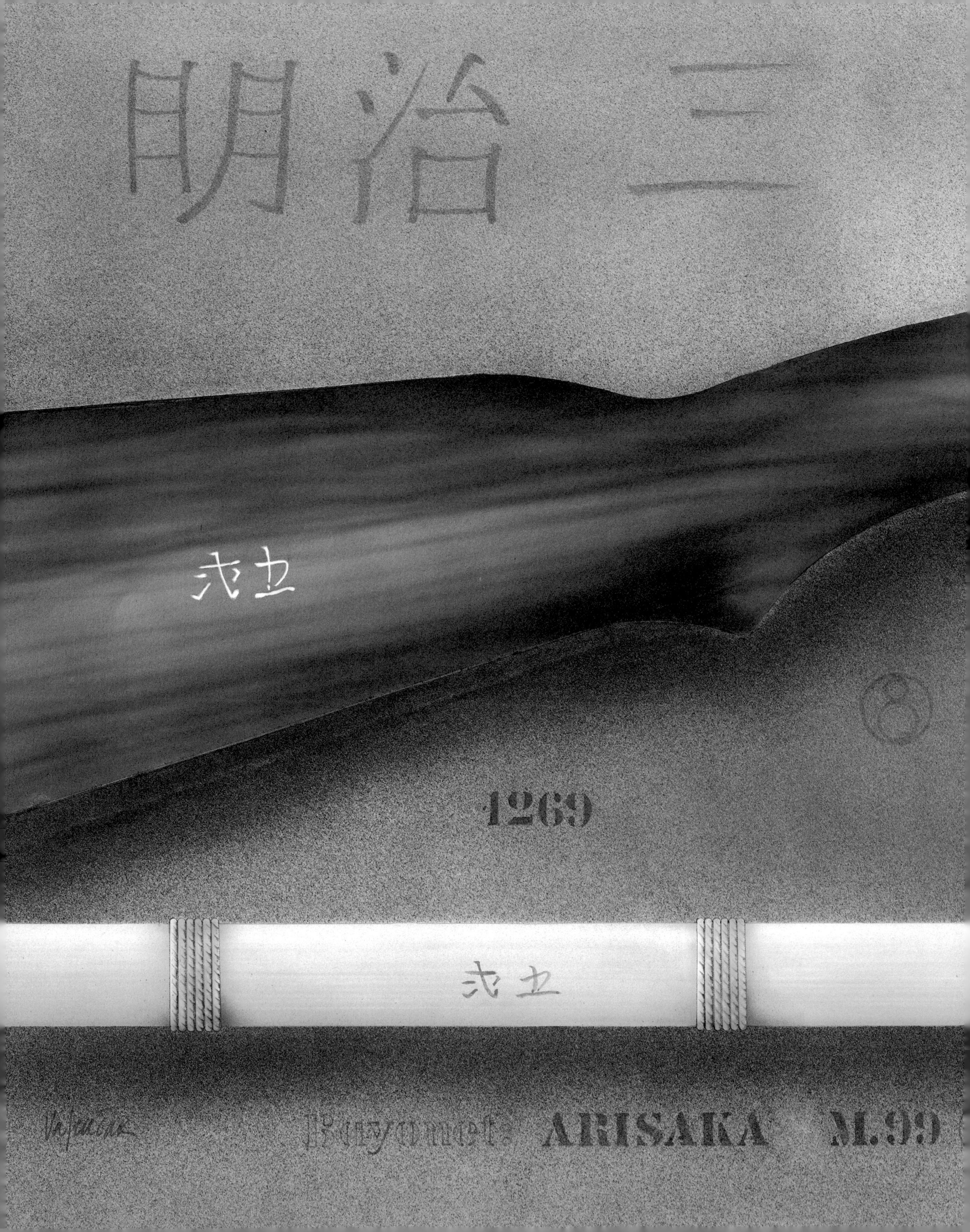

明治 三

弐立

⑧

1269

弐立

Vajaucka Baïonnet. ARISAKA M.99

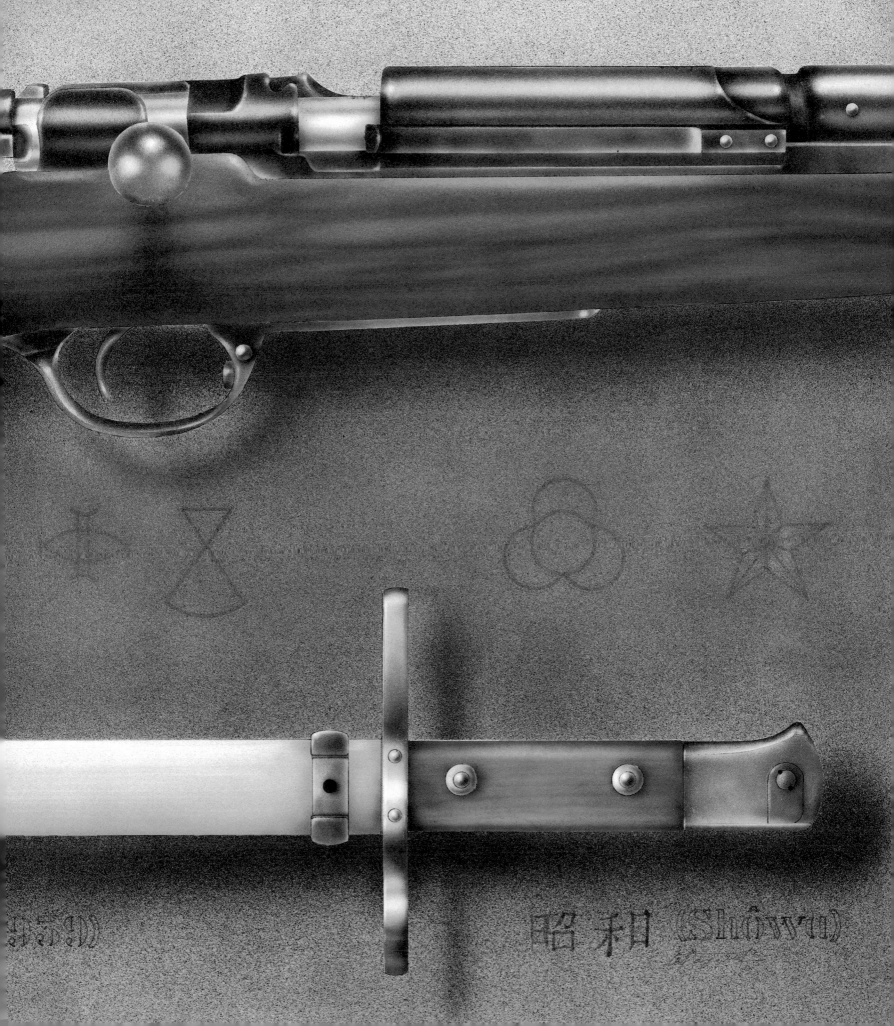

SELF-LOADING PISTOLS

Browning, Ruby

Although they were the last word in technology, pistols were second-class weapons in World War I. This is quite understandable in view of the range of modern rifles and the mass use of machine-guns. Nevertheless, there was no country in Europe and even in America, that did not try to obtain this weapon, if only for its officers. On the other hand, pistols were more useful than rifles for fighting in the trenches.

On the eve of the war, Europe was flooded with pistols based on Browning's blow-back principle. The strong Belgian industry and a number of foreign copies made this weapon cheap and available to almost everyone who wished to own one. Apart from this, the *Fabrique Nationale* at Herstal near Liège offered its pistols to many armies, so that Browning's models became the most widely used weapon of the Great War.

John Moses Browning's patents were received in Belgium with great enthusiasm. The *Fabrique Nationale* immediately started production of a whole series of his pistols which flooded Europe in a short time. True, the first successful pistols constructed in FN-Browning coproduction, the Model 1900 (patented March 21, 1899), was not accepted as a service weapon by any European army, but the following model, M.1903 (9 mm Browning calibre), was chosen by Belgium, Turkey, Denmark, the Netherlands

and Sweden, the last starting production under licence, naming the weapon M.07. By the beginning of the war, the Liège company had produced the no less popular M.1910 in standard FN calibres of 7.65 and 9 mm.

More should be said of a weapon which was intended by Browning and the FN exclusively for the civilian market, but which had a different fate. The pistol in question is the M.1906, based on the 1903 military model. It was, however, of much smaller dimensions and instead of a concealed hammer had a stricker. Precisely because of its practical size, the M.1906 soon won its place on the world market. Seeing an opportunity for high profits, perceptive Spanish companies were amongst the first to start mass production of copies of this pistol. Amongst them was Gabilondo y Urresti of Elgobar, Eibar, which in 1914 started production of a similar weapon of 7.65 mm calibre (9 cartridge capacity) with the intention of selling it on the South American market. But World War I broke out at this time, suddenly giving the Spaniards unlimited possibilities of selling the weapons to the military. Aware that France had practically no automatic pistols, Gabilondo immediately contacted Paris, offering his latest product.

After a number of tests, the French Army adopted Gabilondo's version of the Browning, under the commercial name of Ruby, as its service weapon. During May

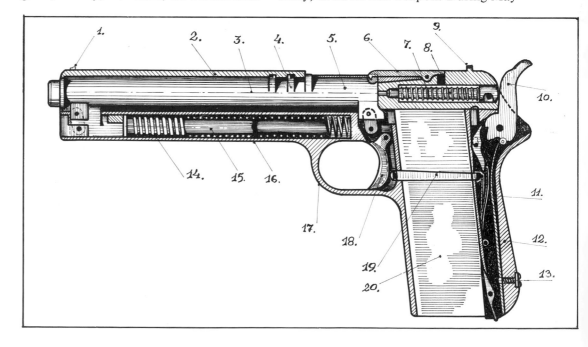

1915, the French government signed an agreement with the Elgobar Company by which the producer undertook to deliver 10,000 pistols a month to the army. Only two months later the monthly consignment was raised to 20,000! Realizing that he would never be able to meet this quota, Gabilondo involved the firms of *Bruno Salaveria y Cia, Eceolaza y Vicinai y Cia, Hijos de Angel Echeverria* and *Armera Elgoibaressa* in the business. In addition, a new company was founded in Guernica,

S. A. Alkartasuna (Alkar), with the principal task of producing Ruby pistols. The final number of weapons delivered to France by Spain is not known, but it is obvious that Gabilondo alone dispatched about 150–200,000 Ruby pistols to Paris!

In line with the agreement about allied aid, by October 1, 1916, France had sent 5,000 Ruby pistols of 7.65 mm calibre to Serbia. This particular consignment today causes a great deal of confusion amongst authors. In 1931 and 1933, the Kingdom

of Yugoslavia, which had inherited all Serbia's arms, repaired the obsolete Ruby pistols and re-sealed them with the following inscription: *PIŠTOLJ 7,65 mm/ VTZ 1933.* Confused by the Spanish and Yugoslav markings, authors (amongst them J. Howard Mathews) have devised two theories about these weapons: that Yugoslavia either bought some new pistols from Spain in the interwar period, or produced them itself in the Arsenal in Kragujevac!

Advance of Franco-Serbian troops.

RUBY M. 1914 PISTOL
- **Calibre** .... 7.65 mm
- **Rifling** 7
- **Capacity** 9
- **Length** .... 150 mm
- **Length of barrel** .... 82 mm
- **Weight** .... 810 gr

BROWNING SYSTEM PISTOL FROM 1897
1. front sight; 2. slide; 3. barrel; 4. locking lugs; 5. chamber; 6. extractor; 7. firing pin; 8. firing pin spring; 9. rear sight; 10. hammer; 11. mainspring; 12. mainspring housing; 13. mainspring screw; 14. recoil spring; 15. recoil spring guide; 16. housing; 17. trigger-guard; 18. trigger; 19. lever; 20. magazine; 21. sear; 22. disconnector.

Overleaf:
M.1915 Ruby pistol.

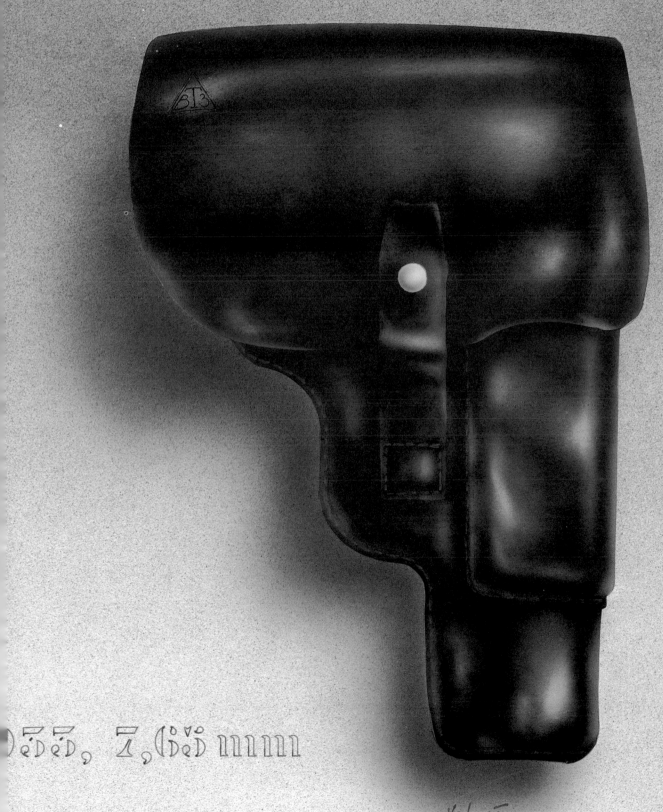

0ꝺꝺ, 7,6ꝺ mm

Valentar

Colt M.1911

In the USA, the fate of Browning's pistol solutions was somewhat different, though no less significant. Browning offered his pistol designes exclusively to the famed Colt Company. This firm, taught by its experience in the mid-19th century, when it had refused Rollin White's patent, without hesitation bought the technical documentation for four Browning pistols in 1896. This was to prove an excellent move. Colt did not hurry into production. His prospering business with the revolver, so popular in the US, enabled the company to undertake studious and lengthy research and improve the new type of weapon, as well as await the results of Browning's European tour.

Thus it was only in 1900 that a version of the so-called Colt 1900 Sporting Model pistol was produced, based on the improved Browning patent from April 20, 1897, and using the first modern ˙38 ACP ammunition. In view of the fact that the pistol was just entering the American market, only 3,000 of the Colt 1900 were manufactured, the Army and Navy taking about 200 of these for testing purposes. In line with its programme, the Colt Company started production, two years later, of a pistol based on a patent from September 9, 1902.

Colt by tradition seemed to have the luck of war experience aiding the sale of his weapons. This time as well, the poor performance of the revolver in the Spanish--American War on Cuba forced the army to seriously reconsider the question of pistols and new, stronger ammunition.

At the open competition in 1906, the government decided on the new ˙45 mm calibre bullet submitted by the Francotte Arsenal and the Colt Company. Colt even developed the corresponding pistol for the ammunition, based on the former, rather successful M.1902. Seeing the possibility of obtaining a state concession, Browning returned from Belgium and started improving this weapon in order to satisfy the rigorous demands of the US Army.

After much work, Browning and Colt, retaining all the favourable characteristics of the M.1905 and the Belgian M.1903 FN, completed a new military pistol in 1911. At the competition, this weapon easily triumphed over such competitors as the Savage M.1910 and the Luger. Finally, on March 29, 1911, the Colt M.1911 was adopted as the service pistol of the US Army.

Immediately after being granted the concession, the Colt factory started serial production of the M.1911 pistol, calibre ˙45 ACP. The state Arsenal in Springfield was also gradually equipped to manufacture these weapons.

At the time when the USA entered World War I, there were only 55,553 M.1911 pistols available in the arsenals. The American custom of issuing this

General Pershing and his staff on board "The Invieta".

COLT

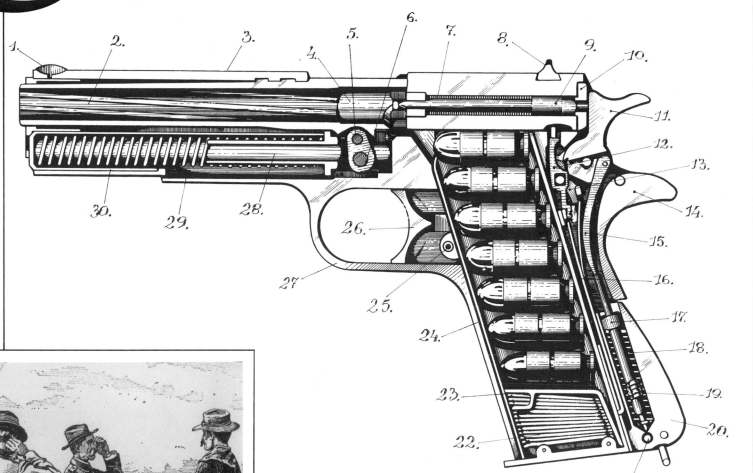

American troops, beginning of 20th century.

COLT M. 1911 PISTOL
- Calibre .... 11.43 mm ('45)
- Rifling 6
- Capacity 7
- Length .... 216 mm
- Length of barrel .... 127 mm
- Weight .... 1,100 gr

weapon to all officers, NCOs and soldiers who could prove their need for it caused an enormous demand for the M.1911 Colt. On the other hand, although equipped for the production of pistols, the Springfield Arsenal had to concentrate on turning out the necessary rifles. The burden of the total production thus fell on the Colt Company, which tried to engage some other well-known US company in the work. It seems that at that moment only Remington was prepared to accept the challenge. But by the end of the war, of the total of 450,000 pistols produced, Remington had made only 13,152. The M.1911 pistol soon became one of the most popular firearms in the world and was the basis for the development of most automatic pistols. Absolutely safe, with a terrific muzzle velocity, it was the soldiers' favourite weapon. However, accurate shooting with this powerful weapon, weighing 1,130 grammes, required much practice. At the moment of detonation, the chamber was subjected to a pressure of 1000 kg/cm², and the bullet, weighing 36 grammes, had a muzzle velocity of 262 m/s!

COLT M.1911

1. front sight; 2. barrel; 3. slide; 4. chamber; 5. link pin; 6. link; 7. firing pin spring; 8. rear sight; 9. firing pin; 10. firing pin stop; 11. hammer; 12. disconnector; 13. sear; 14. grip safety; 15. hammer strut; 16. sear spring; 17. main spring cap; 18. main spring; 19. housing pin retainer; 20. main spring housing; 21. housing pin: 22. magazine spring; 23. follower; 24. receiver; 25. magazine catch; 26. trigger; 27. trigger-guard; 28. recoil spring guide; 29. recoil spring; 30. plug.

Including the modification from 1926 (M.1911 A-1), Colt's pistol withstood the competition of the revolvers so favoured in America and remained the service pistol of the US Army for almost 70 years.

Overleaf:
M.1911 Colt system pistol with holster.

COLT

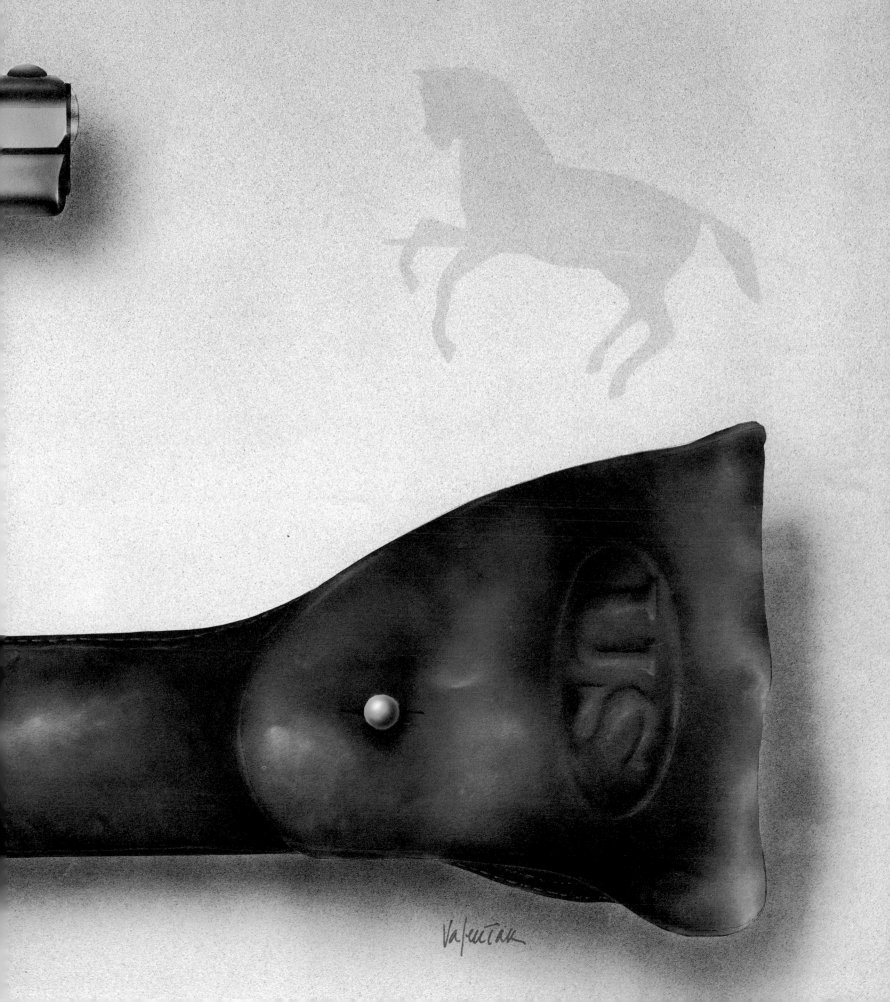

Roth-Steyr M.1907, Steyr M.1912

Austria-Hungary had a number of talented constructors of automatic arms. Unfortunately, the conservative military echelons in Vienna did not show particular interest in the suggestions of Schönberger, Kromar and Mannlicher.

Towards the end of the 19th century another gifted man, Karel Krnka, son of the Czech constructor Sylvester Krnka, appeared on the scene. In his patent bureau in Prague he constructed a weapon with bolt-action locking on the principle of long recoil and 90° rotation of the barrel. When the pistol was fired, the barrel and bolt together recoiled about 0.5 inch within the hollow receiver. During this operation, the grooves in the bolt caused the barrel to turn through 90 degrees.

In 1898, Krnka was appointed constructor and head manager of the famous Georg Roth ammunitions factory in Vienna, to which he transferred all the documentation for the new weapon. With the aid of the factory designers, Karel developed, through the transitional 1899 and 1904 models, the famous Austrian M.1907 pistol. The following year this weapon was adopted as the service weapon of the Austrian calvalry, with the official name *8 mm Repetierpistole 07*. As the first series was manufactured in the ÖEWG factory in Steyr, and the project originated in Roth's construction bureau, the pistol was unofficially called the Roth--Steyr.

The new pistol was of sound construction and excellent quality. Its distinguishing feature was the magazine, placed in the butt, which was loaded by a charger with 10 cartridges.

By 1914, the factories in Budapest (Fegyvergyar) and Steyr produced about 90,000 of these 07 pistols.

When the production of these cavalry pistols was in full swing, the factory in Steyr also started making more modern weapons to use 9 mm ammunition. There are some indications that the major role in the development of the new pistol was played by the factory construction bureau headed by engineer Konrad Murgthaler. The main feature of this pistol, loaded by an 8-cartridge charger, was the locked--breech mechanism operated by the barrel rotating thoughout 60°. The preliminary designs for such a pistol were finished in 1909, and the *Sellier und Bellot* and *Hirtenberger Patronenfabrik* (ammunitions factories) were asked to make a project for appropriate 9 mm calibre cartridges. That some year, after the death of G. Roth, Karel Krnka was appointed technical consultant and director of the construction department of the Hintenberg works. He was thus given an ideal opportunity to see the plans for the competition's new pistol. Adopting an arrogant attitude, Krnka made a number of criticisms and unwarranted demands as regards details of the pistol's construction. In order to avoid further complications, the Board of the ÖEWG left the development of the ammunition exclusively to the S and B factory, which Krnka took as an insult. With the aid of his many connections and the influence of the Regent, Franz Ferdinand, *Kaisertreu* ("faithful to the Emperor" Karel Krnka's pseudonym) managed to prevent the new pistol from being accepted by the army, for the next few years at least.

The first series of 500 of these weapons was produced in 1911. In the following year, the pistol was somewhat modified, and namend the Steyr 12 *(Selbstlade Pistole M.12)*. Because (unlike the 07) it had a hammer, this pistol was also sometimes called Hahn-Steyr *(Hahn = hammer)*.

The new Austrian weapon was adopted in 1911 by Romania, which by 1916 had received 56,000 pistols, and Chile which bought a total of 14,000 Steyr M.12.

In the critical days of 1914, following the assassination of Franz Ferdinand, no obstacle remained in the way of the M.12: that same year it was adopted as an Austrian Army weapon and 250,000 were produced by ÖEWG alone by the end of the war. Moreover, in the period between 1914 and 1918, three interesting versions of the M.12 appeared.

As early as 1914 Austrian pilots complained of the small capacity of the M.12

Austrian flagship "Viribus Unitis".

magazine. To satisfy their demands, the factory in Steyr lengthened the butt, increasing the capacity to 16 cartridges!

The following year, Italy joined the war against Austria-Hungary, and the imperial soldiers on the Dolomite front first came up against the Villar-Perosa automatics, in comparison with which the

sent 50 prototypes of the automatic Steyr pistols with 16-cartridge capacity to the front. This created the famous M.12/ P.16 weapon, which by 1918 had been produced in a series of 9,873 guns.

Finally, a very rare navy pistol (produced in only 1,200 copies) should be mentioned – the *Steyr M.12 Marine.*

This weapon was created in May 1915

STEYR M. 1912 PISTOL	
- Calibre	9 mm
- Rifling	4
- Capacity	8
- Length	216 mm
- Length of barrel	129 mm
- Weight	955 gr

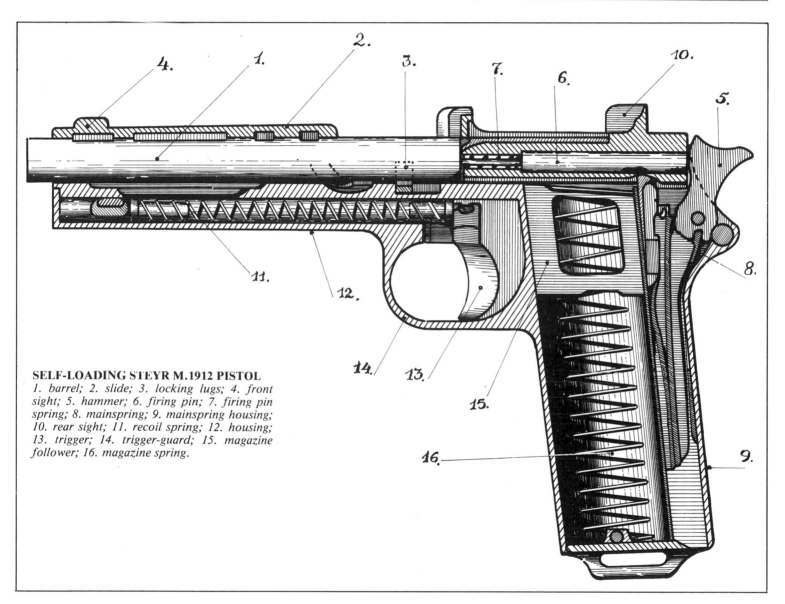

SELF-LOADING STEYR M.1912 PISTOL
1. barrel; 2. slide; 3. locking lugs; 4. front sight; 5. hammer; 6. firing pin; 7. firing pin spring; 8. mainspring; 9. mainspring housing; 10. rear sight; 11. recoil spring; 12. housing; 13. trigger; 14. trigger-guard; 15. magazine follower; 16. magazine spring.

M.12 appeared indicrous. The intelligent Major Fuchs, commander of the Innsbruck II Batallion, remembered the pilot weapons with 16 cartridges, and immediately ordered eight for one of his shock units. Although these pistols were better than the standard ones, they could still not measure up to the automatics. Fuchs then turned to the Steyr factory, suggesting that they make an automatic version of the M.12. The ÖEWG Board accepted this idea and already in February 1916

by lengthening the barrel of the standard pistol to 165 mm, and adding to the upper part of the slide a leaf backsight graduated from 20 to 125 m. This gun also had a wooden holster which could be used as a butt.

Overleaf:
Austrian Marine Steyr M.12 with a drawing of the holster-butt.

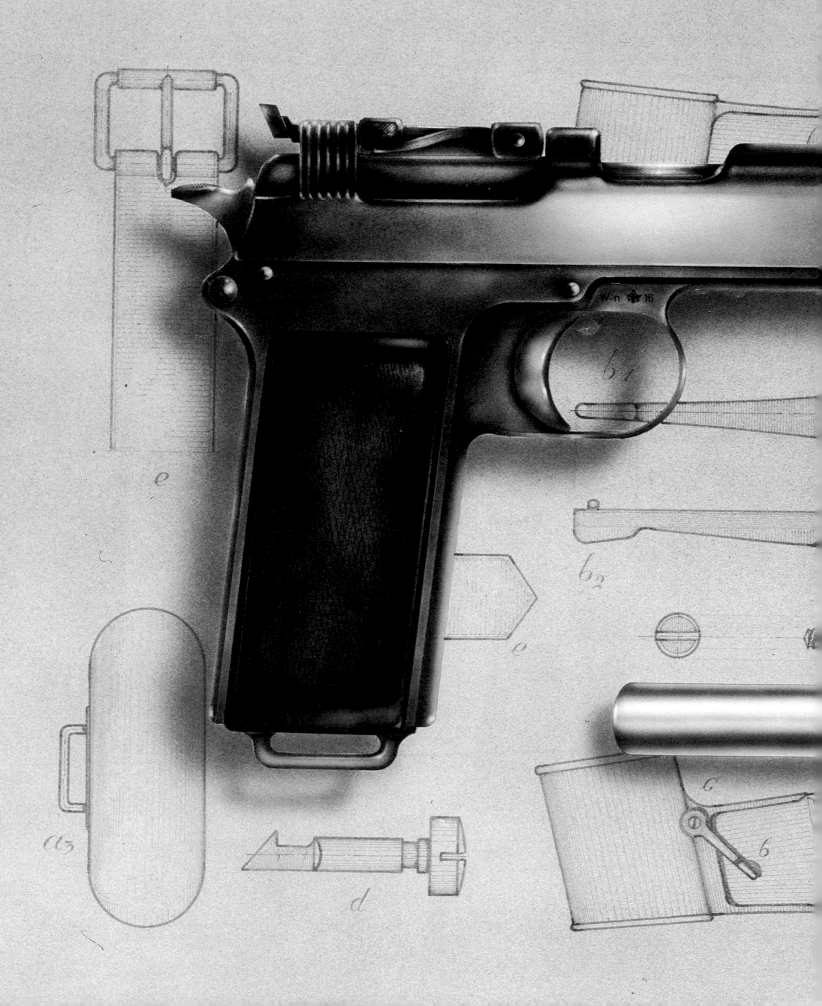

9mm Steyr

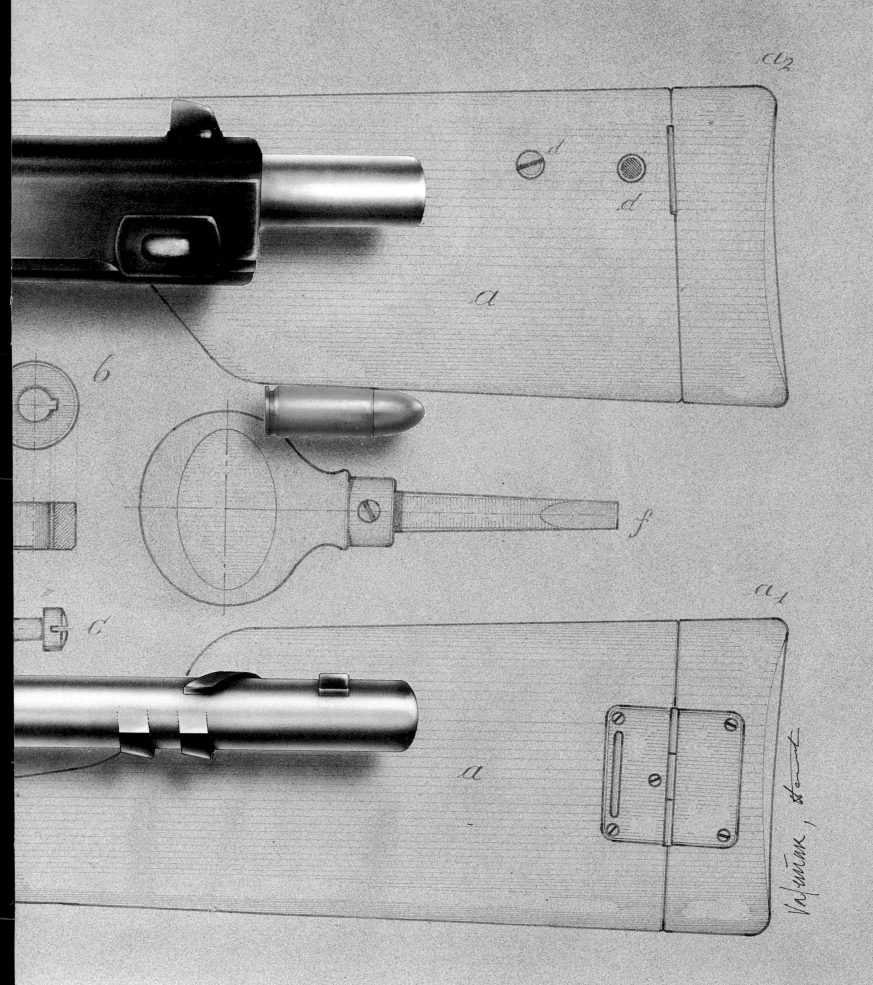

Glisenti-Brixia

In the early 20th century Italy considered the possibility of replacing its revolvers by the more modern self-loading pistols. The favourable experiences of the Navy with the Mauseer C-96, as well as neighbouring Austria's decision to switch to Roth-Steyr pistols, made this question all the more urgent. An opportunity to resolve this problem arose on July 30, 1905, when the famous Piedmontese, Colonel Abiel Bethel Revelli, patented his first solution of an automatic pistol with blow-back operation.

After a number of tests and troop testing, Revelli's weapon was adopted for the Italian Army in 1910, and its production given to two companies in Gardone Val Trompia: *Real Fabbricca d'Armi Glisenti* (later *Societa Siderurgica Glisenti)* and *Meccanica Tempini*. With an eye to advertising, the first producer named the weapon Glisenti, the second Brixia. Even before World War I this dualism confused experts so that in 1910 the Italian Army came up with the idea of naming it Glisenti-Brixia!

Glisenti, Francesco, died September 5, 1887, in Brescia. Manufacturer and constructor of weapons in the Brescia arms centre in Northern Italy. Also deserves credit for developing the metallurgical industry in that region, and was active in the movement for the unification of Italy. His workshop produced Chamelot-Delvigne revolvers for the Italian armed forces.

GLISENTI M. 1910 PISTOL	
- Calibre	9 mm
- Rifling	6
- Capacity	7
- Length	210 mm
- Length of barrel	99 mm
- Weight	820 gr

Right:
March of the Italian infantry on hill 1050.

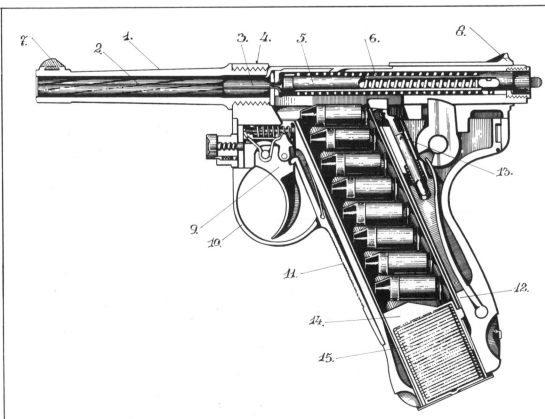

SELF-LOADING GLISENTI-BRIXIA M.1910 PISTOL
1. barrel; 2. grooves; 3. chamber; 4. receiver; 5. firing pin; 6. firing pin spring; 7. front sight; 8. rear sight; 9. trigger; 10. trigger-guard; 11. grip safety; 12. mainspring housing; 13. disconnector, sear and searspring; 14. magazine follower; 15. magazine spring.

French President Poincaré decorates an Italian Bersaglieri captain.

The first types of M.1910 weapons had rather poor grip safety, which was eliminated only on some commercial (Brixia) guns. The pistol used special 9 mm Glisenti ammunition, similar to the Luger cartridge of the same calibre but achieving about 25% less power.

The Glisenti-Brixia M.1910 was a rather reliable and good quality weapon, made by the best semi-handcraft methods of the early 20th century, but is not particularly popular during the war, primarily because of its complicated mechanism. For the reason, Italian officers warmly welcomed the appearance of the first Beretta.

Overleaf:
Italian M.1910 Glisenti-Brixia pistol.

263

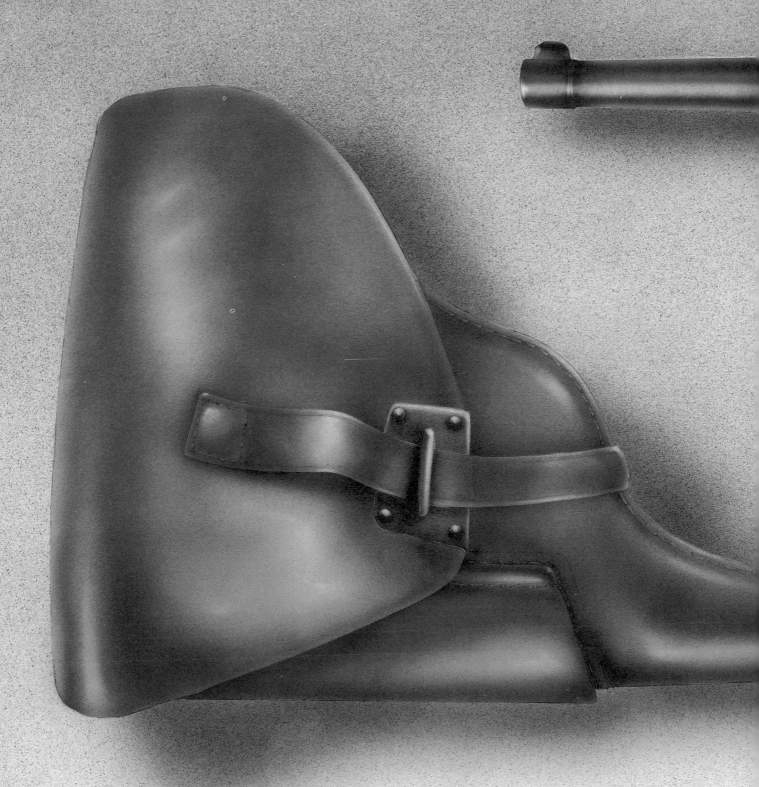

Valentak

Beretta

Beretta, Pietro, born April 22, 1870, in Gardone V.T., died May 1, 1957. After the death of his father, took over the family factory. Outstanding as an expert on machine production of arms with exchangeable parts, which was particularly significant for arming the military forces.

Italian soldiers draw a siege gun up to a height of 2000 meters.

The Italian house of Beretta ranks among the gunsmith families with the longest tradition in the world. Its roots go back as far as the 16th century, and the company was officially registered in 1680. The factory gained a great deal in production potential after reorganizations in 1880 and 1903. From this time on, under the technical leadership of Tullio Marengoni, Beretta turned with great enthusiasm to the development of automatic weapons.

In May 1915, when Italy finally decided to enter the war, the official army pistol was the Glisenti-Brixia M.1910, while the navy used the Mauser C-96. The chronic weakness of these self-loading small-arms enabled Beretta to place its own type of pistol. In the first year of war, the most famous Gardone Val Trompia factory offered the army the *Beretta 1915* the first of the famous Beretta pistols.

The first Beretta pistol, it must be said, did not perform as well as its successors. Its construction seems to have been based on the M.1910 Mauser, except that it had a concealed hammer.

Beretta started production of two types of block-back *Brevetto 1915* (Pattern 1915) pistols: in the 7.65 mm Browning and the 9 mm Glisenti calibres. Whereas the first version probably derived from a civilian pistol, the second was an attempt at simplifying handling and ammunition production for the army. The main constructional difference between these two pistols was in the type of extractor: in the model with smaller ammunition, the case was ejected upwards from the front

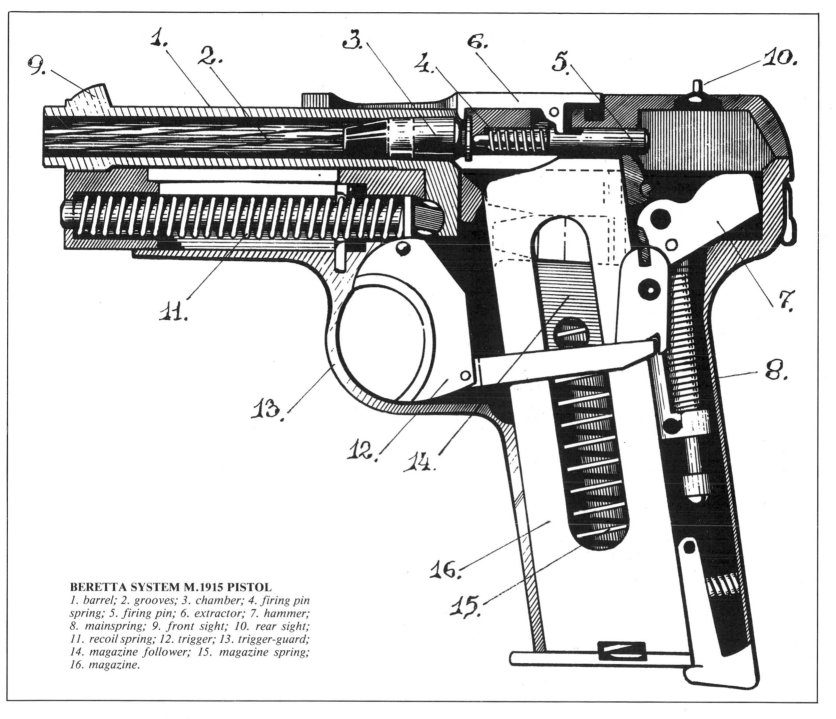

BERETTA SYSTEM M.1915 PISTOL
*1. barrel; 2. grooves; 3. chamber; 4. firing pin
spring; 5. firing pin; 6. extractor; 7. hammer;
8. mainspring; 9. front sight; 10. rear sight;
11. recoil spring; 12. trigger; 13. trigger-guard;
14. magazine follower; 15. magazine spring;
16. magazine.*

part of the breech by the firing pin, while
the 9 mm calibre pistol had a lever extractor.

After the war, Beretta adapted the
M.1915 pistols as a somewhat improved
commercial version M.1915/1919, the
starting point for its conquest of the
world market.

BERETTA M. 1915 PISTOL	
- Calibre	9 mm
- Rifling	
- Capacity	
- Length	167 mm
- Length of barrel	94.5 mm
- Weight	850 gr

*Italian King Victor Emanuel with General
Staff watches operations at Isonzo.*

*Overleaf:
Italian M.1915 Beretta pistol.*

BREVETTO 1915 cal. 9mm GLISENTI

CALCIO-FONDINA MODELLO 1923

Nambu
(Taisho 4 nen)

The Japanese disdain for small firearms has already been mentioned. In fact, self-loading pistols were still more popular in this country than revolvers, especially the unfortunate *Meiji 26 Nen Kenju*. Despite this fact, it was primarily intended for officers, and was not bc to be found in the equipment of couriers and military policemen, as was the rule in other armies.

The first Japanese version of the automatic pistol appeared towards the turn of the century in the form of the un-successful construction of Tomishiro Comuro. In 1897, the famous Colonel Kijiro Nambu, who subsequently, with the rank of general, was to become the main armaments constructor and consultant of the Japanese Army, also started working on pistols.

After a number of prototypes, Nambu considered his project of a self-loading pistol completed in 1909. In his work he used the constructions of the Mauser C-96, Luger P-08 and, above all, Revelli's

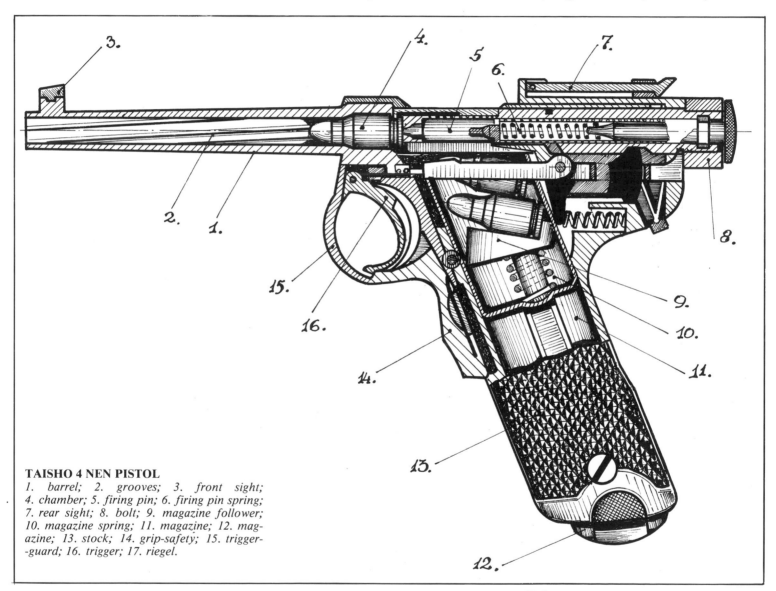

TAISHO 4 NEN PISTOL
1. barrel; 2. grooves; 3. front sight; 4. chamber; 5. firing pin; 6. firing pin spring; 7. rear sight; 8. bolt; 9. magazine follower; 10. magazine spring; 11. magazine; 12. magazine; 13. stock; 14. grip-safety; 15. trigger-guard; 16. trigger; 17. riegel.

Right:
Japanese marines watch conquest of Manila, spring 1942. World War II.

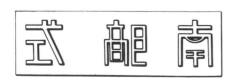

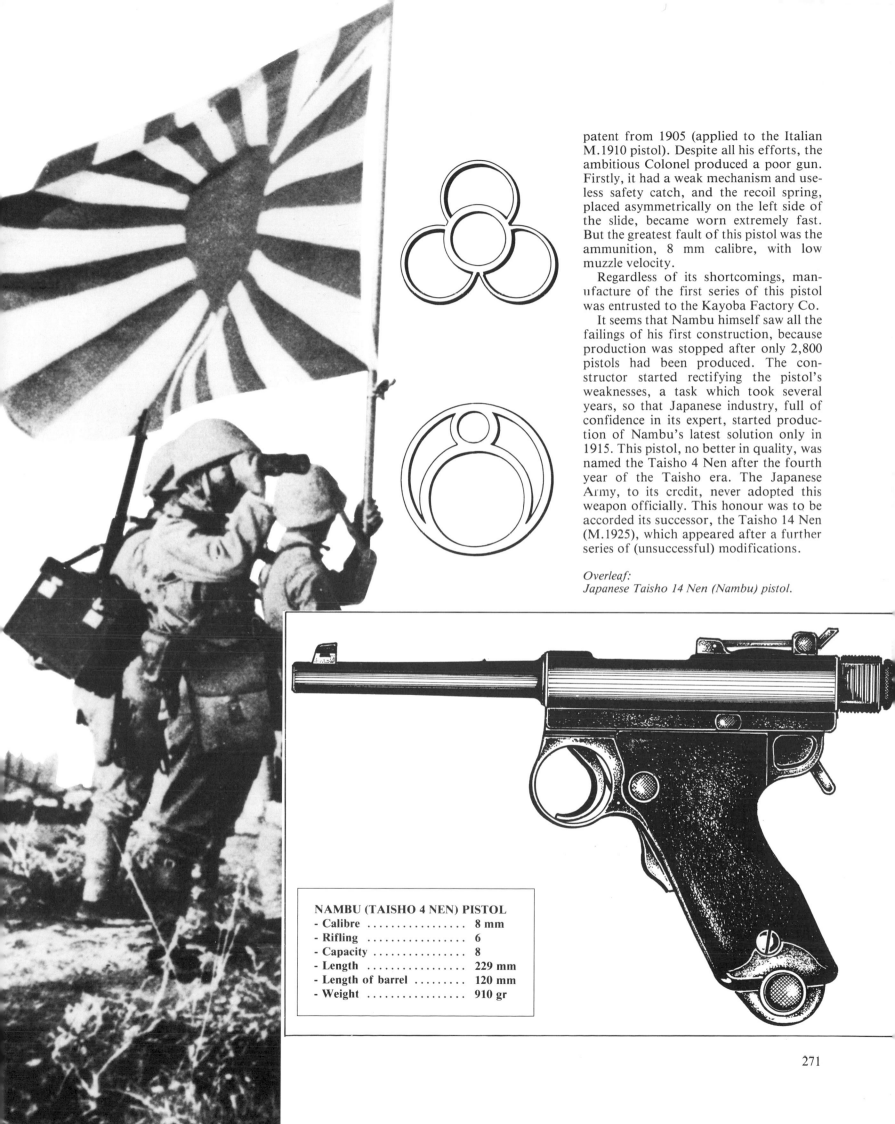

patent from 1905 (applied to the Italian M.1910 pistol). Despite all his efforts, the ambitious Colonel produced a poor gun. Firstly, it had a weak mechanism and useless safety catch, and the recoil spring, placed asymmetrically on the left side of the slide, became worn extremely fast. But the greatest fault of this pistol was the ammunition, 8 mm calibre, with low muzzle velocity.

Regardless of its shortcomings, manufacture of the first series of this pistol was entrusted to the Kayoba Factory Co.

It seems that Nambu himself saw all the failings of his first construction, because production was stopped after only 2,800 pistols had been produced. The constructor started rectifying the pistol's weaknesses, a task which took several years, so that Japanese industry, full of confidence in its expert, started production of Nambu's latest solution only in 1915. This pistol, no better in quality, was named the Taisho 4 Nen after the fourth year of the Taisho era. The Japanese Army, to its credit, never adopted this weapon officially. This honour was to be accorded its successor, the Taisho 14 Nen (M.1925), which appeared after a further series of (unsuccessful) modifications.

Overleaf:
Japanese Taisho 14 Nen (Nambu) pistol.

NAMBU (TAISHO 4 NEN) PISTOL
- Calibre .... 8 mm
- Rifling 6
- Capacity 8
- Length .... 229 mm
- Length of barrel .... 120 mm
- Weight .... 910 gr

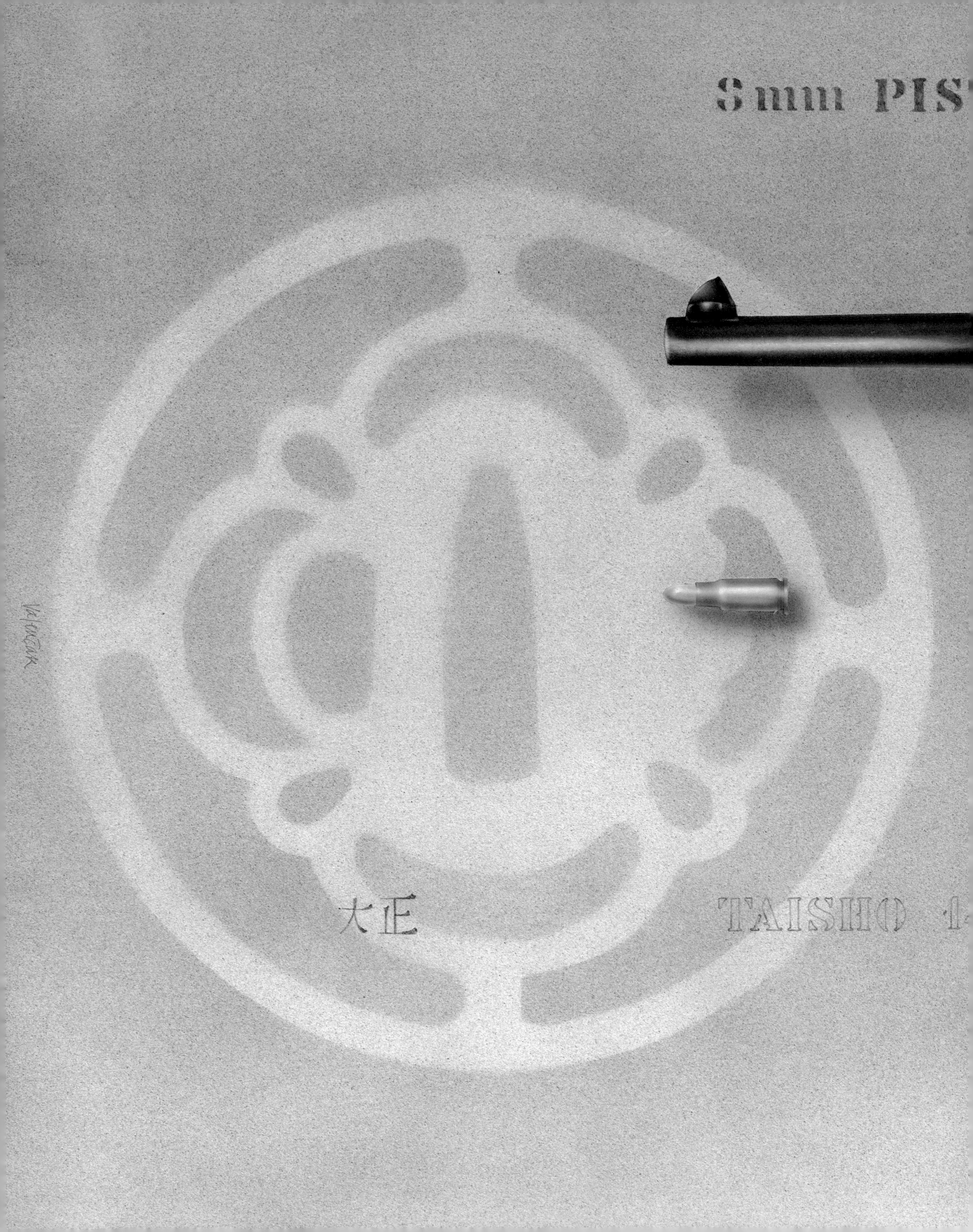

8mm PIST

大正

TAISHO 1

TABLES OF TACTICAL-TECHNICAL DATA

Model	System	State	Calibre mm	Length mm	Length of barrel mm	Weight gr	Rifling

TACTICAL – TECHNICAL DATA OF MUSKETS AND RIFLES

INFANTRY FLINTLOCK MUSKETS

Model	System	State	Calibre mm	Length mm	Length of barrel mm	Weight gr	Rifling
M. 1798	Flintlock	Austria	17,6	1,505	1,125	4,200	.
Brown-Bess	Flintlock	Britain	19,0	1,450	1,040	4,770	.
M. 1777	Flintlock	France	17,5	1,520	1,137	4,300	.
M. 1723/40	Flintlock	Prussia	19,0	1,450	1,040	4,790	.
M. 1808	Flintlock	Russia	17,78	1,460	1,140	4,460	.
M. 1795	Flintlock	USA	17,5	1,510	1,135	3,030	.

INFANTRY MUZZLE-LOADING PERCUSSION RIFLES

Model	System	State	Calibre mm	Length mm	Length of barrel mm	Weight gr	Rifling
M. 1854/II	Lorenz	Austria	13,9	1,335	950	4,120	4
M. 1846	„A tige"	France	17,75	1,285	865	4,200	4
M. 1853	Enfield	Britain	14,7	1,341	990	4,160	3
M. 1855	Springfield	USA	14,73	1,254	838	4,540	3
M. 1854		Russia	17,78	1,480	1,083	4,860	4

SINGLE-SHOT CARTRIDGE RIFLES

TACTICAL – TECHNICAL DATA OF SELF-LOADING PISTOLS

Model	System	State	Calibre mm	Length mm	Length of barrel mm	Weight gr	Rifling
M. 1877	Werndl-Holub	Austria	11,0	1,281	843	4,500	6
M. 1871	Gras	France	11,0	1,300	820	4,000	4
M. 1871	Mauser	Germany	11,0	1,345	855	4,500	4
M. 1870	Berdan No. 2.	Russia	10,67	1,350	830	4,400	6
M. 1871	Henry-Martini Mark I	Britain	11,43	1,231	825	3,950	7
M. 1868	Springfield	USA	12,7	1,321	914	4,200	3

SYSTEM AND MODEL	Bergmann M. 1903	Borchardt-Luger (Parabellum)	Browning	G. Roth (Muster II)	Mannlicher M. 1901/1906	Mauser C-96
Principle of operation	Short recoil of barrel	Short recoil of barrel	blow-back	Short recoil of barrel	blow-back	Short recoil of barrel
Position of magazine	In front of trigger-guard	In butt	In butt	In butt	In butt	In front of trigger-guard
Number of parts	41	57	45	30	42	43
Calibre (mm)	7,63	7,65	7,65	8	7,65	7,63
Number of grooves	4	4	5	4	4	4
Length and direction of rifling (mm)	Left-hand	250 right-hand	440 left-hand	250 right-hand	260 right-hand	250 right-hand
Length of barrel (mm)	100	122	102	125	140	140
Length of sight's line (mm)	170	215	130	156	124	238
Length of pistol (mm)	250	237	163	225	222	290
Weight of pistol (gr)	900	835	600	990	950	1,180
Capacity	10	8	7	10	10	10
Weight of bullet (gr)	5,5	6	4,8	7,5	5,57	5,5
Charge weight – smokeless powder (gr)		0,33	0,2	0,26	0,24	0,5
Total length of cartridges (mm)	35	29,8	25	29	28,5	35
Weight of cartridges (gr)	10,7	10,5	7,7	10,39	8,8	10,7
Muzzle velocity (m/s)	400	305 at 15 m from muzzle	270	305 at 12,5 m from muzzle	320 at 12.5 m from muzzle	415 at 10 m from muzzle
Height of pistol (mm)	150	135	102	150	155	150
Weight of charger or magazine (gr)	charger 14	Lee-type magazine 55	Lee-type magazine 45	charger 14,08	charger 14	charger 14
Penetration force of bullet	Fired from a distance of 12 m into a fir tree, penetrates 35 cm	Fired from a distance of 50 m into a fir tree, penetrates 16 cm	Fired from a distance of 10 m into a fir tree, penetrates 10 cm	Fired from a distance of 25 m into a fir tree, penetrates 26 cm	Fired from a distance of 50 paces into a spruce tree, penetrates 14 cm	Fired from a distance of 0.5 m into a fir tree, penetrates 26 cm

TACTICAL – TECHNICAL DATA OF REPEATING RIFLES

According to the Austro-Hungarian Naval Almanach from 1912

[1] ogival flat-based bullet

[2] round-nosed bullet D

[3] ogival bullet U

[4] at 25 m from muzzle velocity of 678 m/s.

State			Denmark
Model			M. 1889
System			Krag-Jörgensen
Calibre		mm	8
Weight without bayonet and with empty magazine		kg	4,3
Weight with bayonet and loaded magazine		kg	4,71
Mouvement of breech-bolt			turn-bolt
Rifling	Number of grooves		6
	Length of rifling in calibres		37,5
Number of cartridges in magazine			5
Weight of empty clip or charger		gr	
Cartridge	Weight	gr	30
	Length	mm	76
Charge weiht – smokeless powder		gr	2,9
Bullet	Weight	gr	15,43
	Length	mm	28
Length in calibres			3,75
Number of cartridges per man			120
Back sight graduated to distance		in meters or paces (x)	2,100
Maximum range		in meters or paces (x)	3,500
Maximum pressure			2,500
Muzzle velocity		m/s	624
Muzzle energy		kgm	306

Germany[1]	France[2]	Great-Britain[3]	Italy	Japan	Austria	Romania	Russia	Spain
1. 1888 & M. 98	M. 86/93	M. 89/II	M. 1891	38 & 05	M. 1895	M. 1893	M. 1891	M. 1893
Mauser	Lebel	Lee-Metford	Mannlicher	Murata	Mannlicher	Mannlicher	Mosin	Mauser
7,9	8	7,7	6,5	6,5	8	8	7,62	7
3,8	4,18	4,1	3,8	3,9	3,65	3,845	3,9	3,95
4,35	4,78	4,6	4,1	4,4	3,96	3,965	4,29	4,4
turn-bolt	turn-bolt	turn-bolt	turn-bolt	turn-bolt	straight-pull	turn-bolt	turn-bolt	turn-bolt
4	4	7	4	6	4	4	4	4
30,4	30	33	36,1	33,3	31,3	30,78	30	31,4
5	1 + 8	10	5	5	5	5	5	5
.	.	.	.	8,5	16,5	10,2	8	10
23,85	29	28,3	21,5	22,85	29,4	21,9	23,46	24,2
80,3	.	80,5	83	76	76	76,5	76	78
3,2	3,1	2,2	2,1	2,05	2,75	2,1	2,133	2,48
10	12,8	14	10,5	10,5	15,8	10,5	13,5	11,6
28	39,2	31,5	30,5	32,55	31,8	31,4	30,23	31
3,5	4,9	4,1	4,69	5	4	4,83	3,97	4,34
150	.	115	200	60 – 120	100	130	150	150
2,000	2,400	1,740	2,000	2,000	2,600[x]	2,000	2,700[x]	2,000
4,000	4,500	.	over 4,000	4,000	4,000[x]	.	.	over 4,000
3,200	.	2,740	under 4,000	.	2,800	3,000	2,900	under 4,000
860	725	655	709	700[4]	620	726	610	728
390	344	306	269	277	310	282,4	265	314

277

TABLE OF MARKINGS
AND
MAKERS' SEALS

1   2   3   4

11   12   13   14

1. Potsdammagaz, Germany, founded 1722.
2. Potsdammagaz, initials S & D = Splittgerber & Daum (1722 – 1774).
3. Potsdammagaz, initials DSE = David Splittgerber, Seel, Erben, (1775 – 1795).
4. Potsdam, initials GS = Gebrüder Schickler (1796 – 1853).
5. Potsdam, initials GS.
6. Königliche Gewehr- und Munitionsfabrik – Spandau. In 1854, the Potsdam factory was moved to Spandau, where it continued work until 1945.
7. Königliche Gewehr- und Munitionsfabrik – Erfuhrt (1815 – 1862), Germany.
8. Königliche Gewehr- und Munitionsfabrik – Danzig (1815 – 1919), Germany.
9. V. C. Schilling & Co., Suhl, Germany.
10. Typical butt-marking disc, before 1915 (5th Garde-Füsilier-Regiment Company, weapon number 201).
11. Gotha, Germany, 19th century.
12. Sachsen, Germany, 18th century.
13. Deutsche Waffen- und Munitionsfabrik, Berlin, Germany. This factory came into being as a result of the development of Ludwig Löwe & Co.
14. Waffenfabrik Mauser, Oberndorf am Neckar, Germany, founded 1873.
15. The national eagle with the year of production on Austrian military weapons.
16. ÖEWG, Österreichische Waffenfabrik--Gesellschaft, Steyr, Austria.
17. First proof-mark, Ferlach, Austria, after 1822.
18. Second proof-mark, Ferlach.
19. Proof-mark, Vejprty, Bohemia, after 1822.
20. First proof-mark, Vienna, Austria, after 1822.
21. Second proof-mark, Vienna.
22. Leopold Gasser K.u.K. Hof- und Armee--Waffenfabrik, Ottakring, Austria, founded 1862.
23. Augsburg, Germany, beginning of the 19th century.
24. St. Etienne, France, after 1825.
25. Mutzig, France, up to 1867.
26. Saileville, France, middle of 19th century.
27. Chatellerault, France, end of 19th century.
28. Paris, proof-mark, about 1810.
29. Birmingham, England, about 1813.
30. National Arms & Ammunition Company Limited, Birmingham, Warwickshire, England.

21   22   23   24

31   32   33   34

41   42   43   44

31. Arms factory of Peter the Great, Tula, Russia, founded 1712; brand from the 1730/1740 period.
32. Tula, 1740 – 1780.
33. Tula, 1780 – 1830.
34. Tula, second half of the 19th century.
35. Izevsk arms factory, Russia, founded 1807.
36. Sestroreck arms factory, Russia, founded 1721.
37. Proof-mark, Liège, Belgium.
38. FN, Fabrique Nationale d'Armes de Guerre, Herstall near Liège, founded 1889.
39. Smith & Wesson, Springfield, Massachusets, USA.
40. Colt's Patent Firearms Manufacturing Co., Hartford, Connecticut, USA.

41. Colt.
42. Pietro Beretta, Gardone Vall Trompia, Italy.
43. The Italian navy (Regia Marina) sign on military weapons.
44. The Italian national coat of arms on military weapons.
45. Royal arms factory, Torino, Italy.
46. Royal arms factory, Brescia, Italy.
47. Initials of the Italian king Victor Emanuel II (1849 – 1878).
48. Namby factory, Japan.
49. Nagoya arsenal, Japan.
50. Tokyo arsenal, Japan.
51. Types of Japanese markings on Namby pistols.
52. Tokyo Gas & Electric Co., Japan.
53. Tower arsenal, London.

5   6   7   8   9   10

15   16   17   18   19   20

25   26   27   28   29   30

35   36   37   38   39   40

45   46   47   48   49   50

  TOWER

51   52   53

BIBLIOGRAPHY:

A. Gluckman: *Identifying old US Muskets, Rifles, Carbines,* New York, 1965

J. Walter: *The German Rifle,* London, 1979

Major J. E. Hicks: *French Military Weapons 1717—1938,* New Milford, Conn, 1973

W. Moore: *Weapons of the American Revolution and accoutrements,* New York, 1967

Major F. Myatt M. C.: *The Illustraded Encyclopedia of Pistols and Revolvers,* London, 1980

U. Pericoli: *1815 — The Armies at Waterloo,* London 1973

J. Howard Mathews: *Firearms Identification,* Springfield, 1973

W. H. B. Smith — J. E. Smith: *Small Arms of the World,* Harrisburg, Pa, 1962

Col. H. C. B. Rogers: *Weapons of the British Soldier,* London, 1972

Neal, W. K.: *Spanish Guns and Pistols,* London 1955

J. B. Hughes, Jr.: *Mexican Military Arms — The Cartridge period 1866—1967,* Houston, Texas

J. E. Serven: *Colt Firearms 1836—1960,* Santa Anna, California 1960

W. K. Neal — R. G. Jings: *Smith and Wesson 1837—1945. A Handbook for Collectors,* South Brunswick, N.Y. — London, 1966

G. W. P. Swenson: *Das Gewehr — Die Geschichte einer Waffe,* Stuttgart, 1973

J. Lugs: *Handfeuerwaffen, I—II,* Berlin 1962

A. Dolleczek: *Monografie der k.u.k. österr.-ungar. Blank- und Handfeuerwaffen,* Wien, 1896

Wilhelm v. Plönnies und Herrmann Weygand: *Die deutsche Gewehrfrage mit Berücksichtigung der neuesten europäischen Ordonanz-Modelle,* Darmstadt und Leipzig, 1872

H. Schmid: *Handbuch für Unteroffiziere,* Wien, 1916

K. Milovanović, *Artiljerija,* Beograd 1879

N. Naumović, *Taktika,* Beograd 1901

V. V. Mavrodin: *Iz istorii otechestvennogo oružija,* Leningrad, 1981

I. P. Pastuhov, S. E. Plotnikov: *Rasskazi o strelkovom oružii,* Moskva, 1983

V. V. Bahirev, I. I. Kirillov: *Konstruktor V. A. Degtjarev,* Moskva, 1983

D. Venner: *Les Armes Russes et Sovietiques,* Bordaux, 1980

A. Seaton: *The Russian Army of the Napoleonic Wars,* Norwich, 1973

A. Seaton: *The Austro-Hungarian Army of the Napoleonic Wars,* Norwich, 1973

F. Wilkinson: *A Source Book of World War I Weapons and Uniforms,* London, 1978

M. Morin: *Le Armi Portatili dell'Impero austro-ungarico,* Firenze, 1981

S. Musciarelli: *Dizionario Delle Armi,* Arnoldo Mondadori Editore, anno sine

Brigadier P. Young DSO MC: *The Fighting Man,* London, 1981

Deutsches Waffen-Journal, Schwäbisch Hall, 1968—1985

Diana, Armi, Rivista d'informazione internazionale, Firenze, 1967—1985

The Gun Digest, Chicago, current issues

The American Rifleman, Washington, current issues

AMI, Bruxelles, current issues

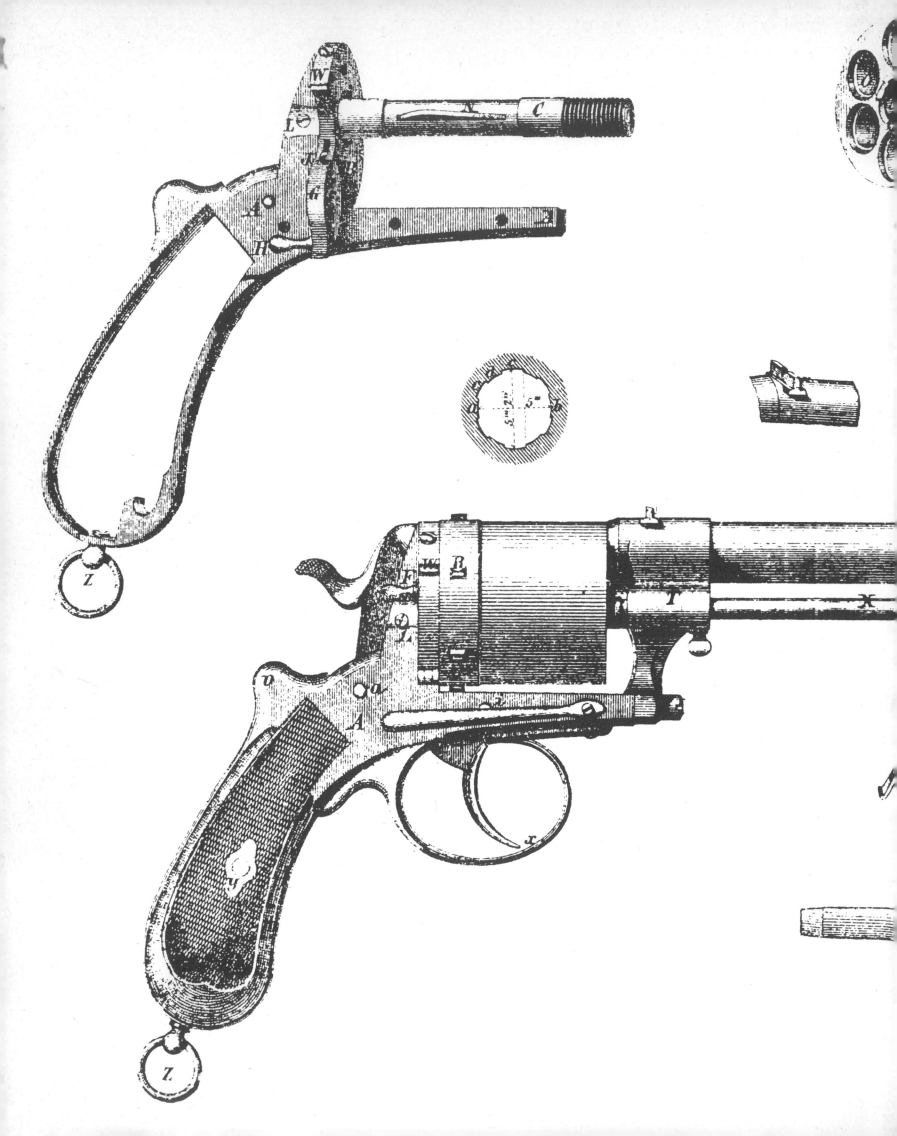